WOLF WARRIORS

THE NATIONAL WOLFWATCHER COALITION ANTHOLOGY

EDITED BY
JONATHAN W. THURSTON

A THURSTON HOWL PUBLICATIONS BOOK

ISBN 978-0-9908902-0-1

Library of Congress Control Number: 2014917534

WOLF WARRIORS

Copyright © 2014 by Jonathan W. Thurston

First Edition, 2014. All rights reserved.

A Thurston Howl Publications Book
Published by Thurston Howl Publications
Murfreesboro, TN

Mailing address:
4072 Hwy 200
Huron, TN 38345

jonathan.w.thurston@vanderbilt.edu

Cover design by Matt Cowan and Marshall Stevens

Printed in the United States of America

10 9 8 7 6 5 4 3 2 1

ACKNOWLEDGMENTS

"Hunt Begins" by A.M. Duvall. Copyright © 2014 by A.M. Duvall.

"wolf howl" by Adrian Lilly. Copyright © 2014 by Adrian Lilly.

"They Hunt Us Too" by Alexander Clark. Copyright © 2014 by Alexander Clark.

"Wolfe" by Ambuja Raj. Copyright © 2014 by Ambuja Raj.

"Crying Wolf" by Bernadette Burger. Copyright © 2014 by Bernadette Burger.

"Yellow Eyes Dancing in Sunlight" by Beverly Ray. Copyright © 2014 by Beverly Ray.

"The Watcher" by Candace B. Gallagher. Copyright © 2014 by Candace B. Gallagher.

"The Wolves of Brooklyn" by Catherynne M. Valente. Copyright © 2014 by Catherynne M. Valente. Originally published by *Fantasy Magazine* in 2011.

"Wolf Girl" by Celia Castro. Copyright © 2014 by Celia Castro.

"Fun in the Snow" and "Howling Practice" by Chelsea Dub. Copyright © 2014 by Chelsea Dub.

"Fruit of Their Frightened Selves" by Chloe Viner. Copyright © 2014 by Chloe Viner.

"John Kindevarg" and "Lives Intertwined" by Chris Albert. Copyright © 2014 by Chris Albert.

"Two Wolves," "Howl," and "Wolf and Antlers" by Colette Korva. Copyright © 2014 by Colette Korva.

"The Wild" by Connie Sparks. Copyright © 2014 by Connie Sparks.

"Endangered Means There is Still Time—A Status Update on the Red Wolf" by Cornelia Hutt. Copyright © 2014 by Cornelia Hutt.

"Perspective on the Mount" by CS Mowgli. Copyright © 2014 by CS Mowgli.

"What's the Time, Mr. Wolf?" and "Children of the Forest" by Darren Greenidge. Copyright © 2014 by Darren Greenidge.

"Fell's Dream" by David Clement-Davies. Copyright © 2014 by David Clement-Davies.

"Invasives" by Debra Rook. Copyright © 2014 by Debra Rook.

To my grandparents, John and Linda, for their constant support. To my grandmother, Debbie, for her encouragement and putting up with my tangential rants. To my friend Dustin, who has helped me to embrace who I am and follow my dreams. To my ever-faithful Temerita, my dog who still insists she is a cat, despite everyone's attempts to tell her otherwise.

CONTENTS

A Letter From the National Wolfwatcher Coalition

Just four short years ago a group of friends had a vision—to form an organization that speaks solely for the wolf. What emerged was the National Wolfwatcher Coalition.

Our statistics speak for themselves: More than thirteen million hits on our website www.wolfwatcher.org; over 420,000 likes on Facebook, with posts reaching one million advocates; over 1,600 supporters follow us on Twitter, and through our newly established Pinterest account nearly 400 people have found us. We have extended our reach around the world with friends in many foreign countries including France, England, Germany, Italy, Mexico, Canada, Ukraine, New Zealand, and Australia.

The mission of the National Wolfwatcher Coalition is straightforward: to educate and advocate for the long-term recovery and preservation of wolves utilizing the best available science. We believe in using peer-reviewed data and encourage comments on wolf-related affairs following the principles of democracy.

We have no membership dues. We do not sell or share our mailing list. We do not send out solicitations begging for money. We do not mail you merchandise you did not request, and we do not inundate your inbox with emails. We have an electronic newsletter that we send out when we have important information to share, and if you no longer wish to receive the alerts, it is easy to unsubscribe. We rely on social media and supporters who seek us out for information.

The National Wolfwatcher Coalition is an all-volunteer organization. None of our board members or volunteers receive any compensation. They work out of their homes, donate their time, energy, and talents to educate and advocate for wolves.

We do not maintain an office, and that helps to keep our expenses down. We also do not maintain a facility with captive wolves.

A core group of volunteers works every day on behalf of wolves.

Our volunteers are scattered across the country but work on issues in every region where there is a current population of wolves. Our goal is to find middle ground and encourage the use of non-lethal methods to resolve conflicts. Volunteers attend meetings, hearings, and workshops and participate by providing testimony on a variety of topics including delisting, hunting, and trapping regulations.

Volunteers scour the newspapers, publications looking for articles to share; we have a letter-writing team that submits letters to the editor. A volunteer set up and maintains our Junior Wolfwatcher site where children can learn about the different types of wolves, where they live, what they eat, how they hunt, and what makes wolves so important.

We are able to advocate for wolves because of the generous donations from our supporters and through the purchase of shirts and other merchandise available for sale at our website store. The National Wolfwatcher Coalition is also listed as a non-profit organization that you can support with your purchases through smile.amazon.com or through a link on Pinterest. This financial support has allowed us to foster relationships with other like-minded organizations.

We wish to thank Jonathan Thurston for putting together this anthology and donating the proceeds to the National Wolfwatcher Coalition. And of course, special thanks to all who submitted art work, poetry, prose, and stories. This anthology would not have been possible without your contributions. Your dedication to helping wolves is truly appreciated.

These are critical times for wolves. The century-old fears, myths, and hatred toward the wolf still exist today. Wolves are now a hunted game animal in every state where they have lost their federal protection. Wolf policies allow for liberal killing of wolves involved with conflicts. With today's anti-wolf political climate, it can sometimes be discouraging, but we are a strong pack. We will not give up the fight for wolves, not today, not tomorrow, or the next day. And, with your continuing support, we can ensure future generations will hear wolves howl.

Board of Directors
National Wolfwatcher Coalition

INTRODUCTION

Wolves walk a fine line, between angels and demons, between dreams and reality, somewhere between the world of light and the world of shadows. There are those who would kill them for their strength and those who would tame them for their beauty. Even scientists today dispute how dangerous wolves truly are. One of the only things we can accurately say about all wolves is that they have been a part of our history, literature, and culture since recorded time. Inherent in this dualism, this walking alongside humans even as they dodge our spears, bullets, and traps, wolves are fighters: they are warriors that stand dignified against a raging war of corrupt politics and hatred rooted solely in myths.

For authors like Jack London and Ernest Thompson Seton, the wolves' midnight howls were enough voices to prompt them to action, to preserve the forest warriors. However, in today's society, the wolf's voice has become mute. Gunshots ring across the fields, and their echoes linger, howls unheard. Through this silence, people have arisen to help give wolves their voices back. Some of these people have contributed to this very anthology, but make note that even these contributors mark only a small percentage of the warriors that speak for wolves. Warriors that *are* wolves and warriors that *speak* for wolves work together, creating one enormous pack, the titular Wolf Warriors.

However, these warriors present their voices in different ways. Some have contributed short stories and flash fiction. Others have contributed essays and poetry. Yet others have sent in artwork and photography. Each work is wolf-themed, yet the cast of wolf characters throughout the anthology is as diverse as the contributors themselves. From wolf cubs to elder wolves, from wolves that will do anything to survive to wolves that will risk their lives to save anyone, even dogs, from wolves that can become humans to intelligent wolves that fight for their own rights, *Wolf Warriors* has something for everyone.

Many award-winning and best-selling authors and artists have volunteered their contributions to this anthology. Check out David Clement-Davies' short story sequel to the best-selling *Fell* entitled "Fell's Dream," where Fell's waking world becomes distorted with that of dreams, and he must question whether his entire life is the product of fate or his own genuine choices and emotions. Another example is Hugo-award winner Catherynne M. Valente and her short story "The Wolves of Brooklyn," in which Camille considers the man-eating wolves that have invaded Brooklyn and fights against the raid in her own, unique way. Our third featured contributor is award-winning artist Lauren Strohacker: observe the ways that she uses mixed media involving light and darkness to recreate the wolf in all its beauty.

The book you hold now contains many more authors and artists than these, and the wolves you encounter will put you through the full spectrum of human emotion. You will smile. You will laugh. You will cry. You will howl. So, tread forward, one paw after another, and join the ranks of both human and lupine Wolf Warriors. Hear their voices and raise your own, for the greatest warriors are not the ones who have the sharpest swords or the sturdiest shields, but the ones who join in the battle cry and inspire more around them to give all they've got to protect the things that are most worth protecting.

A salute to the National Wolfwatcher Coalition for continuing to educate. A salute to the many contributors of this anthology. And, of course, a final salute to you the reader.

I hope you enjoy all of these wonderful contributions.

Jonathan W. Thurston
Editor

FELL'S DREAM
DAVID CLEMENT-DAVIES

Bio

David Clement-Davies is the British author of Fire Bringer, The Sight, Fell, *and many other wonderful novels and short stories. He has been on the Long List for the Carnegie Medal and has won the Parents' Choice Award for his novels. He studied English and History at Edinburgh University and Westminister School. He is now the founder of Phoenix Ark Press, a crowd-funded publisher, where he is working on re-printing* Fire Bringer, *writing and editing* Dragon in the Post, *and publishing* Light of the White Bear. *He fights against much of mainstream publishing and the political cynicism he claims is prevalent throughout it.*

Here he tells the story of the black wolf Fell after his adventures through two novels are finished. He finds his entire life put into question by his true love. What is real? What is dreaming?

"We are such stuff as dreams are made of, and our little life is rounded by a sleep."
The Tempest—William Shakespeare

The darkened cave loomed about the sleeping, sleek black wolf and in its center lay the charred remains of a human fire. A fire which some time before, perhaps a year, had blazed to cook raw meat, bring warmth and cheer, and in the circle of a human world to light the minds of those who gazed and wondered, as they watched its shadows dancing on the walls, sometimes illuminating images painted there in simple ochre pigment, millennia before, of men of stick, of fields and running deer—the dawn of art and making. Did primitive minds see in those totem images what modern terms of science know and limit in the miracle, or did they grasp at wondrous shapes immortal, of gods and demons, spirits and heroes too?

Never men of language, learning nor much debate, those ancient fire makers, nor deep philosophy either. Never hearing of the mighty worlds of Greece or Rome, the great Socrates or his pupil Plato, the sweep of time repeating, but hunters reared to fight on instinct and survive. Human shapes were gone now though from the womb of these mossy rock walls, so the drowsy cavern had returned to animals alone and creeping things, the insects of the dark. Only the dozing wolf retained some distant sense of a human passing and their threatened return. For this strange creature was no ordinary Varg, the wolfen name of wolf, but this was the black wolf Fell, the loner whose power to see and know had long become a legend. The Sight they called it, both gift and curse, which made him see so deep it even gave him glimpse of human minds and the shapes of thoughts themselves.

Fell of the mountaintops, he was called, Fell the fighter of the world, Fell who could see in the dark yet not become it. Whose journeys through the wildest lands of Transylvania had brought him joy and sorrow, shown both dark and light, and a taste of good and evil, then set his teeth against experience itself. Hurt Fell, traveller beneath the ice, redeemed by Larka, his dearest sister, and her burning love and courage. But Fell was saved by another too, his dear mate Tarlar, companion of his wandering years. Fell, whose heart and fighting power had protected a human girl and brought her to her destiny at last.

The legendary wolf's thick black coat was snowing now, flecked with age, and as he lay there breathing gently in the dark, Fell's still powerful muzzle twitched with the onset of the dream. His fine strong head turned softly to the left, too long associated with dark and sinister things, for the word sinister itself means 'to the left', and suddenly it was as if he was touching a mighty sea beneath him, one of unformed meanings and struggling life. Who knows if animals dream, like Man or Woman, what forms and mysteries travel through their brains, without that power of words that name the things of the world without, yet sometimes so mislead the human animal too? It is certain that animals dream something though, like catching echoes of experience and unspoken memory, forming into consciousness and thought. Just watch a cat asleep.

What is it that truly differentiates the Human from the animal though? Is it not that very power called self-awareness and recognition too, itself a kind of gazing on, a seeing? As Fell had felt such a sudden recognition gazing on his mate, dear Tarlar, as if she were part of him and his story already, as if all of it was somehow meant to be, like some hidden pattern in the world, or Fell had the power to know things before they even happened and really write his own life story too. What did the wolf now remember? *"We are Masters of our destiny, if only we have the courage to make them."*

Where did it come from though, the very miracle called thought, then language, as shattering sometimes as a Fire from Heaven, or a brilliant lightning bolt? Man meanwhile, that changing primate who always forgets his real origins, thinks that he alone is touched by 'God' or knowing. But Dolphins of the sea and mighty Whales have brains as large as he and larger still. Dolphins too have spindle cells that form to make the very mystery of thinking. Fell knew as he lay there that man was a kind of God form too, out of his myths and storytelling, perhaps, a thing of legend too, if often twisted out of shape. He suddenly wondered though what it all means, or if all of us are only born to die.

Even the fact of trying to think on man began to make Fell stir and growl—for the dream was getting deeper now. Perhaps the shape of it was defined by his final thoughts, that Autumn day, sparked by the sight of a forking path without, as he wandered from his kill. He wondered then what might have been, as older creatures start to ask, if ever his travels had taken a different path. If white-furred Larka had not been there at the citadel, Roman Harja, in this mighty land beyond the Forests, Transylvania, had not brought him from his mountain lair, then given herself on the bridge, fighting bitter Morgra, their aunt, to change his power to light and bring him from the shadows. That wounded wolf, battling in the savagery of the world, born to the fight of nature, who others had labelled Evil and who thought himself for a time the Dark One himself, dreadful Wolfbane.

"Fell, dearest Fell."

The voice was faint, half-echoing in the cave, and the dozing creature stirred and his muzzle twitched.

"Tarlar, is that you?"

Fell did not know now if the voice was within him or without, but at the thought of her his heart leaped, as it always did, as if she were a part of his very being, another Self. Or in his meeting her his true Self had become complete. The beautiful, brave-eyed she-wolf Tarlar, who had jumped to his side to fight for love and all of nature too—the making of Fell's world anew, the bringer and the mother of his cubs. So Fell had freed himself at last, yet given a generous howl to all the lonely of the earth, the lost and suffering and in pain, a deep farewell, but dared to live himself, with her at his side. To live for ourselves at last is a mighty thing and not the same as selfishness, at all, for journeys of courage free others too into their hope and power.

Fell wondered now whatever might have become of him if that path had been different though and Tarlar had just not understood, understood that he could never win without her at his side, nor be truly whole. With the wondering came a kind of sickness in his belly and an agonizing ache. The wolf was sweating now and felt a nameless fear.

"WonderousTarlar, come lie down beside me."

"Black Fell, you are nothing but a fool."

It was as if the air in the cave was suddenly made of ice, and from without its very mouth looked like some Evil Eye.

"A fool, my love?"

The wolf's eyes opened sharply in the dark, and there she stood, her fine fur shining in the shadows, touched by slanting moonlight, her eyes like burning coals—his loyal, loving Tarlar.

"Fool, Tarlar?" whispered Fell dully again, twitching his ears, "But what are you saying, love?"

"Love?" came the strangely cold reply, "A dream can never love, and you are nothing but a dream."

"A dream?"

"A thing of story, Fell. Impossible. A mere unconscious beast. No creature then of living flesh and bone but simply a legend and a lie."

The standing wolf was growling now, and her eyes were full of sudden scorn.

"Why do you talk to me so, my Tarlar?" whispered Fell, "I see you standing here, my love, my deep salvation. You are part of me forever. For not only in their mating do true lovers enter the cave of one another's being and so must take care in parting. A carelessness can kill."

Now the she-wolf's eyes were shining defiantly, and there anger was in them too.

"No foolish Fell, it never happened, the thing of which you dreamt."

"Never happened?"

"I'm nothing but your deep dream too. A story, Fell. For that I hate you too."

"Hate me, Tarlar?"

The male wolf's breathing now was shallow and constrained, the pain was getting worse, and Fell's long, greying tail began to twitch.

"You," growled Tarlar, "You make us all a myth, Fell, an almost human thing. Creatures of mighty journeys, things of human words, when Lera, real animals, are simply what they are. I know you not."

"But you, sweetest Tarlar, you jumped to my side. You came to me in the dark. Please Tarlar, no. Do not call it just a story."

"Please?" came the drappa's snarl and with it the dragga, the alpha male, began to rise in the cave, "You talk like a weakling cub, a human boy, a Sikla, no alpha wolf at all, but mere Omega. Those who run with the she-wolves do not linger in the dark, consumed by guilt, feeding on their pain, hiding away in the cave of themselves, thinking themselves the world alone. A dragga jumps to a drappa's side to find his mate and power, not the other way around."

"No," said Fell pitifully, and suddenly he felt the stoniness of the cave all about him, as if he had become it, and thought of his pack brother Kar in another cave too, touching madness there, until he saw himself again and knew his purpose, "You saw my loneliness, so understood and came, even as I brought that human girl to freedom— Alina Sculcuvant. You said you loved me, Tarlar, and we fought for all of nature. We ran beneath the stars, so wild and free, so very happy. A beautiful and holy thing."

"It did not happen Fell, except in story. I love you not."

It was as if there was a cry around them now, a bitter screech, as though the molecules of lightless air were forming sounds, reverberating a crow-like'*kraaaaar*'. It sounded like despair ,or empty death, pecked at by jackdaws. Fell's tail had raised, and although quite old he felt the urge to show his teeth and prove his dominance again.

"But Tarlar, we are connected," Fell growled, with rising fury now, "like everything that is. Yet in our story, by far more than mere chance. The Sight has shown it true. My life is yours. We two are one, forever. That is our meaning."

"My life, you say?" said the she-wolf with a snarl, "weak words of a wolf that ever thought himself the center of the world. A dreamer, liar, and a fool. You are like all the foolish Draggas, Fell, arrogant and vain. As hollow as this cave."

"Hollow?" growled Fell, and somewhere the wolf remembered a distant, booming oracle, a growl as deep as the drum beat of the world. "But did you not see within me? My love for you was like entering a giant cavern, Tarlar, made of myself, no—my very Self. Or like the Self of the world. There all things flowed free, in thought but also fact, as if I were a very God. Like matter at the forming of the stars, a magic making as powerful as everything. A flowing river of hope and deep connection. A startling mystery. For all must flow."

"Connection?" hissed his mate, "Magic? There is no magic, fool. There are no legends, prophecies, nor miracles either. Nothing exists but all the hardness of the real and savage world, of fighting nature. The winning or the dying. The jaws of the wild wolf, Fell, that dare not fail , as you have failed."

"There is," growled Fell with bitter anguish now, feeling a weakness in his legs at words of failure, "Everything is magic, Tarlar, veiled by human words, a miracle like fire, a real seeing. A moving energy that we must not betray but feed, then pass on to our cubs, the hope of the future. It bubbles like a spring, the energy, Tarlar, The Sight , if only creatures trust. The way we look at one another, my love, can burn or bless. A curse, or blessing, held in the eye of being. I loved you at once, dear Tarlar, so long ago, because I knew you looked not with the eyes of deceit, but the eyes of love. At the real me too, in all the darkness, the real all of us."

"Love?" snarled the she-wolf now, and suddenly Fell felt as if he were falling through the floor of the cave itself, "You are deceived and trick your memory. You fight to make things different from the truth they really are because you cannot take the pain and grief of real life. So you tell feeble stories that try to bring us others hope. See my wolf eyes then, Fell Failingpaw, and burn and be ashamed. I never came. I am not here; this is a dream, but in the dream I love another now and you are all alone once more."

"Another?"

"Kar."

"Kar?" gasped Fell in horror and in that moment it was as if his mate had undone each of Larka's gifts, the white she-wolf his sister, and worse, with Kar, the pack brother of his youth. The law of the pack, the law that unlike human animals protects their own, was broken.

"But why?"

"You are Evil, and the dark, wicked Fell, with that power of shadows that you have, and now deny. You always were."

"Evil, Tarlar? No, would you un-write all that my sister did and knew in her love? Deny? The power of The Sight is also curse, and so I sought to simply live and love, to find a happiness with you. To have a life."

Fell's being felt a dagger-pierce at the impossible words, and he thought of Morgra now, who had begun a legend in her longing to have cubs and called him Wolfbane. Suddenly he thought the moonlight come because it seemed shapes were moving in the cave walls, as man's fire once had made those paintings dance, in fact and in their minds. But in these shapes were spectral Varg, the spirit wolves that told of another world beyond, of death and meadows red, where none return from except with a Summoning Howl, and of a mighty battle too, in the field of Kosov. As the wolf lay there sleeping, or standing before his mate, wrapped in swirling images, the black wolf wondered now if all was fantasy, and life was nothing but a tale, a dream, surrounded by a river of deepest sleep—Eternity.

Then the wolf seemed to hear a dreaming human mind, a soldier's sleeping thoughts, stirring for the fight, that seemed to say that all that story, all this too, even here and now, was nothing more than human voices warring. Nothing more than a man and woman standing in a room, accusing one another of not showing enough love.

It was the image before Fell's mind's eye now though that seared his brain and tore into his heart, like Morgra's claws. Tarlar's dark betrayal, yet not just that alone, but closest to his very heart and center, with the wise wolf Kar. His powerful mind saw them running together now, beneath the stars, walking in glorious sunlight together, and it made his body keen with pain.

Then it was as if the cave had darkened, the backs of his eyes uncoupled from his mind, a weakening in his very seeing, in his piercing of the darkness of the world. For all of us must penetrate the dark of ignorance, of mystery and of fear. Tarlar was dimmer now, less clear, less real. No thing of touch and sense at all, of taste and smell, that we must know as we grasp the world and great reality. Must grasp as we hold on to the living fact of love, which like everything worth having is no mere idea but an act.

"NO TARLAR," snarled Fell, and now the helpless rage began to come, the myriad thoughts, the violent feelings from a wolf who Tarlar herself had said had felt more than any she had ever known. Yet had Fell dreamt all that and was he dreaming now? Why should a dream, in the caves of our minds, not be as real as what we know when waking? Fell felt the sting of hate and despair, and in his flaring thoughts he wanted to jump at the drappa, to tear her throat, to fight and kill his beloved Tarlar. To take revenge.

Everything that had happened in his triumph and his joy, Fell's freeing, was in that instant swept away, and Fell was lost, alone again, falling, falling forever, looking up at her, as if from an ice cave, or a well, where his claws could make no purchase on the walls. The pain was so extreme it seemed to last for years, this scrabbling fall, his mind to tear in half, his being to be nothing but a hollow thing of anger, made of stone—an empty cave. Then the bitter howl went up—"*aooooooooow.*"

"Please Tarlar," Fell growled now, so desperately, when his call was done, "why do we slay each other's souls, in fear and hate, not lift each other up? That is real love, and the forgiving of our flaws. You said you loved me: it is a sacred word."

"Love comes and goes, poor fool, like life itself. I found myself in another's eyes, that's all."

"Another's eyes? But why with Kar? It is so cruel."

"Pitiful Fell, haven't you learned the greatest truth of life, especially in the wild, that life is just unfair?"

"Unfair?"

Tarlar's eyes were shining once more, but now with a savage pride and growing scorn, as if this younger creature than the black wolf had learned some universal truth no other knew, some words of brilliance, and in those words he hated her, his mate. Fell, who had seen so much of mind and Man, of mighty Evolution that ties us all together, even at the level of smallest atom, of the savage but glorious beauty of the world and being. Fell knew life could be unfair, of course, could be so harsh, knew above all others, for he had truly seen the dark abyss. But in his coming this feeling creature Fell had fought to see beyond such simple, brutal truths, to see forever, to look through the dark and back to light again.

Unfair? Do not even human cubs seek first a fairness in the world that Fell had always hunted for and what justice now was living in her words, what brute stupidity? It seemed the wolf would rather be a Man than suffer this. The scorn of Tarlar's ignorance for his journey, his power, and all he had done and learned, all they had together, made mock of everything, even the truth itself. Why had she not told him before? Because of her secret Self and desire to protect her heart alone. In that darkest moment Fell felt something deep inside him snap, his trust in anything.

The agony was like feeling everything alive caught in its suffering and its journey through to death. The hate and rage grew like a darkening storm of horror. Fell felt himself at war, with spectres everywhere, lost now, and in that raging pain came visions of their murdered cubs, of dying worlds and warring souls, of rapine and of war. Yet there was no power in this hate, this rage, and even as Fell made to spring at her his legs gave way, and he was on the ground again, struggling on his side. Or was Fell sleeping still, and was he real? Fell knew then the greatest secret, that you can never fight into a place of love, for it can kill you.

"Kill me then, cruel Tarlar," whimpered the black wolf bitterly, "your sacrifice to the dying fire. Take out my throat and stop those words you hate, my stories. For you have killed me in my heart and mind and body, murderous, cowardly she-wolf. You who I thought so gentle and so true, so innocent and pure."

"Because I am flesh and blood, no image and no abstract. A real she-wolf."

"You with the eyes of cold deceit, all along, knowing only your own right to harm and seize your happiness at any cost."

"Mad and raging wolf," hissed Tarlar indignantly, "Evil beast."

"Evil?" wailed Fell, "A beast? Not evil, Tarlar, but destroyed by beauty and a fearful, terrible betrayal. You kill my faith. *Beware the betrayer, whose meaning is strife.*"

As he lay there now remembering the peace that she had brought him one, thinking of the words of a legend and a prophecy, this poor, dark creature Fell began to moan, and everything around him black-ened. For Fell knew the secret law, that dragga and drappa, masculine and feminine, forms that move within us all, are made by life to mingle and conjoin, compelled to mingle, and in their proper union is both light and true, right seeing. Sometimes so blazing it holds a visionary hue. Yet if they harm each other, or harm themselves, each one of us can go so dark it seems there is no meaning anymore, no light nor hope. Each one of us can go blind.

"Tarlar," whispered Fell, "I cannot breath. I'm going blind, and not with age but pain. The dark is terrible."

Then Fell knew the truest male secret, that he had found his real power and his mate by making a journey deep inside himself and then in fact. So Fell had won his prize, always held by being well and whole within. So comes the recognition, like a God and Goddess walking to-gether, wreathed in beauty and in peace. Yet in the end wild Tarlar had just not understood him.

Evil? Such labels we put on one another's forms, in ignorance and fear, and so produce much evil too, as Larka's love had brought Fell such redemption. It is the harming of the wholeness that causes wretched things. For wretched were the black wolf's warring thoughts now, as the energy of hate began to choke him, and in his mind his claws lashed out, as if he could slay the world and use his teeth to end all suffering, or just his own. He felt the death of love and life and hope.

"Fell, dear Fell. She did not understand. She had not read your sto-ry well."

"Dear Fell?" he growled and started at the voice.

Fell turned his sightless head toward his mate, yet Tarlar had start-ed too, in the cave.

"Who's there?" the she-wolf whispered.

There was a ghastly silence now, an echo of nothingness and loss so many feel. Yet Tarlar padded forward, as if her Fell were leading her, compelling her, writing her like a story. Her tail was raised; her jaws, powerful as twenty dogs, were primed to bite, the bloodlust coming on.

"Kill me then Tarlar, end it now," moaned Fell, "Forever. For just like Man, the Varg prefer their crudest law, their cruel triumphs, so they make life unfair. For they are made for one thing only, not a faith but war and fear, vicious freedoms, and their deep hypocrisies too. Believing themselves so good when they are bad, and their negligence does such harm. We break real connections at our peril, Tarlar, and I know that it can truly mar the world, take out the better eye of The Sight. That is no story."

Tarlar was snarling now, her growls filling the chamber, angry at Fell for his supine helplessness, his weakness. But ready to kill him too, to sink her canines in his throat. She knew too she had killed the wolf already, in spirit, and now at last came time for Fell to die. Tarlar dipped down on her haunches now, prone to pounce, to fly at Fell's windpipe, skin and blood. Yet just before she sprang a shape came jumping from the wall itself. Fell thought it a spectre, but its shining light was brilliant and pure, and suddenly the cave was filled with hope again.

"Stand, faithless she-wolf," growled a mighty voice, that echoed out like thunder, "for you shall not kill my brother. Ever. He who has helped so many in his journeying. In his stories."

"Larka?" whispered Fell in wonder.

Cruel Tarlar was cowering now, quaking, blinded by this miracle, the vision standing before her , that her ignorance refused to even believe, her carelessness and blindness,. For there stood the white wolf, the other part of Fell, the white wolf Larka, and a legend too. She who had died, slain by human hand, but always come in times of peril.

"You," whispered Tarlar bitterly.

"What have you done?" Fell's spectral sister snarled, "What have you done to Fell and why? Come dear Fell, come back to the light."

Larka's force and meaning came not then in human words but deepest growls of feeling.

"Be gone. You do not exist," said Tarlar coldly in the cave, "you cannot, and he is nothing either. A pointless dream."

"Faithless Tarlar," whispered Larka angrily, "How can you say this wolf lying before you does not even exist? You made the pact in both your hearts and minds."

"A dream," said Tarlar angrily again. "No wolf can speak, nor wield a power of Seeing."

"A dream that dreamt you too, perhaps, cold, brittle Tarlar?" said Larka with a smile. "For how do you stand here now, if you are but a dream, or simply a story too? Then this betrayal is not real either, dearest Fell," she added, looking at her brother, "For nothing is set and some may write the stories of their lives, or write them once again. Our dreaming minds are always seeking the proper pattern of things and a deepest healing too."

A strange confusion seemed to enter Tarlar's eyes, some painful paradox, where reality and story now were one, and Fell stirred hopefully on the floor of the cave. Suddenly those dead charred embers blazed, and the human fire was lit once more and a voice seemed to say "always return to the fire."

"Never," whispered his mate though, "Fell must die. To free the wolf from the stories of Men forever and back into their own pure truth again, their natural reality. To free us from foolish legends and The Sight, which itself is just a lie, a dark religion."

"A Lie?" said Larka, "I and Fell have proven the power of The Sight, in story and in fact, and the blinding harm we do by betrayal and broken connections. Shown that all of us are dark and light, but with man's words, his blindnesses, we sometimes split the world in half. As Fell is black and I am white. No, none can live within the war of opposites and still be whole. But you, dark Tarlar, secret thing, because you have no real faith, would call him Evil itself and send my brother blind, you who said you loved him? Do you not know the power that love can give us, but the grave responsibility?"

Now Larka was growling, showing her teeth, and something shamed came into Tarlar's glittering eyes, but the bloodlust was even greater, and so she sprang at Fell. Larka rose to meet her, two shewolves lunging to battle in the dark above the dream fire and Fell knew now that with all of Larka's power she must surely kill his mate. Even in his bleak despair, his agony, Fell could not see his Tarlar killed.

"NO," cried Fell, "Larka, let her go, dearest sister. Remember all we saw and Larka's blessing too. Remember."

Even as he said it the she-wolves struck, but like a cloud of stardust his sister Larka vanished in a shimmering haze, and Tarlar was held there suspended in mid-air. Although it seemed that particles of light were flowing through her now, like electricity, making her fur translucent in the flames, it was as if time itself had stopped, and Fell now heard another voice, telling him a story:

"Once there was a beast, dear Fell" it whispered gently, "that had fallen under an ancient spell and curse. A man of savage darkness, in the clever, harming things he made and did with his mind and hands, because of naked vulnerability and to give him what he thought was power. But one day on the mountainsides that he rarely visited he saw a beautiful she-wolf, whose fur was black and white, and in her running tread he saw such wild freedom and such joy he longed to run with her forever. So with his clever, calculating mind he dug an earth trap and caught her in a net, then took her to a cave the mouth of which he sealed with golden bars. So every day he came to her and talked to her of his cunning world, yet ached for her to love him and make him free of his curse. This creature frightened the wild wolf, with his strange sounds she could not interpret, his bars inside and out, but with time she came to understand him too, then saw what he really feared, the savagery inside himself and all his guilt at being part of the pain of the world. So one day when his heart was breaking in his chains he sunk on the cave floor, close to death and the she wolf rose and padded towards the human. The she wolf looked at him with care, the eyes of love, for though he had barred the cave to make her prison, he had given her fine food and fresh warm straw and with her he was always kind, except when she pined and howled to escape from him. Now the creature felt such care and compassion for a fellow animal that she licked his face and nuzzled him with her snout, and in that moment of no deceit the curse was lifted, and there lay a fine wild dragga on the cave floor, a wild, unconscious animal. Waking to life, in wordless growls he whispered this: *"Beloved, you must always be free to leave me, yet remember this, for you the door of my cage is always open"*. With that the bars of man-dug gold dissolved like magic, and out they ran, into the lovely air, together, no longer guilty of their truest natures, nor fearing anything at all."

The dreaming story ended, the fairy tale, and as it did so Fell seemed to understand that all the myths are there to show the bridge between our hoping hearts and often hard reality, in the search for our higher selves. But that we are only free when we learn to trust and free each other too, for all real journeys are kinds of transformations. Then he looked again at Tarlar's floating, shimmering features and wondered if this was nothing but a dream, for in the magic of Larka's sacred light

Fell saw other features there, that of her, his sister Larka, and of Tarlar too, of his old nurse Brassa and of Morgra also. Have you not noticed how lovers' faces always change? "Forgive," a voice seemed to say, and Tarlar vanished too, as if she were dissolving back into the very cave wall. The fire was gone as well. Had it all really been nothing but a dream, a chimera of the mind's great ocean and its darkest depths?

Light was coming now outside, and with deep trepidation in his heart Fell awoke and yawned and licked his lips. For a moment fear and grief threatened to invade him once again, but as he rose and lifted his tail he saw her through the cave mouth, coming eagerly up the hill in the morning sunlight, and her eyes were smiling brilliantly—his Tarlar.

"A dream," Fell whispered, with a gladdening heart, as light as morning, and thinking of his living cubs, "All just a bitter dream, or nightmare. Yet if, my love, if I had lost you in another way, dear Tarlar, through illness, chance or death, would I not have had to let my suffering vanish too, to continue on my journey? So we must learn to hold on tightly but to let go lightly too, and use the stories we tell as kinds of exorcisms against the dark."

As he said it a wind came licking through the cave, both clean and fresh, the deepest sigh, and it was as if the strange wolf knew that all was simply breathing in and out. Fell padded forward, and as his forepaws touched the remnants of human fire they broke a branch turned to charcoal by the long dead heat. The sharp snap echoed loudly and woke him fully, and another story seemed to come to his searching mind, or perhaps a lesson. A story of the world of the mind and dreams themselves being like primitive men in a cave, watching fire-lit shadows on a wall and mistaking them for what exists without, in hope or fear. Then Fell knew that we are both things of flesh and blood and bone and pure ideas too, mind, archetypes of perfect being and form, and that the two weave together like a river through the land. Fell knew that we must not confuse the two though, projecting abstract fears on one another and that to really live we must live not in a cave, but in the real world. But that if we are not careful we can throw such shadows on one another as to kill the very soul. It is only love that truly gives that power and grave responsibility.

The wolf walked on, fearful to look back now, to ask if Larka had really come to him once more, fearful to know the truth of dreams themselves. For they live beneath us like a sea. Perhaps it was the thought of Tarlar's dream words that was too painful to really bear, but in the half light, Fell did not stop to know if this had really happened or was a dream. How could a creature such as he?

Fell did not see then, as the wolf approached the opening of the cave, no more an Evil Eye, that there, on the wall, between the stick men and the running deer, now ran an ochre she-wolf, patterned on stone by ancient hands, or by his magic dream. For the truth of life is something always remains of our passing, even as all lets go. He knew this too, that although every creature ages, fails, comes to its natural span and suffers grief, there is no real death, because what remains is the ever repeating pattern of lives and beings' greatest stories. They come and come again and in their making we continue too—in Art.

"Go, dear Fell, go once again and live."

Fell raised his thick, proud tail now at the freeing voice and sprang clear of the cave into the glistening morning air. Then, with hope flowing through his beating heart again, brave Fell was running out once more, out in the wondrous world, proud and alive and free. While at his side, though even in this golden morning light her face seemed changing still, through many beings and many lives, came a beautiful, moving she-wolf.

LAUREN STROHACKER
ANIMAL LAND

Bio

Lauren Strohacker was born in Amherst, Ohio, in 1983. She received a BFA (2006) from The Ohio State University and an MFA (2011) from Arizona State University. Strohacker currently lives and works in Scottsdale, Arizona, where her work examines the ever-growing conflict between humans and animals as our manufactured environments (physical and economical) expand into natural habitats. Aligned with wildlife conservationists, Strohacker installs interdisciplinary visual simulations of native species, effectively "reintroducing" animals into the urban landscape. The simulations function as artificial encounters meant to question the public's commitment to wildlife, foster dialogue about cohabitation, and critique the highly politicized (non-public) debates and decisions on wildlife regulations that subvert animal sovereignty. Through collaboration with wildlife organizations such as Defenders of Wildlife, Strohacker creates ephemeral public artwork and exhibits the documentation of that work throughout Arizona.

Animal Land reimagines traditional wildlife encounters in a contemporary format—through technology in an urban space with human inhabitants. Large format video projections generate synthetic animals, native to each location, that are completely decontextualized. Void of environment, sound, and color, they are activated only by electricity, light, and cityscape. Novel human/animal relationships are realized as manmade forms and sounds interrupt the projection, causing space shifts between resolution (physical sense) and sparking faded memories of true animal encounters (metaphysical sense). Both real and imaginary interactions with animals influence human perceptions of cohabitation vs. conflict, a dichotomy that ultimately determines the fate of native species, traditional habitats, and the uncertain results of synanthropic urprise—as wild spaces decline in the expansion of civilization. Collaborators, Strohacker and Sollars, are responding to nature on the verge of collapse due to the politicization and exploitation of land and wildlife management, and investigating a future where genuine interactions between humans and non-human animals may not exist. Quietly detached, *Animal Land* is a visual metaphor of this long, unfolding narrative that wavers between displacement, reintroduction and loss. Animal Land, is created in collaboration with artist, Kendra Sollars and local wildlife rehabilitation/education centers, including Southwest Wildlife Conservation Center, Liberty Wildlife, and Tucson Wildlife Center.

NO(w)HERE: Tempe Center for the Arts and Tucson

NO(w)HERE is an ephemeral site-specific public work designed to incite awareness about the Mexican Gray Wolf, which remains the most endangered mammal in North America. Paper apparitions of this embattled predator appear in cities of the Southwest. The number of paper wolves corresponds to the current Mexican Gray Wolf count, giving a visual reference to their surprise—population. Commissioned by Defenders of Wildlife for Wolf Awareness Week, Tucson AZ, 2011. Photography by local Tucson photographers. Commissioned by Grand Canyon Wolf Recovery for Wolf Awareness Week, Flagstaff AZ, 2009. Photography by Nathan Renn.

Animal Land. Lauren Strohacker & Kendra Sollars. Video projection.
2014. Photo Credit: Kendra Sollars.

Animal Land. Lauren Strohacker & Kendra Sollars. Video projection.
2014. Photo Credit: Kendra Sollars.

NO(w)HERE: Tempe Center for the Arts. Lauren Strohacker.
Vinyl on glass. 2013. Photo Credit: Lauren Strohacker.

NO(w)HERE: Tempe Center for the Arts. Lauren Strohacker.
Vinyl on glass. 2013. Photo Credit: Lauren Strohacker.

NO(w)HERE: Tucson, Arizona. Lauren Strohacker. Paper and public space. 2011. Photo Credit: Shiloh Walkosak (photo contest winner).

CATHERYNNE M. VALENTE
THE WOLVES OF BROOKLYN

Bio

Catherynne M. Valente is a New York Times bestselling writer from Washington and is best-known for her novels in the Fairyland *series, the novels in the* Orphan's Tale *series, and* Palimpsest. *She has won the Hugo Award, the Lambda Literary Award, the Mythopoeic Award, and more. Along with novels, she has written acclaimed short stories, poems, and even nonfiction. She has studied at UC San Diego and Edinburgh University, where she studied the Classics. She lives on an island off the coast of Maine with a small but growing menagerie of beasts, some of which are human.*

The following story was originally printed by Fantasy Magazine *in 2011 and is reprinted here with minimal edits. It follows young Camille in a wolf-infested Brooklyn as she finds her own unique way of coming to terms with the new danger that has threatened everyone's way of living.*

It was snowing when the wolves first came, loping down Flatbush Ave, lithe and fast, panting clouds, their paws landing with a soft, heavy sound like bombs falling somewhere far away. Everyone saw them. Everyone will tell you about it, even if they were in Pittsburgh that weekend. Even if they slept through it. Even if their mothers called up on Monday and asked what in the world was going on out there in that Babylon they chose to live in. No, the collective everyone looked out of their walk-up windows the moment they came and saw those long shapes, their fur frosted and tinkling, streaming up the sidewalks like a flood, like a wave, and the foam had teeth.

These days, we go to work. We come home. We put on dresses the color of steel and suits the color of winter. We go to cafes and drink lattes with whiskey and without sugar or bars where we drink whiskey without ice and without water. Bars aren't noisy anymore. It's a murmur, not a roar. They keep the music turned down so we can talk. So we can tell our wolf stories. Outside the windows, where the frost crackles the jambs, they stand and press their noses to the glass, fogging it with their breath.

Camille sits with her elbow crossing her knee, her dress glittering ice because they like it that way. They watch you, when you shine. Her lavender hair catches the lamplight, expensive, swooping and glossy, rich punk girl's hair. She says:

"I was walking to the store for coffee. We always run out; I just never think of it until it's already gone. I thought I'd get some cookies, too. The kind with jam in the middle, that look like a red eye. I guess that doesn't matter. You know, I always f— up jokes, too. Anyway, it was snowing, and I just wanted some coffee and cookies and then it was walking next to me. He was walking next to me. A big one, as big as a horse, and white, so white in the snow and the streetlight, his fur so thick your hands could disappear in it. All I could think of was the horse I used to love when I was a kid. Boreal. My mom used to drive me to the stables every morning and I'd brush him and say his name over and over, and the wolf was white like Boreal, and tall like him, and I started running because, well, s—, he's a wolf. Running toward the store, like I could still get coffee and cookies. He ran with me. So fast, and I had my red coat on and we were running together through the snow, his breath puffing out next to me, and I saw that his eyes were gold. Not yellow, but gold. I was red and he was gold and we were running so fast together, as fast as Boreal and I used to run; faster. We ran past the store, into the park, and snow flew out under my feet like feathers. I stopped by that little footbridge—the wolf was gone and I had just kept on running out into the frozen grass."

The wolves never cross the bridges. Sometimes they run right up to them, and sniff the air like Brooklyn has a musk and it fades at the edges, like they accidentally came too close to the end of the world. They turn around and walk back into the borough with their tails down. They stop right at Queens, too. They won't cross the borders; they know their home. For awhile no one talked about anything else, and all our friends in Manhattan wanted to come and see them, photograph them, write about them. I mean, wouldn't you? But there were incidents—like any dog, they don't like strangers. This girl Marjorie Guste wanted to do a whole installation about them, with audio and everything. She brought a film crew and a couple of models to look beautiful next to them and she never got a shot. The wolves hid from her. They jumped onto the roofs of brownstones, dipped into alleys and crawled into sewer gratings. We could see where they'd gone sometimes, but when MG swung her lens around they'd be gone, leaping across the treetops in the snow.

Geoffrey, despite the name, is a girl. It's a joke left over from when she was a kid and hated being the four hundredth Jenny in her grade. She's got green sequins on, like a cigarette girl from some old movie theatre. I love how her chin points, like the bottom of a heart. We dated for awhile, when I was still going to school. We were too lazy, though. The way you just wake up sometimes and the house is a disaster but you can't remember how it really got that way, except that how it got that way is that you didn't do the dishes or pick up your clothes. Every day you made a choice not to do those things and it added up to not being able to get to the door over the coffee mugs and paperbacks piled up on the floor. But still, she was at my house the night the wolves came, because laziness goes both ways.

She says: "Most of the time, you know, I really like them. They're peaceful. Quiet. But the other week I was down on Vanderbilt and I saw one come up out of the street. Like, ok, the street cracked open—you know there's never any traffic anymore so it was just cold and quiet and the storm was still blowing, and the street came open like it had popped a seam. Two white paws came up, and then the whole wolf, kicking and scrabbling its hind legs against the road to get a grip on it. Just like a fat little puppy. It climbed out and then it bit the edge of the hole it had made and dragged the street back together. I looked around—you know how it is now. Not a soul on the sidewalk. No one else saw. The wolf looked at me and its tongue lolled out, red in the snow, really red, like it had just eaten. Then it trotted off. I went out and touched the place where it broke through. The road was hot, like an iron."

The wolves have eaten people. Why be coy about it? Not a lot of people. But it's happened. As near as anyone can figure, the first one they ate was a Russian girl named Yelena. They surrounded her and she stood very still, so as not to startle them. Finally, she said: "I'm lonely," because it's weird but you tell the wolves things, sometimes. You can't help it, all these old wounds come open and suddenly you're confessing to a wolf who never says anything back. She said: "I'm lonely," and they ate her in the street. They didn't leave any blood. They're fastidious like that. Since then I know of about four or five others, and well, that's just not enough to really scare people. Obviously, you'll be special, that they'll look at you with those huge eyes and you'll understand something about each other, about the tundra and blood and Brooklyn and winter, and they'll mark you but pass you by. For most of us that's just what happens. My friend Daniel got eaten, though. It's surprising how you can get used to that. I don't know what he said to them. To tell you the truth, I didn't know Daniel that well.

Seth's eyes have grown dark circles. He came wearing a threadbare 1950s chic suit: thin tie, grey lapels, wolf pack boy with a rat pack look. The truth is I've known Seth since seventh grade, but we never talk about it. We lived on the same sunny broad Spielbergian cul-de-sac, we conquered the old baseball diamond where we, the weird bookish kids, kept taking big steps backward until we were far too outfield to ever have to catch a ball. We'd talk about poetry instead: Browning (Elizabeth only), Whitman, Plath. We came back east hoping to be, what? A writer and a dancer, I guess is the official line. We run with the same crowd, the crowd that has an official line, but we're not really friends anymore. We used to conjugate French verbs and ride our bikes home through the rain.

He says: "I came out to go to the restaurant one morning and one was sitting in my hallway. He still had snow on his ears; he took up the whole stairwell. He just stood there, looking at me, the snow melting into his fur and the light that never gets fixed flickering and popping. His eyes were dark, really dark, almost black, but I think they might actually have been purple, if I could have gotten close enough. He just stared, and I stared, and I sat down on my doorstep eventually. We watched each other until my shift would have ended. I reached out to touch him; I don't know why I thought I could, I just liked how black his nose was, how white and deep his fur looked. He made me think of..." And Seth looks at me as though I am a pin in his memory and he wants to pull me out, so that the next part can be his alone, so that I can retroactively never have pulled down willow branches for a crown, "...of this one place I used to go when I was a kid, in the woods by my school, and I'd make little acorn pyramids or mulberry rings on the ground before first period, and they were always gone when I got back, like someone had taken them, like they were gifts. The wolf looked like the kind of thing that might have seen a bunch of sticks and moss and taken them as tribute. But he didn't let me touch him, he howled instead–have you heard one howl yet? It's like a freight train. The lightbulb shattered. I went inside like that was my shift, sitting with a wolf all day not saying anything. The next morning he'd gone off."

Seth was my first kiss. I never think about that anymore.

I know this guy named David–he never comes out to the I, but I see him sometimes, sitting on a bench, his long thin hair in a ponytail, punching a netbook with a little plastic snow-cover over it. The snow never stops anymore. You do your best. He's trying to track them, to see if they have patterns, migration or hunting or mating patterns, something that can be charted. Like a subway map. A wolf map. He thinks he's getting close–there's a structure, he says. A repetition. He can almost see it. More data, he always needs more data.

Ruben always looks sharper than the rest of us. Three-piece, bow tie, pocket watch and chain, hair like a sculpture of some kind of exotic bird. Somehow his hair doesn't really look affected, though. He looks like he was born that way, like he was raised by a very serious family of tropical cranes. He wasn't, though. He's a fourth generation why-can't-you-marry-a-nice-Jewish-girl Brooklynite. He belongs here more than any of us.

He says: "I keep wondering why. I mean, don't any of you wonder why? Why us, why them, why here? I feel like no one even asks that question, when to me it seems such an obvious thing. I asked my uncle and he said: son, sometimes you have to just let the world be itself. I asked my mom and she said: Ruben, sometimes I think everything is broken and that's its natural state. And, well, I think that's bulls––. Like, ok, it's either zoological or metaphysical. Either they are real wolves and they migrated here, or they didn't, and they aren't."

Camille interrupts him. She puts her hand on his knee. She says: "Does it matter? Does it really matter?"

He glares at her. You aren't supposed to interrupt. That's the ritual. It's the unspoken law. "Of course it matters. Don't you ever wake up and hope they'll be gone? Don't you ever drink your coffee and look out your window and eat your f––ing cruller and think for just a moment there won't be a wolf on your doorstep, watching you, waiting for you to come out? They could leave someday. Any day." But we all know they won't. We can't say how we know. It's the same way we know that Coca-Cola will keep making Coke. It's a fact of the world. Ruben is really upset—he's breaking another rule but none of us say anything. We don't come here to get upset. It doesn't accomplish anything. "I asked one of them once. She'd followed me home from the F train—what I mean is she'd been all the way down on the platform, and when I got off she trotted up after me and followed me, me, specifically. And I turned around in the snow, the f—ing snow that never ends and I yelled: why? Why are you here? What are you doing? What do you want? I guess that sounds dumb, like a scene in a movie if this were happening in a movie and DiCaprio or whoever was having his big cathartic moment. But I wanted to know so badly. And she—I noticed it was a she. A bitch. She bent her head. God, they are so tall. So tall. Like statues. She bent her head and she licked my cheek. Like I was a baby. She did it just exactly like I was her puppy. Tender, kind. She pressed her forehead against mine and shut her eyes and then she ran off. Like it hadn't even happened."

There's going to be a movie. We heard about it a couple of months ago. Not DiCaprio, though. Some other actor no one's heard of. They expect it to be his big breakthrough. And the love interest has red hair, I remember that. It seems so far away; really, it has nothing to do with us. It's not like they'll film on location: CGI, all the way. Some of the locals are pissed about it—it's exploiting our situation, it'll just bring stupid kids out here wanting to be part of it, part of something, anything, and they'll be wolf food. But s—, you kind of have to make a movie about this, don't you? I would, if I didn't live here. Nothing's real until there's a movie about it.

Of course people want to be a part of it. They want to touch it, just for a second. They come in from the West Coast, from Ohio, from England, from Japan, from anywhere, just to say they saw one. Just to reach out their hand and be counted, be a witness, to have been there when the wolves came. But of course they weren't there, and the wolves are ours. They belong to us. We're the ones they eat, after all. And despite all the posturing and feather-display about who's been closest, deepest, longest, we want to be part of it, too. We're like kids running up to the edge of the old lady's house on the edge of town, telling each other she's a witch, daring Ruben or Seth or Geoff to go just a little closer, just a little further, to throw a rock at her window or knock on the door. Except there really is a witch in there, and we all know it's not a game.

Anyway, the outsiders stopped showing up so much after Yelena. It's less fun, now.

But it's the biggest thing that will ever happen to us. It's a gravitational object you can't get around or through, you only fall deeper in. And the thing is we want to get deeper in. Closer, further, knocking on the door. That's why we dress this way; that's why we tell our stories while the wolves watch us outside the I window, our audience and our play all at once.

"Anna," Seth says to me, and I warm automatically at the sound of his voice, straightening my shoulders and turning toward him like I always did, like I did in California when I didn't know what snow looked like yet, and I thought I loved him because I'd never kissed anyone else. "You never say anything. It's your turn. It's been your turn for months."

I am wearing red. I always wear red. Tiny gold coins on tinier gold ropes ring my waist in criss-crossed patterns, like a Greek goddess of come-hither, and my shoes have those ballet straps that wind all the way up my calves. My hair is down and it is black. They like it, when my hair is down. They follow me with their eyes. I've never said so to Ruben but they are always there when I get off the train, always panting a little on the dark platform, always bright-eyed, covered in melting snowflakes.

I say: "I like listening. They do, too, you know. Sometimes I think that's all they do: listen. Well. After Daniel—I knew him, I'm not sure if I've ever told you guys that. From that summer when I interned downtown. After Daniel I started feeling very strange, like something was stuck in me. It's not that I wanted revenge or anything. I didn't know him that well and I just don't think like that. I don't think in patterns—if this, then that. The point is, I started following one of them. A male, and I knew him because his nose was almost totally white, like he'd lost the black of it along the way. I started following him, all over the place, wherever he went, which wasn't really very far from my apartment. It's like they have territories. Maybe I was his territory. Maybe he was mine—because at some point I started taking my old archery stuff with me. My sister and I had both taken lessons as kids, but she stuck with it and I didn't. Seth—well, Seth probably remembers. There was awhile there when I went to school with a backpack over one shoulder and a bow over the other. Little Artemis of Central California. I started doing that again. It didn't seem to bother the wolf. He'd run down the 7th av like he had an appointment and I'd run after him. And one day, while he was waiting for the light to change, I dropped to one knee, nocked an arrow, and shot him. I didn't mean to do it. I didn't set out to. It doesn't seem to have happened in a linear way when I think about it. I mean, yes, I followed him, but I wasn't hunting him. Except I guess I was. Because I'd packed a big kitchen knife and I don't even remember doing that. You know there's never any traffic down there anymore, so I just gutted him right there on the median, and his blood steamed in the snowfall, and I guess I brought a cooler, too, because I packed all the meat away that I could, and some organs. It took a long time. I skinned him, too. It's really hard work, rendering an animal. But there's an instinct to it. Everyone used to know how to do this. I took it all home and I separated everything out and started curing it, salting it, smoking it." I twist a big orange glass ring on my finger and don't look at anyone. "I have wolf sausages, wolf cutlets, wolf bacon, wolf roasts, wolf loin, even wolf soup in plastic containers in my fridge. I eat it every day. It tastes…" I don't want to talk about how it tastes. It tastes perfect. It tastes new. "They all know me now, I'm pretty sure. Once, a younger one, skinny, with a black tip on her tail, saw me by the co-op and crawled toward me on her belly, whining. I watched her do it, bowing her head, not looking me in the eye. I reached out my hand and petted her. Her fur felt so rough and thick. We were…exchanging dominance. I've had dogs before. I know how that works. And I started wearing red."

I tell them they can come by. There's plenty of meat to share. It never seems to run out, in fact. They won't—most of them. They don't look at me the same way after that. In a week or so Seth will show up at my door. He'll just appear, in a white coat with fur on the hood, full of melting snowflakes. And I'll pour the soup into steel bowls and we'll sit together, with our knees touching.

This is what Brooklyn is like now. It's empty. A few of us stayed, two hundred people in Williamsburg, a hundred in Park Slope, maybe fifty in Brooklyn Heights. Less towards the bay, but you still find people sometimes, in clusters, in pairs. You can just walk down the middle of any street and it's so silent you forget how to talk. Everyone moved away or just disappeared. Some we know were eaten, some—well, people are hard to keep track of. You have to let go of that kind of thinking—no one is permanent. The Hasidim were the last big group to go. They called the wolves qliphoth—empty, impure shells, left over from the creation of the world. A wolf swallowed a little boy named Ezra whole. He played the piano.

It snows forever. The wolves own this town. They're talking about shutting off subway service, and the bridges, too. Just closing up shop. I guess I understand that. I'm not angry about it. I just hope the lights stay on. We still get wifi, but I wonder how long that can really last.

We go to the I every night, shining in our sequins and suits, and it feels like the old days. It feels like church. We go into Manhattan less and less. All those rooftop chickens and beehives and knitters and alleyway gardeners comprise the post-wolf economy. We trade, we huddle, nobody locks the doors anymore. Seth brings eggs for breakfast most mornings, from his bantams, those he has left. Down on Court Street, there's a general sort of market that turns into dancing and old guitars and drums at night, an accordion yawns out the dusk and there's a girl with silk ribbons who turns and turns, like she can't stop. The wolves come to watch and they wait in a circle for us to finish, and sometimes, sometimes they dance, too.

One has a torn ear. I've started following her when I can. I don't remember picking up my bow again, but it's there, all the same, hanging from me like a long, thin tail.

SARAH DIERINGER
WISE WOLF

Bio

Sarah Dieringer is 19 years old and was born and currently resides in Wenatchee, Washington. She has been painting for around 7 years. She gets her inspiration mainly from animals and nature, but mostly focuses on her passion for wolves. Her favorite mediums to use are Acrylic and charcoal chalk. She's following a career path that with hopefully someday lead her to working with the Yellowstone National-al Park wolves, which has been a life-long dream.

Wise Wolf. Sarah Dieringer. Acrylics.

MELISSA FAITH CABLE
WOLF CHILDREN

Bio

Melissa Faith Cable is 20 years of age and lives in Newfoundland, Canada. She loves to write and explore the worlds of creativity and imagination, showing them to this world for all to see. Cooking and learning are two of her biggest hobbies, and she has a passionate love for wolves and any form of wolf relations in mythology.

She's a girl that is trapped
Between two different worlds
A land of the humans
A land of the wolves
Hidden there in fur and skin
Her heart is torn, broken within
Whispering sweet words
Of the world in which we thrived
A new found hope
They might survive
The wolf-children
In this life.

NATAŠA VRETENAR
ALPHAS

Bio

Playing with light is Nataša Vretenar's lifelong passion, both as an Optical Engineer and as an artist. She fell deeply in love with Wild West, wide-open spaces, and the amazing colors of the Western North America. She lived in and visited different countries, and she feels that her travel experiences have influenced her art profoundly. She is an avid traveler and nature enthusiast. Instead of realistically portraying landscapes, flora, and fauna, she tries to capture emotion related to experiencing nature. She strives to achieve this by applying thick texture to her canvases, playing with light by using dozens of acrylic paint glazes, metallic paints, bright colors, and different acrylic mediums. Her paintings are 3D expressions of dramatic layers of paint applied by palette knives, and completed with intricate brushwork to create additional depth. She has had numerous art exhibits in Edmonton and St. Albert, AB, as well as Colorado.

Alphas. Nataša Vretenar. Acrylics.

JUSTIN K. ARTHUR
NO HARD FEELINGS

Bio

Justin Kyle Arthur currently resides in Columbia, Missouri. This is his first major publication. His hobbies and personal interests include reading, writing, playing games, and some crafting. He is currently hard at work tweaking and fine-tuning his first novel while also starting on his second one.

All things considered, you're a beautiful animal.

You're a bit far away, and I lost my glasses some time ago, but I can still tell. Your coat has seen better days, but it must still be warm. I always liked those yellow eyes, even if you're the first wolf I've really met. And quite possibly the last.

We're both here in this field. Winter has yet to come but food is only going to get scarcer from now. It isn't surprising that you're trying this, and I can't say I blame you for it.

You approach me alone, growling, primed to pounce and attack me. Maybe you have a pack waiting just inside the trees, but I think it's just you. I can relate, even if I've only been in these woods for a few weeks. I'd tell you how that happened, but I doubt you're interested.

What actually matters is that we're both tired and hungry. I haven't eaten anything good in some time and I can only imagine how hard it is for you to hunt alone. The desperation you must be feeling if you're approaching me out in the open, if only because I can't outrun you. I can relate. I know next to nothing about surviving in the wild.

The distance between us continues to close, both of us with hair standing on end. Your teeth are bared, and my knife is out. It's just one of those Swiss army knives, but it has proven to be a lifesaver so far. But you're the first live animal it will be used on. Can't imagine the same goes for you, but that's to be expected.

I try to not look you directly in the eyes; my dog always hated that, and I'd rather not rush into this. Though I suppose it's just delaying the inevitable. Both of us can hear our stomachs growling. Little chance for either of us that we'll eat heartily after we're finished with each other. I have no idea how long I'll have to go until I find a road or high-way again, and for you the fight to survive never ends.

You look ready to pounce. I bring up my knife, my muscles tens-ing. Any second now you'll launch at me, probably go for my throat to make it quick. I think wolves do that. When you attack I'll try to stab at you, pierce your skull to get it over with. And once it's done the winner won't have to go to sleep hungry.

As much as I fear for my own life, I can't blame you for what you're doing. I'm doing the same thing. No matter who survives, no hard feelings, okay?

LIATH MACTIRE
SONGS

Bio

Liath Mactire developed a passion for science fiction by stumbling across the ur-priseingly large collection in his primary school's library. Having devoured them all in short order he went on to larger libraries and never stopped. He now creates his own stories with the hope that in some small measure they'll bring to others the same pleasure that authors like Heinlein, Clarke, and Asimov have given him. This story joins other works of writing and photography that up to now could only be found on the Internet in such corners as The Chakat's Den, Fur Affinity, *and* SoFurry. *He first heard about the anthology through the Furry Writers' Guild and hopes to be a member of the group someday. He lives in Toronto, Ontario, Canada in a home that his sprawl of cats allows him and his wife to share.*

Here Liath details the account of Blackpaw the Alpha and his descriptions of a universe where wolves are not only intelligent but also capable of speech, walking, and fighting for their own rights. Read on to see for yourself where the line would be between human and animal if animals were smarter.

I sat back on my haunches, my forepaws placed carefully before me, and looked to the night sky. My eyes took in the many stars painting unfamiliar patterns on that dark canvas. Here was a sky that had never held the Moon that listened to the serenades of the Old Ones.

I filled my lungs, opened my muzzle, and began singing in the Old Tongue:

"I AM WOLF."

"I am Blackpaw on Grey of the Three Sweetwater Lakes in the Snow! I am Alpha! My teeth are long and sharp; my jaw is strong. My prey will never elude me as I chase them from first light of the sun to the last light of the moon."

I sang of Eirwyn my Alpha female, her beauty, her strength, the loving mother of my cubs. My three daughters, my two sons. Some of those now with their own mates and their own cubs, all gathered in the circle about me. The strength, the cunning of the members of the pack, of our love for our cubs, of our rich lives.

"The pack is Strong. We are..."

A shriek of sound exploded in my ears, issued from an apparition the Old Ones would have only called a monster, as it laid a fleshless clawed hand on my shoulder. Generations of instinct from the Old Ones kicked in, taking control of the levels of my brain that direct my limbs, faster than my slightly muddled conscious thoughts could process. My hind legs launched me virtually straight up, as I twisted about, opening my jaws with a snarl, ready to sink my teeth into that arm.

As my leap reached its peak, a powerful bundle of four limbs and sharp teeth intercepted my trajectory, bearing me off to the side where I landed heavily. I found myself laying on my back, slightly stunned, the breath pushed out of my chest by the forepaws standing there, as a powerful set of jaws closed on my throat with an implicit threat.

It was only then, as my beloved Alpha gripped my throat in a way that garnered my rapt attention, that my conscious mind caught up with the message being whispered into the back of my mind. It was the output of the bundle of nano-circuitry that sat at the base of my skull—this acts as a translator for us, among its other purposes.

A thought, and it started to play back from the beginning the translation of that burst of sound that had so startled me.

"Gentlefur, I must ask you to please not to make so much noise out of consideration for the other patrons, or I will have to ask you to vacate our restaurant."

As I lay there contemplating this through the slight haze induced by my earlier tumbler of the local equivalent of whiskey, another whisper entered my brain, this time from my Alpha.

"Husband, if you end up running afoul of the law I will leave your sorry tail locked up here until the next time we make this port. Now, apologize to the waiter." Her jaws were somewhat encumbered, so she "spoke" to me via her own nano-circuitry implant.

I agreed with the wisdom of her suggestion. She let me up, and I apologized to the waiter—although after all these years his kind still looked like animated skeletons to me, and their voices like a motor shaft with a failed bearing.

The Old Tongue as noise! The very idea!

As my human friend Stuart (from whom I'd learned to appreciate a fine whiskey) once said, "The Old Tongue is to wolves as the bagpipe is to the Scots. It is a sound of wild beauty not fully appreciated by the untutored ears of the common crowd." We then downed another "wee dram" or two to confirm the wisdom of his observation. The beauty of the howls, growls, barks, and yips of the Old Tongue resonates to our soul, but I can understand that not everyone thinks so.

I am wolf—for those not fluent in the Old Ones tongue my name is Donal. We call ourselves wolf, although the human geneticists who first created us in the late 21st Century Terran Common Era termed us SmartWolfs, a registered trademark of Applied Sentient Genetics Corporation. They used the genome of the Canis lupus, the Old Ones, as the basis for our genome. They created us originally to address the technical limitations of early spaceships.

I know, 'SmartWolfs,' not very grammatical. It's their own language, but I don't know why they would ignore the most basic rules— but then they did build in us a strong bias to following rules, so maybe that is why we find it so unnatural. One of the important humans at Applied Sentient Genetics was from an 'LUC' (Large Urban Community) where a favourite 'LST' (Local Sports Team) was the 'Maple Leafs.'

This use of abbreviations and acronyms was common back then— it all had to do with 'texting' and 'twittering' as they called it.

In any case, for the first time in over a century this 'LST' won their league championships, the 'Stanley Cup' (odd name—it is obviously a bowl). This was an 'RBT' (Really Big Thing), so the spelling of our given name became an homage to that event.

That entry in the record books doesn't mean much to us, but it does have a link to something that is very important to all Terran sentients. That team was from a 'city', as they were then termed, in one of those old-fashioned nation-states, called Canada.

Most non-furs don't remember that name the way we furs do. Many of these labels faded away after the Terran cultural unification that came about during that chaotic period of dealing with the after-effects of global warming. After the global scale efforts required to cure the fever that humanity had induced in the ecosystem, the concept of nations didn't seem to matter so much anymore.

We furs do remember that name—they were the first government to recognize all sentient beings, natural or created, as 'persons' under the law.

Until then we were just property.

PROPERTY!!!

The thought of that always made my hackles rise, and the tales I could tell you of The Bad Times...

Well, those are stories for another time.

The Canadians treated us pretty well in the end, even if some of their politicians would make the pace of a glacier look like an avalanche. Fortunately we received support from human lawyers, scientists, and other humans in our struggle to obtain personhood—and they were more aggressive than a pack of the Old Ones. As the human saying goes, they were real sons of bitches, but they were our sons (and daughters) of bitches.

The ultimate irony was that most of the pressure that came to bear was due to the actions of the company itself. Technology changed, and our services were not as needed for space travel. They needed new markets for us, so we were placed as personal service workers for senior and disabled humans—like seeing-eye dogs and other service animals. We could do much more, and didn't need a salary like humans. What they didn't fully appreciate was how attached our humans would become to us. In that era, many non-sentient companion animals were treated virtually as surrogate children. Consider that situation, and then add companion animals that you could have a conversation with. Our "parents" became our most stalwart allies in our struggle to be free.

Part of what they obtained for us was a region of their nation as a permanent home. It was in the range of the Old Ones, next to one of their National Parks that housed many of the packs. Eventually we were ceded full governmental authority over our land.

So, we are a bit of contradiction—many of us tied to the lands and forests of the Old Ones, and others calling the empty space between the stars and planets their home.

From a distance you might not recognize that we are different from the Old Ones. The geneticists didn't make too many obvious changes—in part to avoid the rules of the day. Experimentation on the human genome was forbidden, but although they used human DNA in our creation there was not enough for our genome to be considered human.

They gave us uplifted brains, elongated some of the bones in our forepaws, added a few more, and modified our throats to make us able to speak directly to humans. The changed bones in the forepaws allow us to have "fingers" and "thumbs," but when we curl them up we're still able to run on our four legs. Our hind legs were modified to allow us to better balance on our haunches so that we could use our forepaws as hands when working. We are able to walk on our hind legs, but it is tiring. Our metabolisms were modified to avoid the effects of prolonged exposure to micro-gravity, which was always a problem for humans in the era before artificial gravity became practical.

We were required to have nano-circuitry implants as part of the controls that were placed on us. For that reason our cubs do not receive them until they reach an age that they can truly give consent, and properly control them rather than be controlled by them. When we reach our age of reason we can then make the decision about receiving the implants as free beings.

Of course, there are days when some parents would wish them for their cubs, choice or not.

What made us useful to the early spaceship builders was that we mass about half of an adult human, and on four paws we don't need those tall corridors and rooms that a human would need. So while humans would travel in artificial hibernation, we would maintain and pilot the ships. With our fur, the ships didn't need to be kept as warm as a human would require. The reduction in our demands on the energy production on the ships, as well as the smaller volume and mass of the crew area, allowed for more payload. For some of our early "employers" it was also convenient that we were expendable when human crews weren't.

Even now, with energy not being as critical as it once was in those early flights, we could make a better profit on our ships with the reduced overhead (literally). We did sacrifice a little of that advantage for our pack's comfort.

But I digress, as a whitemuzzle will. It sometimes seems my mind grows paws of its own and treads unbidden down unexpected trails.

This evening in the open-air restaurant came to its end. All were satisfied with the fine meal we had shared in celebration of a profitable cargo. Each adult member of the pack is a shareholder in our business, so each would see the benefit of their hard work when at last our trail took us back to our homeworld and the forest land of our kind. For the moment, full bellies and the late hour combined to make us all look forward to the comforts of our dens. For the cubs, even the boundless energy of youth was starting to fade, one or two struggling to keep their eyes open amid their yawns.

We made our way back to the landing area where we had left our heavy cargo lifter (an HCL, as a human would say) in order to make the trip back above the atmosphere to the parking orbit where our ship, *Sweetwater Sunrise*, was waiting.

The stroll back to the lifter took longer than you might think—the cubs always made it hard to just travel on a straight trail, seemingly engaging in an act of super-atomic fission. The adults would take an oath that there were at least twice as many of them when they were moving as when they were standing still. With the resilience of the young, they were able to push back their earlier sleepiness, at least for a while.

A human might say directing cubs is like "herding cats" —although one must be certain that your listeners understand you mean *Felis domesticus*, and not *Panthera tigris altaica sapiens*. I know many of the latter, and they have no sense of humor when it comes to expressions like that— and at 200kg and 3 meters from nose to tail tip they have the means and the temperament to enforce their views.

We reached the lifter's airlock and authenticated ourselves with the on-ship Electronic Intelligence. The adults and juveniles fell to donning their spacesuits, while the cubs were secured in an emergency escape ball. This was one of our cargo lifters, and so it didn't have the triply redundant life support systems of passenger lifters. We would never thoughtlessly risk members of the pack, so everyone needed to be sealed in, one way or another, before the lifter took off. Too many furs, not just wolves, lost their lives during the Bad Times—it has made us careful even now.

Modern suits are made of materials and in a manner that speed up the process of getting them on and off. We thank our ancestors too that the suits now have a separate tail structure. The early suits required us to stuff our tails down one of the legs—an idea that only a tailless human would think to be sensible.

Once they had their suits on Meriel, my second daughter, and Kenta headed forward to perform the pre-flight checks. Kenta is a litter mate of our Beta male—they joined us from another pack as part of our need to strengthen the genetics of the pack.

The Old Ones didn't pay attention to genetic diversity, but we try to keep our gene pool diverse. There is also the desire for wider horizons that causes some of our young ones to leave their birth pack to search for adventure, opportunity, and mates. For those of us who find our way among the stars, our children may also split into new packs when a new ship is commissioned.

These are our Wandering Children.

As a parent, your heart aches at the distance that it puts between you and your cherished cubs (and aren't they always cubs, regardless of their age?), but you share the joy of their adventure.

Necessity dictates it, but we miss our young pack members when they set their paws on these unknown trails.

The packs have made it a firm tradition that these Wandering Children are to be warmly welcomed, as each pack would want their Wandering Children greeted by another pack. They may stay with their new packs, but some have the wanderlust and will move on to another pack after a time, sometimes many times, until they find a permanent home.

The addition of the adopted pack members, in addition to multiple mated pairs from within the pack, encourages the goal of genetic diversity. The Old Ones might have made do with just Alphas having litters, but we can't. While we don't control the hearts of the young ones when they choose their mates, there is a strong tradition of not choosing a mate that is too close by blood. All of this does mean that nearly every pack has a blood tie to every other pack—pack celebrations often take on the scale of a global holiday.

From the way Meriel and Kenta act, I think they may declare themselves as mates someday soon. Eirwyn and I think they will have many fine cubs. I can see the day my mate and I will no longer wish the responsibility of being Alpha. I might encourage a challenge from Kenta, or one of the other promising males.

On that day, after a long, hard fought and determined battle—my dignity must be considered, after all—I'll let him win the status of Alpha Male.

One of these days—but not today.

Some might question this. Would it be better if an Alpha just appointed a successor? Our choice is to carry on this tradition, paralleling the challenges that were used to choose Alphas among the Old Ones.

We honor tradition and the instincts that we inherited from the Old Ones, but try not to be too bound by it.

"Meriel, would you put Maeve up on the display," I called out. In a few moments, our Engineering Chief appeared on the display.

"Hi Donal, the family ready to come home?" asked Maeve.

"Yes Maeve, we're just running the pre-flights. You missed a great meal."

"We'll be happy as long as you've brought us back a 'wolfy bag,'" joked Maeve.

"Of course, can't forget any of the family," I replied with a toothy grin.

"I'll prepare the lifter bay and turn on the 'porch light' for you." By the time we would reach the *Sunrise*, Maeve would have the approach navigation beacons online, and the hatch open for the lifter.

"Thanks—we'll be on our way shortly." We closed the connection, and I joined the rest in the temporary passenger area.

With all preparations completed, Meriel and Kenta lifted off from the spaceport and proceeded to the orbit where the *Sunrise* awaited.

Meriel and Kenta docked the lifter in its bay with their usual care and precision. We all moved to the airlock to disembark from the lifter to the ship. The juvenile and un-mated females bundled the cubs out of their ball, still seemingly as a large ball of fur, and followed us into the airlock.

Maeve met us at the airlock while her mate remained on duty in the bridge. She performed the requisite scans on us all to make sure we did not have unwanted "guests" accompanying us. After we passed her scrutiny, she secured the hatch and wished us a good night as she retired to their den.

"Standard night crew assignments everyone—primary shift for a half shift, then the secondary shift for the other half. Standard rotation will resume in the morning. Don't forget Maeve is waiting for Kaine in her den, so let's get him his relief," I reminded everyone.

Departure day would be a busy day for them as for us all, and they welcomed every moment of sleep they could have in advance.

We all moved into the clothing locker and in a scene of controlled chaos the pack settled back into their shipboard roles. Everyone helped get the paw covers off the cubs, interspersed with the rest of the pack stowing their spacesuits and paw covers. Once back to just their fur the cubs were led (some were carried, already asleep from the day's adventures) to the nursery den off the main living area, behind the un-mated females' den. This layout ensured no wandering cubs, although we would prefer them with us. When we were back on Terra the cubs would join their parents in their dens, but the dangers of space travel, even now, meant that we had the cubs sleep in a den with its own independent life support at the heart of the ship.

On ship we all usually just go about in our fur, but on even the most tolerant planet we always wear our paw covers. When you have as sensitive a sense of smell as that of a wolf, you don't want to find your paws drenched in some awful substance.

Local sensibilities sometimes require more than just paw covers. There are varying degrees of taboos about displaying genitals so we usually wear, well, I guess you might call them breeches. They cover from the middle of the rear legs, with the rear seam split to ease getting them past the tail but then when pulled on they can then be joined together around the abdomen—that seems to mollify most societies. Their one redeeming virtue is that they do have pockets.

It is an odd situation that the planets that are the most able to accept us as fully sentient beings are also the ones that mostly prefer us clothed, while the ones that see us just as intelligent animals are the ones that let us just wear our fur.

We also wear ornaments, some for status markers and others just for vanity, and harnesses for practical purposes like providing pockets and storage pouches. We don't care for clothing—it just makes your fur look odd. The furry equivalent of what humans would term "hat hair." Less is definitely better.

Morning would be arriving all too soon, so we left the night shift to secure the rest of the ship. When underway we'd have a full crew standing watches. Tonight was still a celebration night, in orbit around a safe planet, so all but the single pair standing watch were still off duty. The bachelor males made their way to their den. Some might end up spending part of the "night" with prospective mates—we don't forbid such things to our young, but the pack does expect that partners will be considerate of each other's feelings. Badly handled relationships would result in a loss of social status within the pack, so this rarely happens. The mated pairs wandered through the common area to their dens, everyone bidding the others a good night.

Our common area was one of the things that made being in space for long periods bearable for the pack. As one stepped into it, one was transported back to Terra and our home. It looked and smelled like a forest clearing. There was a dome that displayed a sky that mimicked the time of day, either sun and clouds during the day or stars and moon at night. The floor was covered with soil, grasses, and native plants from the home range. Trees and shrubs ringed the edge, making it look much like home. It even "rained" from time to time to irrigate the living plants. It was part of the life support system, but some might deem it an indulgence. For the pack, this mattered more than the profits they lose.

As we reached our den, Eirwyn asked, "Would you care to brush my fur, my mate? I'm afraid an evening of wearing clothing has left it looking dishevelled."

I replied, tilting my head to the side, showing my best lascivious grin and letting my tongue briefly hang out the side of my jaw, "I am always happy to run my paws through your fur—especially if you will return the favour, my beloved".

We settled in to the pad in our den, and brought out our grooming brushes.

I brushed her fur, long languorous strokes starting on her neck, along her back, all the way to the tip of her tail, I gradually realized from her scent she was interested in more that just a brushing.

When the geneticists modified our skeletons, they also built in the ability to suppress the normal wolf oestrus cycle. The hormonal controls that were used in the Bad Times were beyond our direction, but the nano-circuitry we now have implanted as adults allows us the control of these cycles. Within moments the hormones will flow, giving us the passions of the Old Ones without necessarily triggering fertilization.

Where our...owners...(a word that has a bitter taste on my tongue) once would use this to prevent inconvenient pregnancies we can now decide when to have cubs, or just engage in mating for pleasure.

"My beloved, I do believe you want something more than just a grooming," I observed.

"Surely your sense of smell has not failed you, even with those white hairs showing in your muzzle," she teased with a gleam in her eye. "Given our duty schedules after leaving orbit in the morning, I don't know when next we'll have time to properly enjoy our pleasures." With that, she braced her hind legs, dropped her front legs, and looked back over her shoulder with what anyfur would only term a "come hither" look.

No Alpha would dream of arguing with such an eloquent request.

I formed a thought directed at my nano-circuit, issuing the lovers equivalent of "Cry 'Havoc', and let slip the dogs of war," although this might be better termed "let loose the passion of the wolves!"

"Aah, back to the old standard, none of this exotic human-style this time," I joked with her.

"You know what they say, an oldie but a goodie, my love", she replied. Our jaws interlocked in a playful embrace as I leaned down, our tails sweeping through the air and the soft sounds of our emotions leaving our throats.

The scent of her arousal filled our den—and without the atmosphere purifiers it would have sent every other member of the pack into a frenzy too. Those who weren't already enjoying themselves, in any case.

(I think I'll leave the next part out of this record—we don't need our grandcubs offering critiques of our lovemaking. Let's just say that we were both well and truly satisfied with our recreation.)

The storm in our minds that robbed us of our intelligence had grown to a seething, roiling peak—now these forces of nature started their retreat back to a relaxing calm.

We entered that pleasant haze, that warm glow that follows copulation. We both flopped down on our sides and rested from our earlier exertions, still panting.

Eirwyn turned her head back toward me, and said, "My whitemuzzle, my life love, let us now to sleep—the morning will be here soon, and tomorrow will be long."

I moved to lie by her side. In the lingering euphoria of our emotions, we gradually entered an exhausted, but contented, sleep, our heads side by side and our muzzles touching.

As my conscious mind departed unheard on its silent paws, one last thought ran through my mind:

I am wolf—and on this night, I could want for nothing more.

FRANCES "YOTE" MCKEEVER
LUNAR BABY, CAUTIOUS APPROACH, &
CHAINED BY LUNA

Bio

Frances "Yote" McKeever currently lives in Des Moines, Washington with her fiancé, Scott, and her 3-year-old daughter Elizabeth. She is a self-taught artist working mostly in colored pencil, gouache, and acrylic. Many pieces of her artwork have been submitted into several contests and art shows, earning awards and high appraisals. Frances is a huge fan of the BBC hit television "Doctor Who," which can be seen by the huge collection that decorates her art studio, plays the piano writing her own music, loves the outdoors, and loves coyotes (hence the nickname Yote).

Lunar Baby. Frances "Yote" McKeever. Watercolor and colored pencil. 2011.

Cautious Approach. Frances "Yote" McKeever. Gouache paint. 2014.

Chained by Luna. Frances "Yote" McKeever. Graphite. 2011.

HENRY AKINS
DEATH OF A WARRIOR

Once was a time
in the depths of my mind
that my hands knew the feel of a sword.
A flick of the wrists was all that it took
to follow through on my word.
Where nightmares walked freely
through lands of the fairy,
its borders I was to guard.
My time was spent well
till one day I fell,
about which is told by the bard.
I lay on the field all shrouded in mists,
and ponder if maybe I am dreaming all this.
First a nose,
then shoulders,
and finally a tail.
A wolf through the mists,
slowly parting the veil.
Revealing a path
I'd not seen before.
So I rose,
and I walked
to be seen never more.

CANDACE B. GALLAGHER
THE WATCHER

Bio

Candace Gallagher resides in the tiny mountain town of Jerome, Arizona with her husband, Michael, three rescued dogs (including a wolf hybrid), and a rescued Maine Coon cat. Her artwork has never been published before, but her poetry has. By day, she serves as the Town Manager and Clerk for Jerome. At other times, she and her husband operate an eclectic shop there (The Wary Buffalo), she creates and sells healing gemstone jewelry (Medicine Beads Jewelry), and she enjoys cooking, singing on occasion with a local band, and simply enjoying life every day.

The Watcher. Candace B. Gallagher. Acrylics.

DMITRY GORODETSKY
THREE HOWLING WOLVES & WOLF AND CUB

Bio

Dmitry Gorodetsky is a wood and antler carver from Russia. He has won two awards at the Calgary Wildfowl Art Carving Festival for his mixed media entries "Wild Boar and Laikas" and "Bear and Laikas." He professionally studied carving at the Art Institute at Bryansk, Russia. His hobbies include bone carving, studying animals, and riding his mountain bike.

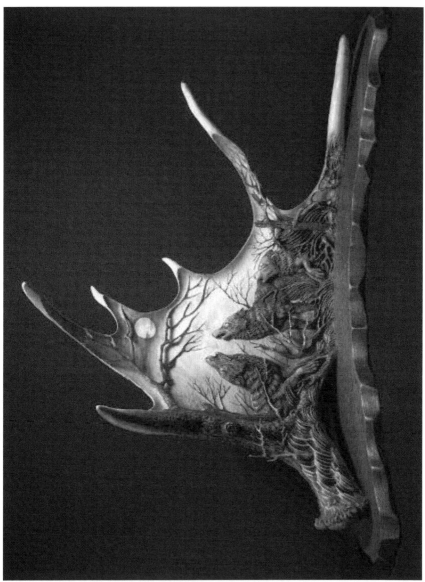

Three Howling Wolves. Dmitry Gorodetsky. Moose antler and wood (stand).

Wolf and Cub. Dmitry Gorodetsky. Mammoth tusk.

DOMINIQUE GOODALL
SHIFTING STANCE

Bio

Dominique Goodall is a modern day pro-wolf Red Riding Hood. Living in the UK, she is only able to see the wolves within the confines of a zoo—or so she thought. A chance meeting, and she got to meet her lupine inspiration in person, culminating in a chance leap and a wolf in her arms for a hug! She often writes fantasy and has a plethora of pets, not limited to her dog and snakes. She is the author of upcoming fantasy, Power of the Song, *and various other titles within* Lupus Animus, *a charity anthology she brought out.*

In this heart-wrenching short story, two creatures fight over expansion of a territory, but the stakes are much higher than just a property gain. Who will come out on top in this struggle for power? Who can lead the packs?

A velvet-black sky spread above the forest, trees forming tall fingers spread upward as though in supplication to the light-granting orb. The moon itself hung there, huge and throwing shadows onto the snow-carpeted ground. Nothing moved within the depths of the ancient forest, boughs laden with snow. The air whistled between the trunks of the trees as a savage frost held the forest in a deep, desperate grip. Deep within hidden dens, animals slumbered, waiting for the warmth of life to renew their energy, to bring about the verdant paradise they adored. Instead, the winter clutched the forest tighter to its chest, in claws which punctured flesh and made it weep. Somewhere in the darkness, a lone voice called. A single voice answered...and then silence fell again.

It was there they met, in dappled shadows. One with fur that blended with the snow beneath her paws, the other with a coat that hid him in the shadows. They came forth alone, their tails held still. A strength flowed through the darker wolf, a soothing calmness that spread around him. Both possessed eyes of brilliant gold, filled with an intelligence both savage and keen. They settled down, the silence of the forest forming around them once again. The thickness of their coats lessened the effect of the wind, and it became a battle of wills as to who would speak first. This contest was one repeated every year, when the moon was high and snow thick upon the ground.

It was the black who broke first, his head tilting to the side as he observed his white companion.

"You know the borders need to change, don't you? We've got litters waiting to be born, and I won't allow any to die." His voice was gruff, underscored with a soft growl. Despite that, he kept the respect he felt in his words. She was stronger than most, and it showed as she grinned at him. He knew she was aware of the way her body moved almost sinuously.

"And you know that if the borders move, we'll be left with less food. I have more elders this year to look after than normal. You'll have to extend yourself elsewhere." Her voice was soft. Almost musical but so quiet he had to strain forward to hear her words.

"We are meant to be negotiating, Shiya! You are meant to be listening to me. You know that, right?" He found the stress getting to him. He heaved himself to his paws, the warmth of his body having left a depression in the snow. He paced, his tail curling over his back. He was careful not to cross a certain line, invisible to the naked eye.

"And I am negotiating, Orphe. I said no. I won't let the elders go without their food. We need the land to hunt as wolves. You don't need to expand your reach to our side. Take the human village and pillage that." She sneered the words at him, still reclining in the snow.

He remembered his hatred for her then. He shook his head back and forth, affecting a calm posture only by breathing in carefully. He exhaled, the plumes of his breath streaming above his head. He shivered in his skin, shifting a little before shaking his maw back and forth.

"We don't hunt the human village. We know better than that. They will hunt us all down. And when they find our own homes, what will we do then? They will know of our existence!" He barked the words out, anger getting the better of him. He dug his claws into the snow, tempted to rip up great chunks and toss them behind him.

He stilled the impulse, knowing a show of strength would hinder him now.

"The humans are weak. If they came upon your dwelling, they would simply think you are einsiedler[1]. That you prefer the wild to the village. I'm sure none would recognize you as werwolf. You don't wear your furs around the humans, right?" She lifted her ears at him, her cool tone enough to make him remember just how little he looked forward to spending this time with her.

"No, but that's not the point! My pack need extra territory. We don't need the human village, we don't want it. We need the forest. The less we have to do with the mensch[2], the better it is for us all. Even you, Shiya. Surely you remember how your eltern[3] were taken for their pelts."

He saw her flinch and prepared to apologize. His ears fell back against his skull as he widened his maw to speak.

"Don't! Just...don't. You don't even deserve to be around me, Orphe. I didn't need to remember that. To know that they died because they loved their coat too much." She whimpered, the sound so soft and heart-breaking that he took a swift step towards her. As soon as he nudged the boundary between their territories, she was up on her paws. "What do you think you're doing, Orphe? Step foot here, and it'll mean *war*. Just as it's always been. Our packs are kept separate for a reason. We can't exist in peace together!"

Her frantic words, snapped from jaws that frothed in sudden rage, made him hesitate. He drew his ears back against his skull, his tail dipped to curl around his inner leg.

"Shiya...Shiya, I'm sorry, okay? I won't pass the border. Let us talk our terms again. There has to be some way we can come to a normal agreement. Just as every generation of our past kin have managed to." He spoke with pride and a confidence that didn't carry on through his body. His tail was still tucked in, his ears still flattened and his head lowered slightly. He knew the contrast between himself and his rival.

---

[1] hermit

[2] men

[3] parents

She stood upright, power flowing through her white-pelted body. She was still, her ears drawn upward. Her tail curled above the level of her back, and her golden eyed focus pressed into his face. She stirred lightly before shaking her maw, smiling. There was malicious intent in her smile, her body drawn onto all four paws as she growled at him.

"There are no terms, Orphe. There's nothing but this border which will exist as it is!" She snarled the words at him, her head lowered as she snarled under her breath and pressed forward, until she *felt* the straining boundaries around her face.

"Dark and light
Shall come to fight
Over land and prey.
Two shall war,
Damaged inside their core
Will charge into the fray.
One will survive,
In order to strive,
None shall ever stray.
When death does come,
All will be glum,
Black or white will slay."

She snapped the words at him, her head lowered as she took a steady step backward. She knew the prophecy. She'd had the words bitten into her. Chewed into her. She'd not delay in stopping a fight that would see her kin and pack killed. She was protecting them, and in her own way, Orphe.

"Go back to the others, Orphe. You aren't getting what you want this time. I conceded last time. This time…I am happy for the borders to stay as they are." She shook her head, disappointed in his actions. Her brow was furrowed, her head tilted as she snarled softly.

She turned to walk away, ignoring the angry bellows of the brute behind her. She soon hesitated as she felt something inside her warp. Her body trembled a little, her eyes closing a little. She shrieked as she turned to meet his bounding leaps. She was shocked, hesitating. She whined softly as she jumped at him, her teeth widened as she pressed her chest to his. She would do what she had to, even if that meant she had to kill Orphe and rule the forest herself.

"Stopp[4]! Nicht[5], Orphe!" When she pulled away from him, blood splattered the ground, and she panted. Whenever she was pressed, whenever stress flooded her, she found herself resorting back to her native tongue. She quivered a little before stepping back, trying to retreat from him. A whine slipped from her muzzle as she wagged her tail slowly. "Orphe...please! We don't need to fight like this!" She barked at him, backing away from the savage brilliance of his golden eyes. His larger body pressed her, forced her into the snow.

"No, Shiya. No! I will take what we need, in the way of the wild."

As he spoke, she found her legs trembling. Small wounds bled more, and her eyes narrowed. She yelped softly, throwing herself forward carelessly. She'd win. She had to win. She shuddered and quivered, her fur bristling. She wouldn't waste time with talking. She would be brave. She snapped at his face, her teeth scissoring at his cheek before she darted away. Despite her weakening wounds, she was faster than he was. Her paws were wider, her body lighter.

"Shiya! Just let me remove you as *alpha*. I'll let you live in the pack! You can even take your band of wolves off...if they are old, they aren't what I want."

She shook her head. She wanted to get away from his words. From the savagery present in his slashing teeth. She shrieked, Shiya's head thrashing as his teeth caught hold of her scruff and tugged her around. She snapped at him, weakened by the blood which renewed falling down her neck. She caught hold of his dangling ear, tugging at it roughly. She panted through the bite until he let her go. Her ears narrowed as she shivered, her hackles lifting. She could smell the copper of her blood, especially when she whirled and blood splattered the snow.

Their panting breaths made the snow melt about their feet. She could see the plumes, her breath exhaled forcefully as she tried to calm herself down. She needed her mind to work properly. She

[4] Stop!

[5] no

whined softly as she shook again. Her toes were numbing in the snow, and she screamed loud enough for Orphe to halt his attack. Snow shot up the sides of his body as he slipped to a halt. Her body convulsed as her legs collapsed, her body undergoing a rapid change. She panted into a face full of bloodied, slushy snow.

"Shiya? Are you okay?"

She heard the whispered voice through hearing that faded as her fur receded. Her naked skin erupted in goose-bumps as long hair fell down to her waist, almost white blonde but no cover. She shuddered as she sat up, kneeling in the snow as she stared at Orphe. Wounds closed slowly as she narrowed her eyes at him, her lip curling in a vague imitation of a snarl.

"Now try and kill me, Orphe. Kill me and let true war wage between our clans. Mine may be older, but yours are carrying young. They are weak compared to those with experience." She smiled slowly, ignoring the growing chill in her feet and fingers.

His heat covered her, his fur warming her against the snow. She sighed softly, fingers caressing the fur of her one-time enemy.

"I have to do it. Shift, Shiya. Shift and show me your throat. Don't make me fight you. I don't want to force against my instincts any longer." She was thankful that she could understand him. Her ears weren't quite keen enough now to catch every nuance of his words, but she forced him from her, sitting upright and noble.

"No! I won't let you. You'd kill them all, just because you can't be bothered! You had plentiful food, but you should have stopped them from breeding."

She snapped the words at him, standing carelessly in the wind. It bit into her bones, made her tremble—but still she continued to stare him down. She knew her wolf-eyes carried over into her human-body. She knew that she had strength in this body others wouldn't know. And yet, she was lean—too skinny for the human form. Her ribs protruded, her hips were clearly identified. She curled her lips in, protecting them from the frost that built slowly along her eyelashes.

"Shiya! You'll die like this! You'll die, and no one can help you! Just shift, please?"

His begging tone came through, suddenly. She barked softly, her body trembling before she gave in to the desperate demands. Fur flowed over her skin, warming her instantly as her body temperature increased. She panted, biting lazily at the snow and thankful to whatever instincts Orphe had that kept him from her in that moment. Her ears fall back before she bit at the snow one last time, letting it melt in her throat before standing on legs made weak by a second shift in such a short time.

Orphe neared her, and she reared up, her claws powering her upward. Her teeth snapped shut around his maw, her eyes narrowed. His blood poured onto her tongue, at once sour and powerful. She released his shrieking body, ignoring the growing weakness of her own to attack again. She pressed her advantage. Her teeth caught his cheek and split it open. He retaliated, her shoulder soon bared almost to the bone. She yelped, the sound shrill enough to carry to the empty wastes she called her home. His answering howl to her rang through the forests in which he hid.

Their battles raged underneath the neutral moon. The snow beneath their paws turned to slush which made lunges and snapping launches turn to scrambles and falls as their bodies tired. They paused between attacks as the moon tired of their antics and the velvet sky lightened along the horizon. Soft yelps of pain became a symphony on the wind. Their shudders became longer as they panted, snatching mouthfuls of bloodied snow to sate the burning thirst. Shiya stopped, panting heavily as she dropped her head forward.

She panted, her tongue draped over her teeth. Blood dripped from a snap that had taken a chunk from it, but she still dipped her head low, protecting her throat during a moment of rest. The wind was dying down around them before Shiya gathered her strength. Orphe was bleeding more than she was, his black coat torn in many places, bloodied gashes showing on through the thick fur. He'd wasted energy trying to topple her, to prove his dominance. She had just tried to kill him. Her chest heaved faintly before she lunged forward, under his chin and up.

Her teeth sank into his throat, despite the thick fur protecting the wounds. He yipped, the sound shrill but soon cut off by her clenching jaw. The hot pulses of his fading life melted the remaining slush at their paws, his body trembling. She held on until he went limp in her grasp. Even then she held on, worrying at the flesh of his throat until he went cold. That was when she dropped him, panting as she stepped back. She slipped in his blood and retched as she stared at his body through listless eyes.

"What have I done?" Her whisper rang out, louder than she intended it. She flinched, swallowing down the bile as she looked about.

She may now have been the undisputed alpha of two packs…but she was also a killer. That fact wouldn't…couldn't, be disputed. She lifted her head to the waning moon. Her song of grief lent chills to anyone awake to listen, her self-recrimination hurting her mind as she lowered her head to press her nose into Orphe's neck fur.

"Abschied[6], old friend. Verzeihen Sie mir[7]."

---

[6] Farewell
[7] Forgive me

CS MOWGLI
PERSPECTIVE ON THE MOUNT

Bio

CS Mowgli grew up and currently lives in the Mid-Atlantic region of the United States; he studied the environmental earth sciences while at college and living in the Virginia Piedmont and takes his authority from an inner consciousness that requires an admiration and respect for life in its many forms of splendor. From as far back as CS can remember, the one creature on this earth that represents to him what humans need but what always seems to elude them is the gray wolf...indeed all wolves...a creature who lives with purpose, cherishes family and has mastered the art of communication. An extended family member of Seacrest Wolf Preserve in Chipley, Florida, where his travels took him over a decade ago, CS leans on his Seacrest family of wolf advocates and cherishes the gift to humanity this educational outreach continues to provide on behalf of the gray wolf, whom he acknowledges seems eternally and unfairly caught somewhere between man's need to be right, no matter how fearful and alone it leaves him, and a desire for reaping the selfish benefits that may follow.

From the heavy weight of things
I climbed the great divide
Atop the mount a sight to see
In freedom I'd survive

Yet there with me inside myself
A fear so all-consuming
The atmosphere grew thin and dim
My spirit bent on ruin

But then astride this sullen soul
A shift in my perspective
As loneliness from cold and grief
Beneath me he had left them.

a Wolf Tribute, as I see it...

JANE LEE MCCRACKEN
THE WOLF'S HOUSE

Bio

Scottish artist Jane Lee McCracken makes intricate multi-layered Biro drawings and constructs multi-media objects and installations inspired by her drawings. Her work is impassioned by childhood memoirs, fairy tales, forests, wolves, and other animals. Along with her continuing interest in war, environmental destruction, and loss and the impact on humans and animals, Jane's work is symbolic of life's brutal reality. Jane lives in the Northeast of England with her husband Rob and their Northern Inuit dog, Lily, her muse. Jane also fundraises through her artwork for endangered and threatened species and is an Official Supporter of Save Wild Tigers, UK.

The Wolf's House. Jane Lee McCracken. Mixed media.

JITKA SANIOVA
WOLF DIVINITY & IN THE LAND CALLED UNIVERSE

Bio

Jitka Saniova is a Czech writer/photographer/visual artist. She loves to write (especially fantasy genre and romances for women) and to create poetic images (mostly photomontages). Since 1995, she has published many books (in the beginning of her career, under a pseudonym), magazines articles, and stories. For almost two years, together with her friend Richard Brookes from California whom she met on the Internet, she has enjoyed writing stories in English. We have written fifteen stories and two fantasy screenplays. The stories have been published in magazines such as Cabaret, The Orphic Chronicles, Black Rose, *and* Dragon Laugh. *They have also written a screenplay "The Wolf Queen" that was under consideration for a production in Australia. Her husband Valentino has brought her to visual art. She loves to photograph (her photos have been used for various book covers) and to create photomontages (every year she publishes* The Angel Calendar *here in Czech Republic). Besides writing and photographing, her other loves are animals (She love all of them; however, wolves, tigers, dogs and jaguars have a special place in her heart) and spiritual/esoteric topics (She likes especially astrology and angels). Anytime they can help with the protection of animals, it makes her and her husband very happy.*

Wolf Divinity. Jitka Saniova. Digital media.

In the Land Called Universe

The wolf's eyes shine by truth
As the wolves have understood
To the mystery of Universe—
To its birth, eternity and sense.

The wolf's eyes looked at me
and told me—I love you,
I'll be the guide for you
In the land called Universe
In the land called Earth
In the land called Soul
In the land called Love.

The wolf touched my soul.
He opened for me the gate
to the mysterious Universe
where the divine Power plays
the game of creation.
Going through the gate
I lived the endless emotion.

I saw millions of stars -
their glare is in us.
I saw planets that give us energy
for realizing our dreams we imagine,
for our missions and plans,
not for cruelty and hate.

The wolf brought me to the place
where rule the night and the day.
They touch each other,
they must remain together.
Every time they're born and die
and yet they are eternal.

The wolf runs on the bridge between stars.
The wolf runs toward eternal love,
he runs toward never-ending passions.
I felt in me the explosion of desires
to run with him and so I did.
We came to the Universal ocean.
Its water refreshed my soul,
Its water caressed me,
Its water made me feel free.
Its water glittered with the light of stars,
Its water made glimmer also my heart.

I didn't feel limits anymore
in time, Universe and my soul.
Love, eternity and the light
filled up my mind.

We approached the land of dreams.
My wolf and I came in.
I saw millions of colorful suns,
their rays penetrated us.
I met a white angel of the innocence,
I looked at the seductive queen of the Night,
I faced the white-gold Lord of the Light.
Green color made hopes grow in me.
The blue created wings for me.
Now I got what are our dreams,
no craziness but they're pieces
of the Universal Higher Truth,
that humans must again discover.

The enigmatic Lord of the Underworld
welcomed me with mysterious words:
"Finally chains around your soul broke,
finally you have again returned home.
Remember, no matter where you live,
your soul wants to be free,

to love and to understand,
to touch endless Universe."

Suddenly the wolf sat down
and looked up with devotion,
love, respect and joy at
the place where souls join.
There was no loneliness,
illness and sadness.
I was feeling as hypnotized
but I knew it's not still time
to go and to remain there.
Wolf and I returned down,
to enjoy our terrestrial life.
that is the greatest gift we've ever got.
I wish all people to have such a friend
who shows them the eternal Universe,
Higher Truth and powerful love
—love that should fill up our world.
Sitting on the beach
on our beautiful Earth,
The wolf's eyes told me:
Space is our father,
Earth is our mother,
Our souls are Love
Love made up the Universe!

NED GANNON
NEW PARABLES & DISAPPEARING

Bio

Painter, illustrator, and writer, Ned Gannon spends his time teaching, illustrating, and advocating for wolves as a part of a whole ecosystem. His artwork has appeared in Communication Arts, Cricket Magazine, the Staten Island Museum, and the International Wolf Center. He teaches in the Department of Art & Design at the University of Wisconsin-Eau Claire.

In the following essay, Gannon connects the real-world struggle for wolves with his artistic fascination and representations of them and the very literature the wolves roam.

In her philosophical treatise on *The Iliad,* Simone Weil argues that power is the central character in Homer's epic. She implies that power's ultimate purpose, in the form of violence, is to rob an individual of their humanity so that they can be crushed, literally. Unless the human spirit is extracted from the body, bludgeoning a fellow human being is unthinkable. So we must demonize that which we oppose—this is the first step in any power relationship in which a party seeks to overpower another. We must cauterize any leaking sympathies. Facts, in these instances, mean nothing, because it is the humanness or spirit of the opposed thing that we hope to diminish or obliterate in order to allow the violence to ensue. In our society this becomes a game of propaganda, of information exchange and of media dominance—in short, who can shout the loudest or most often.

For me, one of the most potent elements of Ronald Dworkin's recent book *Justice for Hedgehogs* was a segment in which he outlines the contradictions in many thinking individuals' outlooks on life. A stated belief that morals are the result of an evolved dynamic between biology, geography, and cultural or environmental factors may lead us to the belief that varied moral outlooks are simply the inevitable and determined outcomes of particular places and times—the obvious answer to the equation. This sense that things are simply the way they are because they have to be can create within a thinking individual a sense that nothing can be done. And yet, the same people shout to close Guantanamo prison, which is surely the product of some equation as well. Dworkin says that this has created, particularly in academic circles, cynicism and skepticism—skepticism has become a moral position for many. Hope is not postmodern. To be truly postmodern may mean to be morally paralyzed between intellect and flickering conscience, as John Berger so beautifully explores in his book, *A Painter of Our Time*.

From 2011-2012, I have been creating, off and on, a series of drawings called the TINAW drawings. Some people have amusingly asked me if this is an Indigenous or Native American term for wolves. It is an acronym I gave the drawings that stands for "This Is Not A Wolf." Besides a reference to Magritte, I wanted to emphasize the existent. Nothing about my drawings replaces wolves' existence in nature. People ask, occasionally though not as often as I would like, why wolves? Depending on my audience, I give varied responses. Sometimes I quote Paul L. Errington, "Of all the native biological constituents of a northern wilderness scene, I should say that the wolves present the greatest test of human wisdom and good intentions." Sometimes I reference Barry Lopez's seminal work, *Of Wolves and Men*, noting that no other animal in human history has been so despised and with the exception of the Russian fairytale, "The Firebird," and a few Siberian and Native American tales, all of western literature has depicted the animal as a nuisance at best and demonic at worst. Yet other times, I reference Douglas Smith's terrific book, *Decade of the Wolf: Returning the Wild to Yellowstone*, in which he outlines the trophic cascade that resulted when the wolf was re-introduced, positively affecting everything from tree species such as Aspen and Cottonwood to beaver populations in the park to healthier fish and bear populations.

But all of my comments are arguments for the preservation of wolves, not explanations of why I draw them. In a letter to Thomas Greevy, Wallace Stevens once wrote, "It is a queer thing that so few reviewers seem to realize that one writes poetry because one must... It is quite possible to have a feeling about the world which creates a need that nothing satisfies except poetry and this has nothing to do with other poets or with anything else." In the end, I draw wolves for the same reason I believe most of us make art. I have a feeling about the world—a belief about the way it is or should be or a passion for something in it—that can't be explained through traditional verbal or written discourse. And I say this as the once creative writing major offspring of two English teachers. These drawings attempt to demonstrate that I recognize the wolf. I recognize it as a taker of life and a giver of life. I recognize it as a nuisance and a creature of awesome endurance, fierce intelligence, and human-like loyalty. I recognize it as a reclusive and mysterious animal and a mythological animal of legend and fear.

In his book, *The Last Wild Wolves*, 2007, Ian McAllister relates, near the end of his text, a story about the dangers of trying to garner sympathy among the masses for something about which they care very little. In an attempt to film a group of wolves living in the British Columbian rain forest for National Geographic, McAllister's team recruited a local outfitter, Raincoast. In November of the same year, McAllister received a letter from the owner of the local store.

> "He informed me that 'our' precious wolves existed no longer, that he had just killed as many of them as he could; he called it 'ungulate enhancement.' He had shot them dead as they played on the beach. I found out later that he had discovered where the National Geographic crew had been filming..." (McAllister)

My reaction to this is to batten down the hatches, or as Simone Weil states, "...to cauterize any leaking sympathies..." for the opposition. My temptation is also to become cynical and skeptical because things seem so out of whack with corporations and money writing legislation for our treatment and management of natural resources that are really the origin of everything and the source from which all things spring. As Barry Lopez has said, "I do not think it comes from some base, atavistic urge, though that may be part of it. I think it is that we simply do not understand our place in the universe and have not the courage to admit it."

But I can't become cynical. I can't because to do so would be to fail at my own moral endeavor, as an activist for wolves, as a teacher, as an artist, and as a human being; because it is sympathy and understanding and patience that instill value in what I do. Many of us feel under fire lately for what we do, for what we value, for who we are, assailed and battered to the point of despair by senselessness.

Early in many semesters, I like to ask my students two questions: "What would you attempt if you knew you could not fail?" and "What is one thing that you feel is absolutely true, and how will the way you think about art change if that thing turned out not to be true?" I don't ask them this to push them toward relativism. I don't really consider myself a moral relativist, even though I believe moral behavior is incredibly convoluted. But as the political landscape descends into an absurd comedy worthy only of Beckett, I often consider what I really want—what I want for my children—and, no, what I want is not "no taxes" on capital gains. What I really want is for my children to understand what is valuable, perhaps beyond what I can teach them, or as Wendell Berry said, "The highest moral behavior is not obedience to law, but obedience to the informed conscience in spite of law." In her book, *The Pine Island Paradox*, Kathleen Dean Moore says,

"Don't all parents want the world for their children? Fellow parents, tell me, wouldn't we do anything for them? To give them big houses, we will cut ancient forests. To give them perfect fruit, we will poison their food with pesticides. To give them the latest technologies, we will reduce entire valleys to toxic dumps. To give them the best education, we will invest in companies that profit from death. To keep them safe, we will deny them the right to privacy, to travel unimpeded, to peacefully assemble. And to give them peace, we will kill other peoples' children or send them to be killed, and amass enough weapons to kill the children again, kill them twenty times if necessary." (Moore)

Are we all children begging for this?

I won't claim to always know what is right. And I don't always know what to value. But in 2012, a lone wandering wolf, first referred to as OR-7, and now dubbed Journey, wandered into Northern California where Gray Wolves had not been sighted since 1924 when the last wolf was trapped there as part of a predator eradication program. And that stirs me beyond the power of words. Because quite literally, if there is hope for wolves, there is hope for us.

Bibliography

Berger, John. *A Painter of Our Time.* New York: Random House, 1996.

California Wolf Center Staff. "Wolves in California." Julian, CA: California Wolf Center. Accessed August 7, 2014.

Dworkin. *Justice for Hedgehogs.* Cambridge, MA: Belknap Press, 2013.

Errington, Paul L. *Of Predation and Life.* Ames, IA: Iowa State University Press: 1969.

Lopez, Barry. *Of Wolves and Men.* New York: Scribner, 1979.

McAllister, Ian, Rob Sanders, and Paul C. Paquet. *The Last Wild Wolves.* Oakland, CA: University of California Press, 2007.

Moore, Kathleen Deane. *Pine Island Paradox.* Minneapolis, MN: Milkweed Editions, 2005.

Smith, Douglas, and Gary Ferguson. *Decade of the Wolf: Returning the Wild to Yellowstone.* Guilford, CT: Globe Pequot Press, 2005.

Stevens, Wallace. *Letters of Wallace Stevens.* New York: Knopf, 1966.

Weil, Simone. *The Iliad or the Poem of Force: A Critical Edition,* 3rd ed. Trans. James P. Holoka. Bern, Switzerland: Peter Lang International Academic Publishers, 2006.

Disappearing. Ned Gannon. India ink and charcoal on Arches.

STEFANIE LEVINAWOLF KIDD
SANTIAGO, ROWYN, & ROMULUS AND REMUS

Bio

Stefanie LevinaWolf Kidd was born and raised in Pittsburgh, Pennsylvania. Being raised in a Pentecostal home, she became an exorcist at the young age of 12. Stefanie has been an animal rights activist since the age of 6. Her main focus in high school was very strong in art and expression; and as a member of every art and music club, she explored many different forms of art. At the age of 19, she graduated from high school with a certificate in Graphic Design. Stefanie soon left home and began working odd jobs in freelance while basically being homeless. In 2007, she worked as an unofficial set photographer on a feature film after answering an ad on Craigslist. It was very risky, but she had nothing to lose. The directors loved her work and meticulous planning, so they decided to approach her with the offer to work on more films. While building her vast network, Stefanie ended up working with several amazing people. After her fourth film, she gained the title of Production Assistant. To this day, she has worked on a total of 18 feature films all over the country. In 2011, she started to write her own films. Stefanie is in the process of officiating her very own entertainment company called Solstice and plans to get a few feature projects off the ground within the next two years. Under the Solstice banner, she is also creating a graphic novel series "Wolven Lycana" which is about the origin legend of the lycan. Her main priority, however, is to reach her ambition of completing her Bachelor's Degree in Advertising at the Art Institute of Pittsburgh.

Santiago. Stefanie LevinaWolf Kidd. Color chalk pastels and Prismacolor markers with charcoal on bristol.

Rowyn. Stefanie LevinaWolf Kidd. Permanent marker on paper.

Romulus and Remus. Stefanie LevinaWolf Kidd. Color chalk pastels and Prismacolor markers with charcoal on bristol.

PIGI
THE WISE RACE WOLF, OMEGA WOLF, & WHITE WOLF

Bio

Pigi (Pierluigi Paviola) is an artist, born in Venice. He began painting as an auto-didact in 2005, during a period of prison that lasted for 23 years. In the context of restriction, he graduated from the Dams of Padua with a dissertation on transcodification from the literary language into film language: he wrote the screenplay based on the story "The Dog Who Has Seen God" by Dino Buzzati, and he drew its story-board. He has had art exhibitions in Venice, Milan, Turin, and more.

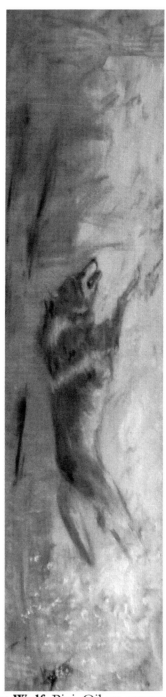

The Wise Race Wolf. Pigi. Oil on canvas, 120 by 30 cm.

Omega Wolf. Pigi. Oil on canvas, 100 by 100 cm.

White Wolf. Pigi. Oil on canvas, 100 by 100 cm.

MICHAEL E. HAYNE
THE LAST ONE

Bio

Michael E. Hayne lives in Tujunga, CA, with four rescued dogs and three rescued cats.

Here a former trapper stumbles across a wolf caught in a trap. As he tries to free the injured animal, he realizes his life is very much in danger.

His eyes were filled with rage and pain, teeth bared in a defiant last stand.

I heard his voice in my head: "Take me if you can. Be prepared to go with me."

The trap held his left rear leg in a tight grip. There was no way out for him. He had already started to chew at his leg, to escape, freedom. If he did succeed, he would not survive. This was not one of my traps. I long ago stopped. But I knew others who were driven to do this, and there was nothing I could do about it.

He snapped at his captured leg. I yelled. That distracted him back to me. He snarled, his voice erupting from his chest. I could feel his heat and smell his breath. I knew his fear. Not of dying. Fear of losing. It was my own fear.

I held up my right hand, palm open toward him, my left hand down close to my side, still in his sight, also open. He looked from one hand to the other. Then he stared at my face. I stared back. I nodded to him, slowly. Again.

He pulled back, teeth still exposed, but not making a sound. I took my right hand and, his eyes following, slowly placed it on the trap. I waited. He did not move. But his eyes never wavered from my hand. I could see I would need both hands to open the trap, to free his leg.

I raised my left hand, palm open, and slowly, while he again watched, moved that hand to the other end of the trap. This would be difficult, as I knew these traps. I placed my hands so I could open the jaws. He roared and snarled and leaped at my hands. I recoiled away, falling backward, yelling as I fell.

"WHAT'S THE MATTER WITH YOU?! I NEED TO OPEN IT

TO GET YOUR LEG OUT! YOU UNDERSTAND ME?! I'M TRY-
ING TO HELP YOU, YOU DUMB MUTT! YOU DON'T LIKE IT,
I'LL LEAVE!!!"

Neither of us moved. We simply stared at each other. I had to
laugh.

"Sorry. Look, I can get you out of this. But don't leap at me again.
Okay?"

I sat up on my haunches and just looked at him, waiting. He barked
and snapped at his captive leg. "STOP IT!!!" I screamed.

He lifted his head, upper lip twitching, teeth still very conspicuous.
A growl from deep in his chest slowly faded to a wary rumble of what
seemed to me a truce. Or perhaps I was just being sentimental. I glared
at him until he looked away, and around us. I followed his gaze.

Almost a dozen wolves surrounded us, standing back in the shadows. I had not heard their approach, nor even felt their presence. That
shook me. All these years in the wood I had come to believe, to place
my life, in my ability to sense another's presence, especially a predator.
Even if I did not see, I always felt them nearby. These wolves had
made no sound at all.

"Okay. It's your game now." I knew, under this situation, I best not
grab my knife, and my rifle certainly was out of the question, being
several feet away from me. I lifted my hands up, palms toward him.
"Well, ol' son, maybe it always was."

Without moving, just using my eyes, I looked from him to the other wolves. No movement at all, frozen in place, waiting. I looked back
at him. He stared at me.

"All or nothing. Your choice."

His eyes never left me, never left my hands. I leaned forward and
grabbed both jaws of the trap and, using all effort I could muster, slowly spread the jaws apart. Sweat dripped in my eyes. For some odd reason I don't know why, I almost laughed at that.

He carefully pulled his leg free, paused, then took a few moments
to lick the wound. I could now see it was not as serious, not broken as
I had thought. I would have preferred to do some care for him, but
that was not within this situation.

I released the jaws and they snapped together with an unpleasant
crack. All the wolves jerked away, then looked at me. "You were very
fortunate, ol' son. Wish I could help more, but that's it, you are on your
own. You take care. Okay?"

Another wolf stepped from the gathered pack, moved to him, and began licking his leg. He joined in. Both licking the wound. I realized this was a female. After a moment, the female rejoined the others gathered round.

He slowly tested his weight on his leg, found it to be sound. At least as far as I could tell. He stepped to the trap, lifted that freed leg and urinated, marking it. Several other wolves came and urinated on the trap. He trotted a couple of paces away, turned to face me, eyes wide, penetrating, something behind those eyes I had seen before.

I held up my hands, again palms showing. "What's your pleasure? Nothing I can do."

Without a backward glance, they quietly and quickly vanished into the wood.

Was I expecting a display of gratitude? I don't know. I did know it was not important. I gathered up my fallen rifle, checked my knife, grabbed my pack, and, with a last look toward where they had disappeared, I set off to continue my journey.

As I said, I gave up trapping a long time ago. Nothing noble about it. Just did not want to do it anymore. Perhaps it was the last wolf I killed. Old battle scarred warrior.

I never saw any of that pack again. I wonder about them. About him. Thank you, ol' son. To this day I still do not know why I feel such gratitude. You were the one freed. Just like that proud and ancient Guardian of the wood.

There are moments when I think, maybe some time in my journeys into the wood, I will meet him again. Or one of his clan. I can only hope. Strange, I know.

John Noland
Red Wolves, Awakening, & Hunters

Bio

John Noland has rescued a cougar cub, but he has never seen a wild wolf puppy and would love to see one. He believes that helping to save wolves is to help save the spirit of the Earth. He grew up in the Midwest for a love for all creatures canine. His earliest memory is of coyotes howling. Now John lives and writes near the ocean in Coos Bay, Oregon. He has published works in The Chicago Review, Orion, Nature Writing 1999 *ed. by John Murray,* The Georgetown Review, The Seattle Review, The Laurel Review, Limestone, Big Muddy, Camas, Intricate Homelands, *and other journals. His poem, "Three Coyotes," was one of the winners in the 2013 Northern Colorado Poetry Contest. John's most recent chapbook,* Midwestern Trees and Shadows, *was published by Finishing Line Press; a previous chapbook,* This Dark Land Where I Live, *won Kulupi Press' "Poetry of Place Contest." His chapbook* The Caged *and the Dying won the 2012 Gribble Press Chapbook Contest; poems from it were published in the March, 2014* Jefferson Monthly.

Red Wolves

They slip through shadows,
A sudden red flash, then
gone.

This is what we know,
mostly
of red wolves
mysteries old, old
but still here,
still dying, still
shouting hossannahs
and defiance
in the gold-breaking
dawn. They roam
lost to those who see

only with their eyes,
blind
to what lies hidden
in earth's dark hills
and in our own roiling blood
where those of us who care
pray to live wider, deeper,
hungry as wolves
running wild trails
in the earth
and in our blood.

Awakening

As the sound rises,
beneath a thin slice of moonlight,
even crawdads in tiny streams
ache with hunger
and a forgetting
they almost remember,
something below
the surface
that awakens the darkness
to attention. Birds
ruffle their wings,
rabbits sink deeper
into shadows.
Howls cut across darkness
like a jagged, bright light
as the night quivers
and what we took for granted
of the world
and its possibilities
opens wider. This song
lives in the forest
and in us, sliding
riding mysterious
blood-rivers
in our flesh

where we hunt
a long-lost beauty
almost gone
from this,
our earth:
Wolves howling
in the dawn.

Hunters

Wolves pass in and out
of thin fog
and sea mist
like spirits
from an earlier
and innocent world.
I have been there,
a hunter of men
working my way
up a long savannah
of grass almost unseen in flare light. Tongues
of flame spurt
in darkness, rifle shots,
even explosions dim
to men overcome
by night's beauty:
Fog, smoke, rifle fire,
rippling flare light,
the distant chatter
of machine guns,
even distant screams
rising like bird cries.
A face suddenly
out of darkness,
then gone.
We are not sure
who we are—
friend or enemy.
Too young to know

Beyond what we are told,
we would like
to reach out, stroke a face,
say, I did not mean
to do this, did not
mean to kill,
did not know
what kill meant.
It was natural, unaware,
even innocent.
In the fog
and the darkness
among silent red wolves,
I cry out, Father,
forgive us, we know
not what we do.
it is the way
of the hunger,
the flickering night-trail
touched by death
and beauty
and the curse of gun fire.
O, wolves
howl for all of us,
sing sorrow
in a dark time.
Forgive us all.

JENNY H. THORNTON WOODLEY
ACROSS THE RIVER

Bio

Jenny H. Thornton Woodley has been writing short stories and poems most of her life. She was raised in Northern Ontario, Canada, where wolves and other wildlife surrounded her. She is a grandmother now, and her favorite thing to do is tell stories to her grandchildren. She has had a poem that she gifted to a local group used as a poster for their children's health department. Her interest in wildlife conservation became more serious as she grew older and realized how little humans were doing to ensure that no more species became a part of the lost ones.

The following story follows the way a bond between a father and his daughter develops through nature. This is a story of love that transcends all generations. What do you all hear when you look across the river?

It was the summer of her fifteenth year, and as promised her father was taking her hiking to the big water fall. They had hiked the trail many times in the past, but this year was special; her father had been ill, and against all odds he had recovered enough to take the long walk into the bush. He would have to walk slowly and take many rests along the way, but they were prepared for that. In her pack she carried dried meat and fruit and a large bottle of grandmother's homemade apple berry juice.

The walk into the falls took over two hours from the main road; they had driven that far in her father's old car, and then left it parked in a small clearing. Several minutes before they saw the falls they heard them; the water crashing over the top to hit the large boulders nestled at the bottom. As they approached the end of the trail they had to choose which way to climb: up to the top where the river could be seen for some distance, or down to the bottom where the rocks lay scattered as if thrown by some giant in a pool of frothy water.

"You choose Daddy, which way is best for you. If we go up first the climb down will be easier; but if we go down first we can rest at the bottom before having to climb back up." She spoke softly; it made no difference to her which way they went, she was just content to be here.

Her father paused and scratched his head as he always did when trying to make an important decision. "I think we should go down first:

we can rest and cool our feet in the pool and perhaps have a little of that juice." He nodded, decision made; and began the slow climb down.

Once there they sat on a large boulder and took off their shoes. They shared some of the juice and a hunk of corn meal bread that her mother had carefully wrapped and put in the pack. The spray of the water hit their faces gently, and they sat for some time relaxing in the sunlight that beamed down on them through the shadows of the rocks and trees. It was good just to be here.

Suddenly from the top of the rock wall came a howl, long and steady and piercing. She shook her head and jumped to her feet gazing upward searching for where the wolf might be. It was mid-morning, not the time of day she associated with the song of the wolf, but there was no doubt there was a wolf up on the ledge somewhere. She loved wolves. She had been taught to respect them; she had also been taught to give them the space they required. Her father had told her many times that wolves fear men, and if given the room they would run and hide rather than confront a human. She scanned the top of the rocks but saw nothing; she hoped the wolf was on the other side of the river.

"Don't worry my girl: that wolf is high up and across the other side." Her father spoke softly, his voice barely heard above the roar of the waterfall. "Let's climb to the top and take a look over there. I don't think it means us any harm, and besides there is a river between us."

Quickly and quietly they climbed to the top, and as they reached a wide flat rock surface they heard the howl again. This time it seemed much closer, and she followed her father's lead as he carefully sat on the rock and put his feet over the edge, dangling his legs and putting his hand up to shield his eyes from the sun. Together they peered across the river, searching the openings in the woods that led to the water's edge.

At first they saw nothing, and then her father gently touched her arm and pointed across the river to a stand of large pine trees; the sight took her breath away. A large gray wolf stood staring over at them, its golden eyes seemed able to look right inside of her and read her thoughts; it kept its gaze locked on hers for several minutes as time stood still. And then, it lifted its head and howled, like a song of greeting that echoed through the space around them. And what happened next thrilled her to her soul: from behind the large wolf appeared another adult wolf, but at her side were two pups. All four wolves stood staring across the river at them as she and her father stared right back.

It was a moment locked in her memory for all time, something she knew would stay with her forever.

After several moments of what appeared to be mutual curiosity the large male lifted his head and let out a long howl, and then nudging the female to follow him he retreated back into the trees, taking his family with him. And just like that the visit ended.

But that was not the last time they saw them: many times over the summer they traveled back to the falls. Often her father would howl as they approached; he said he was calling his brother the wolf to let him know who was coming. Each time they would hear the wolves sing, and each time they would gaze at them across the river. The pups grew bigger and bolder, and late in the summer they began to lag behind when their parents called them to leave. That usually earned them a snap on the behind, and her father laughed and reminded her that even wolves knew they must teach their young to listen to the words of their elders.

For the rest of that summer and into the next two years she and her father made regular hikes into the falls; they told no one of what they saw there because there were many who feared wolves, and there was always a chance that some hunter would go and kill them if they knew where to look. Instead it was a well-cherished secret between father and daughter, and they treasured the visits with the great creatures.

And then the worst thing that could happen to her did; her beloved father died in the fall of the third year. She raged at the heavens and buried herself in pain and sorrow. She did not go out; she stayed in her home and cried, for weeks and weeks. Nothing was the same; the once happy girl was now a shadow of herself, and she spent the winter grieving.

When spring came again she did not go to visit the wolves; she would not go without her father. Those days seemed over, and she struggled to get on with her life, trying to make a new one. Two years later she married and left home, and for a time life was good. She had a son, a beautiful gentle boy who reminded her of her father, and she taught him as her father had taught her. And as with most things, time began to heal her broken heart, and she began to feel that life could be good, even while knowing it would never be the same: those days were gone, and she would have to accept that.

One day when her son was three years old she awoke with the knowledge that it was time to take the boy to the falls; she did not think to see the wolves, for surely they would be gone by now, but she wanted to show her child the place she had shared with her father. They walked in through the old well-known trail, and as they walked she spoke to him of his grandfather, and what a good man he had been and how he had loved all animals. They got to the end of the trail, and something drew her to go to the top, and she followed the path remembering many other such climbs and feeling the loss of her father all over again: maybe this had not been such a good idea.

Suddenly her son began to howl, just as her father had done and tears filled her eyes. She let them flow as she continued climbing, listening to her son howl as if to call the wolves. She thought to let him think maybe they would come, even as she believed it was not going to happen ever again.

They reached the top, and she sat her son beside her on the rocks, and together they peered into the woods across the river. What occurred next sent shivers up her spine: she heard the howl of a wolf, and from the woods appeared a beautiful gray creature, standing proud and strong on the rocks above the falls. At first she thought she was dreaming. Surely that wolf from years past would not still be here, but even as she shook her head she saw the wolf lift his and howl again; long mournful howls that pierced the air as he stood staring over at them. It was like that for several moments. The wolf howled, and her son howled back as if in conversation, and then the great creature howled one last time and retreated out of sight. She sat for a very long time, holding her child and letting all the pain of her losses ease away.

She never knew if it was the same wolf, or perhaps it had been the spirit of him, but she believed that he had come to let her know her father's spirit was safe; he had passed the love of nature onto her child. His great love of all nature would live on. Her heart was lifted once again: she had purpose in her life, and she knew what she must do. She would continue to teach her child the way her father had taught her, and she would encourage others to learn of the wolves and hope that one day the animals would be left in peace.

She never again saw a wolf at the falls: some said hunters had killed them all off shortly after her father's death, but she knew what she and her son had seen that day, and so did the boy. He spoke of it many times to her as he grew into a strong young man, and he carried the love for nature with him into adulthood. She continued to speak of her love of wolves, but never did she speak of the wolves at the falls; it was now a secret she and her son shared. And just in case they were still there somewhere she had no intention of putting any wolves in harm's way. Man would do what man would do. She could only hope they came to their senses before it was too late for the wolves.

KAMEROUN MARES
OKAMI

Bio

Kameroun Mares is a college student living in San Marcos, CA, but originated from La Mesa, CA. She started drawing passionately at the age of 6. She was diagnosed with Acute Lymphoblastic Leukemia along with Type 1 Juvenile Diabetes, and she didn't have any family with her: she was always alone. She is not sure why or how, but somehow her deep passion and love for wolves just came naturally and mysteriously. As she learned more about Wolves, she grew closer and closer to them, the often mistaken, beautiful creatures that are symbols of loyalty and faithful to their pack, no matter what. They are such strong, beautiful creatures who have survived hardships just to survive along with providing balance with nature. Her dream is to get a chance to interact and volunteer to be around with Wolves.

Okami. Kameroun Mares. Ink pen with digital retouching.

GENA BENSON
ALPHA

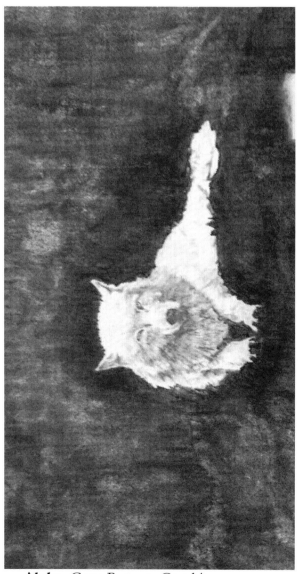

Alpha. Gena Benson. Graphite on paper.

JEFF SETZER
RED WOLF STARE

Bio

Jeff Setzer lives in Lynchburg, VA. He obtained a Bachelor's Degree in Aeronautics and is now a private pilot, a wildlife photographer, and an avid red wolf advocate.

Red Wolf Stare. Jeff Setzer. Photograph.

LINDA PALMER
THE PACK

Bio

Linda Palmer has been writing for pleasure since the third grade and has letters from her teachers predicting she'd be an author. She was the student who loved essay tests, research papers, and reading assignments. Though becoming a writer was never actually a dream, it was something she did naturally and eventually with intent. Silhouette Books published Linda's first novel in 1989 and the next twenty over a ten year period (writing as Linda Varner, her maiden name). In 1999, she took a break to take care of her growing family. She learned that she couldn't not write, however, and began again, changing her genre to young adult/new adult/adult paranormal romance and writing under her married name. She has numerous full-length novels out as e-reads and in print, and there are always more in the works. She also has many novellas and short stories available. In addition, Linda loves creating book covers and does most of her own.

Linda has been a Romance Writers of America (RWA) finalist twice and won the 2011 and 2012 Electronic Publishing Industry Coalition (EPIC) eBook awards in the Young Adult category. She married her junior high school sweetheart many years ago and lives in Arkansas, USA with her family.

Here Annie takes care of her dying grandfather when he says something that ultimately changes her life...and makes the woods outside his house seem so much more alive.

"Tell the pack."

"What?" My gaze shifted to the cards Gramps and I'd been playing to distract him from his pain. Did he mean 'deck' instead of 'pack?' Was I supposed to say something to the kings, queens, jacks, and jokers stacked on the bedside table?

Gramps smiled at my reaction. Realizing he was in the here and now—a rarity the past few hours—I beamed back at him. It was so good to see that twinkle in his baby blues, if only for a nanosecond.

"The werewolves. Let them know when I pass."

My spirits sank. So much for the here and now. "What werewolves?"

"The ones on Rainbow Mountain."

I wasn't sure how to answer. Clearly he was still not with me, a result of his meds, and it wasn't really surprising he saw werewolves wherever he now was. My grandfather, who'd been a writer, loved all things Canis lupus and had paintings and photos of them on every wall of his cabin, as well as wolf afghans, wolf rugs, wolf throw pillows, and wolf figurines. Then there were his books...so many that I had no clue which to read first. Luckily he wasn't the kind of guy to get upset because his granddaughter preferred nonfiction.

"Tell them I'm gone, okay? Ben Caulder, the alpha, will know what to do." Gramps drew in a wheezy breath and closed his eyes. Yeah, he'd definitely left me in spirit again and was probably now deep inside a world of his own making, which was maybe not a bad thing.

The monitor beside his hospital bed bleeped extra loud. I jumped up to hover over him, my panicked eyes on the graphs. His heart rate had slowed, I thought, and looked erratic, but what did I know? My degree was in journalism, not nursing. "Are you hurting? Should I call someone?"

Gramps found my hand somehow and squeezed my fingers. "I'm just fine, Mattie Lou."

Mattie Lou.

He thought he was talking to his only child aka my MIA mother. Well, his memories of her had to be better than mine. Or not. Mattie—she never let me call her Mom—had kept him secret from me all my life for some reason. Maybe he simply wanted closure to their issues, whatever they were. "I'm Annie, Gramps. Your granddaughter."

"Of course you are. Sorry."

My heart twisted. "I love you so much."

Gramps smiled without opening his eyes. "And I love you back." He patted my hand like I was the one dying, and not him.

I watched as he drifted off to sleep, his expression peaceful. He didn't have much longer. Even I could see that. So I scooted my chair closer and sat where I could cling to him, dreading the moment when he left me in body, too.

Two nights later, a howl stopped me in my tracks. One of Gramps' werewolves? Too tired to laugh at that idiocy, I just shook my head. If there was a wolf howling, it wasn't a two-legged one. And for all I knew, it could be a coyote or even a wild dog. I wasn't exactly familiar with sounds of the wild. Sighing, I shifted the urn and my purse to one arm so I could raise the hatch of my car. Somewhere under all the stuff

I'd crammed in back was my overnight bag. If I could find it, I'd leave the rest of the unpacking until morning.

I heard the plaintive howl again and then others, echoing it. I realized the sound was natural for the setting, which meant I might've heard it before, though surely not this close. At any rate, it didn't scare me.

Tell the pack.

Poor Gramps. Or maybe not. Although never a writer the critics considered gifted, he'd had a lot of fans and made a living doing what he loved. I should be so lucky.

The full moon showed me the way from the dirt drive to the front porch of the log cabin built by his father many years ago. It had held up well, I thought, and would do nicely as a home away from home or, if business didn't pick up soon, temporary living quarters until I paid off my student loans. So far my freelance writing career was going nowhere, a fact I'd kept from Gramps so he wouldn't worry. But I somehow scraped by every month and still believed things would get better now that I had more time to write.

When I opened the cabin door, familiar smells assailed me—coffee, cedar, Old Spice. Gramps could've been in the kitchen right then, cooking a late dinner for us. I swear I almost called out to him before I remembered he'd never stand in front of that old stove again. That's when it hit me, that blast of grief I'd somehow held back while I'd done what had to be done. Obituary? Check. Cremation? Check. Packing? Check. Drive back? Check.

My rigid self-control slipped a notch. I suddenly needed air—fresh air and lots of it. Ridding myself of my purse, bag, and the urn, I started back out the door only to pivot and grab the urn again. Full moon, star spangled sky, autumn woods. What better time to scatter his ashes and start the healing process? Gramps had loved this cabin and the surrounding forest as much as he loved the night. Why, I couldn't count the times he'd headed out after dark all alone for a walk. I hadn't followed out of respect for his privacy. Having me underfoot had to be a challenge after all his years alone. It didn't help that he was already sick when I found him, which meant I tended to fuss about his health.

Without bothering to grab a flashlight, I fearlessly headed into the trees, taking a well-worn path. Deep shadows occasionally tricked my eyes into thinking I saw movement peripherally, but every time I looked, there was nothing there. Since I wasn't a rookie to the trails, I pushed on. It wasn't as if I intended to go beyond the area familiar to me.

Another low howl sent a shiver up my spine and made me question my goal. Should I be scared of the local wildlife? I knew wolves wisely avoided humans. But what if a hungry bear was out there or a wild boar? And then there were the snakes—some venomous. I stepped lighter, my gaze shifting from one side to the other. Maybe this wasn't such a good idea, but I'd come this far, and it felt so good to stretch my legs after hours in the car.

A hundred yards from the cabin, I stopped to consider my next move. A stiff breeze shook the tops of the trees on all sides of me. Leaves rained down, a shower that would've been colorful in sunshine, but looked a little creepy by moonlight. I knew there was a bluff just ahead. If I emptied the urn there, Gramps' ashes would catch in the breeze and scatter all over his mountain. That felt right, so I picked up the pace, my destination firmly in mind now that I knew it.

Maybe twenty yards later, I saw the break in the trees. The path was narrow now and more treacherous, thanks to roots and brambles, but I made it all right and stepped into a small clearing. A large rock lay ahead, perfect for star gazing. I set the urn on it and carefully crawled over the top so I could sit with my legs dangling into the dark unknown.

The sky stretched above me like a midnight blue umbrella sprayed with glitter. A cool breeze lifted my hair and tugged at my jacket, but I barely noticed. My gaze was on the full moon. With no city lights to challenge its glow, it had never looked so big, so close. I saw clearly the lunar maria that gave it human features. No wonder our ancestors thought the moon controlled more than the tides. At the moment, I could easily believe that it held sway over the werewolves Gramps wrote about.

Suddenly desperately lonely, I realized how quiet the night had become. I hadn't heard any howls in a while now, which probably meant the animal had bedded down for the night, something I should consider. But not before I did what I'd walked so far to do.

"Hey, there," I said, addressing the man in the moon as if Skip Clayton had taken him over. "I've got your ashes in this urn, and I'm about to toss them into the wind, just like you wanted. As for that other thing you asked me to do... I'd tell the werewolves about your death if I only knew how to find them—"

The tangled brush behind me rustled ominously. Then a pebble skittered past my rock to drop into the dark chasm. Gasping, I twisted to see why. I saw eyes. Lots of eyes, every pair eerily opalescent by moonlight. Stifling a scream, I eased all the way around and stood to face whatever creatures had tracked me there.

A wolf split from the shadows and stepped out of the trees into the clearing. Another followed and then another until there were six, all of them silver in that light and incredibly magnificent. They stood in a half circle, blocking any possible escape into the trees and trapping me between them and the edge of forever. Was I scared? Not one bit. Why? Because they weren't real. Utter exhaustion and Gramps' crazy last request had clearly resulted in a waking dream so surreal that I actually went with the magic.

"Um, hello. Thank you for coming. I'm Annie, Skip's granddaughter. He passed away Wednesday night." Did wolves know about days of the week? Probably not, but werewolves should. Unfortunately, I didn't see any furry men with sharp claws and fangs in my tiny audience, which ruled out the latter possibility. A hysterical giggle bubbled up from nowhere, shocking me. I hadn't made that sound since I was five and Mattie asked some hot guy for directions to the ferry. I'd thought she meant Tinkerbell and giggled with excitement. Fatally embarrassed, she'd slapped me.

But that was then. At twenty-two, I no longer believed in fairies, much less the myth of loving moms.

I didn't believe in werewolves, either, which made these wolves nothing but normal, if mere illusions.

"Um, I'm going to scatter his ashes now. You're welcome to watch if you promise not to eat me afterward." I picked up the urn and showed it to the pack before brazenly turning my back on them. Since I wasn't attacked, I assumed my head was on straight again and climbed onto the rock. Removing the lid of the urn, I carefully tipped it. Gramps' ashes blew over the dark mountainside. I turned to go, squealing when I saw that all six wolves still stood right where I'd left them.

Yeah, as hallucinations went, this one was a doozy and without the help of Grandpa's powerful painkillers.

In the spirit of the moment, I hugged the urn to my chest. "Maybe I should say a few words. I didn't know Skip Clayton until a year ago, when Lucy Williams, a former neighbor, gave me a box she'd been keeping for Mattie, er, my mom. Lucy said she'd read a piece in the local paper and realized it was written by me, which eventually led to her getting my address. I'd been passed from one foster home to the next for years, so didn't really have one until—" I caught myself. "But we're talking about Skip, aren't we? Gramps was wonderful man. Patient, loving, talented. I just wish I'd known him longer. Yeah." Sigh. "Him, I'll miss."

I jumped off the rock, ready to head home. But the wolves had something else in mind. To the one, they tipped their heads back and howled, a gut-wrenching sound as beautiful as taps at a military funeral. When silence reigned again, I had to wipe my eyes with the hem of my shirt.

"Thanks for that. I'm sure he heard you." Although I expected my wolfy companions to vanish like the visions they surely were, they simply stepped aside, making room for me to slip past them. I started walking but didn't get far before I stopped and glanced over my shoulder. "Do real wolves hang out with werewolves? Probably not. But just in case, if you see Ben Caulder, would you ask him to come by the cabin later? Grandpa told me he'd know what to do next."

By the time the clock struck eleven, a hot shower had soothed my physical aches. Mentally, however, I was a train wreck. I not only reeled from the enormity of my loss, I questioned every decision I'd ever made. Worse, I worried about decisions to come. After snagging a Coke from the fridge, I sat at the kitchen table and stared at the urn I'd picked out for Gramps' ashes. It had a wolf motif. Fitting, I thought, and a perfect addition to decor I had no intentions of changing. In fact, I knew right where I'd put it—the mantle.

I wondered briefly if Gramps had a will. By rights, everything should go to Mattie. Would she want the cabin she'd grown up in? I doubted it. But she'd love any money earned from the sale of it, and that's what scared me.

Restless, I left the kitchen and went into the great room, which felt chilly. Was it getting cold out? Since I didn't want to worry with a fire this late, I pulled Gramps' old sweater off the back of a chair and slipped it on over my thermal pajamas. The sight of all his books lured me to the shelves. I read the titles until I came to one that called my name. With book in hand, I settled into my grandfather's leather recliner and covered up with his afghan, the one with the wolves on it. Surrounded by his special scent, I felt very safe and warm.

I began to read and to my surprise was quickly sucked into a tale of love, courage, and mystic transformations. Since the werewolves in this novel weren't the ridiculous two-legged kind, I found it shockingly easy to suspend disbelief and accept that a human could morph into a wolf. In fact, it was a beautiful possibility that piqued my interest and made me want to take notes. Did I have a werewolf novel in me? My doubtful gaze shifted to the bookshelf. Surely every possible plot had already been written.

A knock rattled the front door and scared me to attention. I glanced at the clock. Midnight. Who'd come by so late? Snagging a fireplace tool from the stand, I crept to the door, which didn't have a peep hole, much less a window in it. So I kept the chain lock engaged and flipped on the front light before I opened up. A man was standing on the porch, his finger tips stuffed into the front pockets of his jeans and what looked like a leather pouch tucked under his arm. The tense set of his shoulders hinted that he might be cold. His freezing breath told me why. The temperature had definitely dropped.

He gave me a smile. "Hey."

"Hey." My suspicious gaze swept him from dark brown hair to muddy boots.

"I'm Ben."

"Who?"

"Ben Caulder. Skip's friend."

I must've looked pretty blank.

"I woke you, didn't I? You said you'd be up, and the light was on." He waited for a response I couldn't give. "I'll come back tomorrow." Ben turned to leave.

"Wait."

He stopped.

"You were at the funeral tonight?" If you could even call it that.

"That's right."

"I didn't see you."

"Actually, you did." He winced. "Oh boy. Skip never told you, did he?"

"Told me...?"

"About the pack."

"He mentioned a pack, yeah, right before he died, and he called you the alpha. But I never dreamed—I mean I just figured—" I swallowed hard. "He was pretty out of it by then." Everything hit home at once. "Ohmygod. Are you for real?"

"I should definitely come back tomorrow."

"No, no, no." I couldn't toss the tool or shut the door fast enough, and then my shaking hands fumbled disengaging the stupid chain. But when I finally yanked the door fully open, he was still standing there. "Come in. Please."

"Are you sure?"

"Uh-huh."

He brushed past me to step indoors. "I have Skip's papers. His will. The deed to the cabin. The combination to the safe. Everything's yours."

I just looked at him.

"Maybe you should sit down."

"Okay." Admittedly dazed, I let him lead me into the kitchen and help me into one of the chairs. He clearly knew his way around. "He willed the cabin to me?"

"Yes." Ben sat on the other side of the table and pushed the portfolio toward me. "There's a stipend for Mattie, of course, just in case she turns up someday. But it's not much. He was afraid she'd use the money to—"

"Buy drugs?"

"Well, yeah." He glanced around the kitchen. "You look a little shell-shocked. Are you okay? I could make some coffee or cook something."

"Isn't that my line?"

His brown eyes crinkled at the corners when he laughed. "Guess it is."

"Are you really a—" I just couldn't say it.

"Werewolf? Yeah, I am." He stared at me for a minute. "And you seem to be taking it pretty dang well considering you just found out they exist."

"Only because I'm emotionally numb and absolutely positive I'm hallucinating." I poked his hand, which was resting on the table between us. Flesh. Bones. A big silver ring with a wolf's head on it, just like Gramps'. "Plus, I've been reading this book about—" I belatedly registered his expression. Talk about shell-shocked. "What?"

"N-nothing." His face flushed.

"Come on. Out with it."

"I never dreamed you'd be so damn beautiful."

Now my face flushed.

Ben jumped to his feet, knocking over the chair. "I should go. You're emotionally numb. I'm talking too much. Why don't we start fresh tomorrow?" He straightened the chair and scooped up the pouch.

"Can I keep that?" I pointed to it.

Ben was obviously surprised he held it. "Of course. It's yours." He pushed the pouch toward me.

I followed him out the door. "Do you really turn into a wolf?"

"I do, yeah."

"Did Gramps?"

"No, but he sure as heck wanted to."

"May I watch next time you do it?"

"Sure, if you're still around."

"Oh, I'll be around."

"Does that mean you're keeping the cabin? I worried—I mean I figured you might want to sell. I know you're a city girl." He finger combed his shaggy hair, a move that looked a little self-conscious.

"I'm keeping the cabin."

"For the weekends?"

"For ever, actually."

"Then we'll be seeing a lot of you, I guess."

"I'd like that." I narrowed my gaze. "I have questions, Ben Cauld-er."

"Skip warned me that you might."

"Do you mind?"

"I sort of did, but now, not so much." He leaped off the porch, only to turn and walk backward a few steps. "Is nine too early?"

"Nope."

"I'll bring donuts."

"Something else to look forward to." I couldn't hide my smile.

The smile he gave back was as bright as that big old moon.

NIKCOLE KING
RAMPANT TUESDAY

Bio

Nikcole King (Nikci) is a multi-media artist from the woods of N. California and N. Arizona. She recycles common household items and repurposes them in her jewelry and acrylic paintings. Her signature style for paintings is done on found wood and mostly wafer board (orientated strand board). Nikci's themes contain strong movement, color, nature, and industrial tones. Nikci received her Bachelor of Fine Arts degree in 2011 from Idaho State University and has since been active in her studio. She has been published in Black Rock & Sage *(issue 10), received an award in architectural design and artistic expression, and actively participates in art shows in her current home in S. Idaho.*

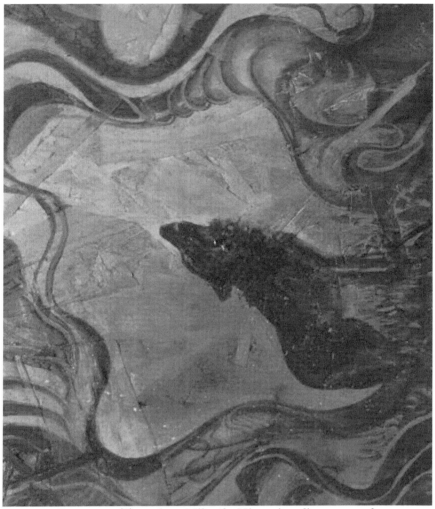

Rampant Tuesday. Nikcole King. Acrylic on wood.

REGAN MORAN
A LAND WITHOUT WOLVES

Bio

Regan Moran lives in Quebec, Canada. Behind his back lies a few hundred acres of Laurentian bush. Hemlock stands with logs too big to carry out with no roads in. Yet, for the last five falls he has resigned my summer freedom and held his head high while he shows up for duty on the three-man cross country ski network crew. They like to think of themselves as an elite band of bushmen, able to clear monster tree snags out of the way. As far as writing is concerned he has been published in the Yukon Sun, *a paper out of Dawson Creek, Yukon and wrote a column here in his area called "WE LIVE HERE TOO" published in the* Main Street, *a monthly out of Lachute, Quebec. He and his wife currently own and operate an increasingly expanding farmer's market from spring to fall.*

His essay here looks closely at the issues of hunting wolves and the ecological as well as cultural implications therein.

There is a wolf at our door, and he wants to come in. In this case our door is the hundreds of acres of bush that we are lucky enough to be living in and around. The wolf wants to come in to our conscious and be welcomed not as a bad dream or a sinister beast of myth, but as a highly useful predator that deserves our respect. An animal so tied to human history, hunted to extinction worldwide, now recognized as an integral part of a healthy forest ecosystem. Not to mention an integral part of a healthy Canadian identity. They want to let them back in the door down south in Maine, New Hampshire, they already have in the mountains of Mexico, Yellowstone Park and other western US states, and the wolves they used to re-populate were Canadian wolves. It has been proven that the wolf has a positive effect on deer and moose populations, eating the old, sick, and weaker animals and consequently strengthening the gene pool.

Just the other day, not far from here, a local illustrious back-woodsman shot a wolf on a frozen lake. He was baiting them. The body doesn't have to be recorded, and there is no tag, like there is for the sacred Deer; in fact if he wanted to, he could have left it to rot. All winter he could have shot every wolf he saw, just like rabbits and other small game. Small game? That's right: the wolf is still considered a small game animal, and so with a hunting license any soul can go kill that which is stronger, wilder, and more free than it will ever be. Canada is one of the only countries left in the world, along with other forward thinking places like Tajikistan and China, that does not protect the wolf. Perhaps he did it just to get close and touch this noble animal, so similar to the dog he feeds every night and gets along with better than family. It's like a lot of things in this land: we feel so rich with our rivers and our forests and our wolves, but the wallet is getting thin, and if you have been to James Bay or watched the news the other night you realize that most of our big rivers are having cement poured in them. The forests aren't as wild, and there is less room for wolves in the new urban mindset. People come here to see them!!! Just like people go to India to see the last of the tiger in game parks. Wolves are already becoming isolated in parks like Mt. Tremblant, but they need more land than this. Wolves should be protected animals, but in this old human landscape they are not, so the hunt should be managed and highly controlled like it is for the deer, to ensure the wolf is not treated as a pest but as one of our greatest assets.

The chief wolf biologist in Quebec, Hélene Jolicourt, has written that it is very hard to know the health of our wolf population because of all the wolf kills that go unrecorded.

Will the wolf survive? Will we?

Early one morning I see big canine tracks meandering in the fresh snow. They continue all the way up to Monfort weaving back and forth, splashes of urine on tree trunks, digging marks in snowbanks. I skidoo left into the woods and come upon the tracks again where they lead to a big patch of blood-splattered snow, deer fur, some stomach remains, and that's it. I dig for bones, hoofs, antlers—there is nothing. For one whole week around the same location I see the solitary big canine tracks, and then they disappear. A year earlier, same time period, I hear a long deep howl from across the lake floating out of a stand of Hemlock. My two huskies hear it too; they look at me and start to howl. A neighbor observes two very large canines poking around a beaver dam. They are here: we live with them.

Imagine a forest with only deer and squirrels! No predators. It seems a weaker place; the humans seem to be softer, more domesticated, like there is something missing inside of them. It's a land without wolves, a bleak place, a place to go shopping. It's not Quebec.

Meanwhile the illustrious local backwoodsman is sitting on his couch drinking coffee and watching Steven and Chris, and the next minute he's shooting a wolf! What a country!

Up on top of Lac Rond there was a guy who lived in a log house at the end of the road when his was the only house up there. Behind the house was, and still is, a good little patch of wilderness. One night walking around his living room he got a funny feeling and walked up to his window, outside was a starry cold winters night, and that's not all— on the other side of the window a wolf was standing up with its two front paws on the window sill looking straight at him. Their eyes met. Then the wolf came down on all four paws and disappeared into the forest.

I AM CANIS LUPUS, AND WE LIVE HERE TOO!

ELIZA HOMAN
WOLF CALL

Bio
Eliza Homan lives in Dublin, Ireland. She has been writing for many years and is a member of Airfield Writers. Eliza has a number of local publications to her name and was highly commended at the McGill School poetry competition some years ago. At present she has just completed a children's story which is in the editing stages. She is a wife, mother, and grandmother. Eliza is a shamanic practitioner, massage therapist, healer, and clairvoyant. Nature is part of her life, and she feels free and at home among its environs.

rain seeped earth
autumn bite in the air
chilled bones

somewhere in the forest
you stood unseen
watching

your spirit had walked with me
now your howl
awakens primal years

lifts my soul
to dance
the hunting of your call

JANET HOBEN
I AM RED WOLF

Bio

Janet Hoben is a lifelong resident of Southern California. She has had numerous letters to the editor published nationwide advocating for wolves, including two that were published in a book given to all members of Congress. Janet is on the Board of Directors of the National Wolfwatcher Coalition and currently serves as their Southeast Regional Director/expert on red wolves.

I am a rustling in the trees
I am a whisper in the wind
I am a howling in the night
I am red wolf

I am the cry of newborn pups
I am the hunter left unseen
I am the pack that's proud and strong
I am red wolf

I am the prayer that's on your lips
I am the cry for one more chance
I am the one who fights to live
I am.......red wolf

SUNDA THEODORE
STARE, COMPANION, & JOURNEY

Bio

Sunda Theodore lives in South Korea. Her interests include art, wolves, and Shamanism.

Stare. Sunda Theodore. Pencil on paper.

Companion. Sunda Theodore. Pencil on paper.

Journey. Sunda Theodore. Pencil on paper.

SHANNON BARNSLEY
WE WERE WOLVES

Bio

Shannon Barnsley is a fantasy writer, poet, and blogger from New Hampshire, currently living in Brooklyn. Her work has appeared in The Concord Monitor *and* Redhead Magazine. *Raised on the* Julie of the Wolves *series and world folktales in a quiet corner of rural New England, Shannon loved wolves from an early age, devouring any book about them she could find, whether fictional, folkloric, or zoological. Though her childhood dream of living with wolves to study them was abandoned in favor of the humanities and a slightly less rugged lifestyle, her love for them remains. Thus, she is thrilled to have a hand in helping wolves through her writing. Shannon holds a degree in Creative Writing/Mythology & Religion from Hampshire College.*

We werewolves, we were wolves
Who walked among the sheep.
You heard our echoes in the wind,
Drifting fitfully to your sleep.

We haunted the corners of your mind,
Prowled the edges of your farm.
Then came the torches, axes, knives,
For fear we'd do you harm.

You shiver beneath the harvest moon
To hear the tell-tale howl.
Mind, latch your door against the wolf
Though man be on the prowl.

We werewolves, we were men,
Jekyll's Hyde, your darker side.
We walked among you, clad in wool.
With us slain, you wore wolf's hide.

We moved in mist, in fog, in shade
To claim those straying from your flocks.
You torched the forest to face us there,
Caged the wolf in dungeons, cells, and stocks.

You think her innocent, your little lost girl,
Caped in Inquisition red.
Yet when she leads you hunting Hyde,
Mind don't slay Jekyll in his stead.

We werewolves, we were wolves,
Lying slain 'neath moonlit skies.
See as you burn the impure lamb
In whose heart darkness lies.

Van Sims
Love

Love. Van Sims. Digital media.

MARCOS CARVALHO
NORTH AMERICAN WOLF

Bio

Marcos da Rocha Carvalho is a designer and illustrator from Rio de Janeiro, Brazil who lives and works in the DC metropolitan area. He has a BFA in Photography from the University of the Arts and an MA in Computer Art from the Savannah College of Art and Design. He loves all things design and art related. He also enjoys traveling, cooking, body-boarding, surfing, martial arts, and just relaxing at the beach. He has had his work shown and published all over the Americas and Europe.

North American Wolf. Marcos Carvalho.

A.M. DUVALL
HUNT BEGINS

Bio

A.M. Duvall lives in Wiarton, Ontario. She has had three poems and a short story published in the Wolf Anthology named Lupus Animus. *She has also had an article published in a newspaper named* The Record, *from Kitchener, ON. Her hobbies include wood burning, jewelry making, as well as occasionally glass fusing. Her cats keep her on the go constantly.*

Suddenly there is the sound of running paws,

Along with the sound of a howl.

Its sound loud, long, and clear.

Leaving others to quake,

Knowing it's on.

The hunt!

CHRIS ALBERT
JOHN KINDEVARG & LIVES INTERTWINED

In Chris Albert's first story, "John Kindevarg," John is wandering on a mountain-top when he realizes a storm is coming. As he struggles to find help, he finds help in the most unlikely place.

In "Lives Intertwined," the children Carrie and Mack learn important life lessons through their neighbor who shares their birthday, a young wolf cub.

When deep or troubling thoughts piled up, there was nothing John Kindevarg liked better than to take a long walk on his hilly Montana ranch. A spring snowstorm had been predicted for later, so John had brought the livestock in the barn. His neighbors would probably leave their cattle out, laughing at his over-cautiousness, but John had seen those snowstorms turn deadly, and he was a careful farmer.

Having carved out a little time, John put on his hat and warm brown Carhartt jacket, shouldered his rifle, and set off on a somewhat unfamiliar path up into the hills. The rifle was for real—this was grizzly country, and they would be waking up soon. And though the wolf packs had never attacked a human, it felt wrong to be out unprotected just in case.

The wolves were one of John's thoughts. Like most ranchers in the area, he was deeply disturbed when faraway federal forces had decided to reintroduce these threats to his livestock, and, until recently, had forbidden him from killing the animals when they threatened. John was a careful rancher, and, thanks to the special livestock guardian dogs that lived among the herds, he had not lost any livestock to predators in some time. The thought weighed on his mind nonetheless.

At the crest of the first little mountain, John looked up. Immediately his thoughts were wiped away by a more pressing problem. Though forecast for later, the clouds had already arrived, and they were dark and low. The snow squall would start very soon, and John was on a mountain with very little cover.

Tamping down panic, John pressed on. Realizing there would be no time to return he quickly sought shelter. Please help. I need help, he thought to no one in particular as he moved up the mountain.

At that moment there was a movement to his right. In a cutaway he had overlooked in his haste stood a magnificent gray wolf. Judging by her belly, she was a female. Standing only 20 yards apart, John locked eyes with her for a long second before she moved quickly away and vanished among the rocks. Unable to distinguish if it were real or imagined, he heard an alto voice "welcome home," followed by a long ripple of laughter.

Behind where the wolf had been was a promising jumble of rocks. As he quickly approached, he spotted an actual cave, big enough for John with room to spare. He settled gratefully into the dark space as the wind picked up and the first flakes fell.

John was a practical man, not given to fancy, so he was disturbed by the woman's voice that had been in his head. He did not believe in fanciful thinking, yet here he was, in a shelter he would have overlooked if it hadn't been for the she-wolf. He didn't know what to make of it.

He turned his thoughts to practical matters. The livestock would be safe. They would miss the evening feeding, but they would be fine. The presence of the wolf worried him a bit—reminding him he would have to be even more careful. John had actually never killed a predator. He found that despite all the bluster, the coyotes that lived nearby seemed to learn the rules and didn't disturb his charges. The only time there had been trouble was when his neighbors had trapped out the resident coyotes and new ones had moved in and tested boundaries and the dogs. They, too, had learned. As for wolves, they were fairly new residents. He had seen tracks, the dogs had barked ferociously at the shadows, but they, too, had bypassed his livestock for easier pickings.

John's mind then wandered to a certain young newcomer in town, a young woman who annoyed the ranchers because she—well—liked wolves. Perhaps he should ask her out for coffee, he thought. He might even mention the encounter he just had, yet he couldn't imagine what she would think when he explained the alto voice he'd heard in his head.

As the storm picked up, John found himself thinking about the nature around this farm that he loved. He loved the raucous ravens that appeared on every carcass and road kill. Did they give back? They certainly were the first to warn of any impending newcomer.

John remembered that he had been annoyed at the last nature show he had watched, overlaid with narrative that spoke only of competition and thievery amongst the creatures of the land. How did they know that the bear robbed the squirrel's stash? What if the stash had been for the bear all along?

Comfortable, sheltered, and warm, John's thoughts dissipated and he drifted off to sleep.

Morning brought a blanket of snow and bright still blue skies. The storm had passed. John, now uncomfortable from a night on hard ground, stretched. He briefly wondered where the wolf had spent the night, since he had clearly been in her place.

Fortunately the path down the mountain was easy to follow, and what would have been treacherous the day before was easy and lovely in the bright sunlight and fresh snow.

Arriving safely back home, he was relieved to find the livestock were fine—if hungry, and eager to kick up and play in the snow.

Life settled back into rhythm, except for a newfound resolve. John actually looked up the young woman in town and asked her on a date. He'd had no idea whatsoever what to suggest, but a trip into the park and dinner afterward seemed to suit her fancy.

She had just arrived at the farm for a second date when two trucks pulled up. The first was a neighbor. "Just wanted to let you know to watch out for your stock," the man said, "I winged a big black wolf this morning. He's hurt, but not dead, and he headed in this general direction." John nodded his thanks, but felt an unfamiliar stab of regret. That would likely be the mountain-wolf's mate. She would have had her pups now, and he would be hunting for the family. If wounded, John's stock would make for easier pickings than the plentiful deer and elk. Moreover, he couldn't help but think, The wolf pups might starve. The woman by his side looked grim.

The second truck was a Fish and Wildlife officer: "I've come to tell you about a road-killed elk up the road apiece," he announced. I know you sometimes feed wild meat to those dogs of yours. You've got my permission to get it if you choose."

Before he even had time to wonder about the remnants of his date, the young woman had touched his arm, "I've got boots and coveralls in the car." John smiled as he realized that evidently the butchering of elk was an acceptable second date.

Together they found the elk carcass and got it in the truck. Together they cut and packaged select portions for the livestock guarding dogs, putting most in the freezer. Then as they drove the rest of the carcass to the base of the wolves' mountain in the wilder parts of his property, John shyly told his date of the walk up the mountain before the spring squall. He even spoke of the lovely voice in his head that somehow led him to find shelter in the wolf's den that he otherwise wouldn't have noticed. She smiled at him, a lovely smile that was simultaneously knowing, and grateful. Together, in quiet understanding, they unloaded the remains of the elk. Though he could hardly believe it, he, John, the rancher, was giving this food to the family of wolves, that the young might survive while their father healed. He had a debt to repay to the lovely she-wolf that had maybe saved his life. He would simply have to be careful with his livestock, but then, he always was.

John looked at his date, and looked up the mountain. "Welcome home," he said out loud, smiling. This time, the long ripple of laughter that followed was nearly the same, but in his own voice.

Lives Intertwined
(Author dedication: to Mrs. Lewis' second grade class, May 8, 2014)

On a windy, stormy April evening, there were three lives born that would be forever intertwined.

Carrie and Mack were twins born to Idaho sheep farmers. They had many things in common with most other children—they lived in a house, attended school, and had friends, but they especially loved the lands of the ranch. Over the years their parents taught them to be responsible. They had to watch the clouds and come home before it stormed. They were expected to know when the grizzly bear woke from a winter's nap so they could be especially careful when approaching brushy thickets. They learned that the wild elk can be pushy and dangerous in the fall during the "rut," or breeding season, when they are competing with each other. They knew to check the weather report before they went outside and take clothes that didn't seem necessary at the moment.

Carrie was blonde and petite. She loved wearing her favorite blue plaid flannel shirt when she went out adventuring. She also wore jeans and leather boots that protected her from rattlesnakes. Her brother Mack had a sandy brown hair, and while he also wore jeans and leather boots, he favored a brown plaid flannel shirt.

Every day after school—or once chores were completed in the summer—the twins would have a snack, change into their favorite clothes, and set out exploring. Now you might think it strange that parents would allow eight-year-olds wander off on their thousand acre farm, but the twins had been well-trained. Their parents had accompanied them almost every day for as long as they could remember. Together they had watched the bear, the rattlesnake, and every other dangerous thing on the farm. So by the time they were eight, their parents felt they had learned to sit still and watch carefully. Most importantly, the children knew they had to pay attention and take care of themselves.

One day in June, when school was nearly out, Carrie and Mack put on their trusty flannel shirts, their jeans, and boots and walked to the far boundary of the farm. They had long ago learned that when you get to a sitting spot, if you sit quietly for fifteen minutes, so that the disturbance you made while arriving settles down, the wild animals go back to business.

That particular day was the first time the twins spotted a very special animal—a wolf—that happened to be born on that same stormy April night they had been born.

The wolf didn't think of herself as having a name, but Carrie and Mack called her Raven, for she was glossy and black like the real ravens that lived around. Like the twins, Raven had learned many things in her eight years. She understood the importance of family, learned there was always a babysitter for the young pups until they could keep up, and understood that if one of her family became injured hunting, the others would provide until that one recovered. She had learned how to hunt the big elk—a dangerous way to make a living—but that is how wolves eat in the world. Most importantly she had learned to stay away from people, for wolves are not often welcomed on farms in Idaho. Sadly, if a wolf is seen by a human it is usually killed, so Raven and her children had learned to fade quietly into the landscape whenever a human was around.

You might think the twins' parents would be worried about two eight-year-olds meeting an experienced wolf, for anything that can hunt and kill an elk surely could hunt and kill people, but despite all the fairy tales about evil wolves, the children had learned that wolves don't hunt humans. They had even Googled it to make sure. They could only find two instances in the recorded history of North America a wild wolf had hurt a human. So they were more fascinated than worried.

The children had been sitting quite still under a tree by the stream bank, when Raven and her five pups came out of the brush. The puppies were discovering the stream, jumping and splashing, playing with the water and with each other, hunting and pouncing on bugs, and being so silly that Carrie and Mack almost laughed out loud several times, but they knew better. The puppies were learning how to pounce, how to be a family, how to get along together. One big male puppy thought he was separated from the family, put his stubby nose into the air, and gave a tiny puppy howl. Later, the children called this puppy "Imbo" after a word a traveler had taught them for "song".

The wind shifted, and Raven suddenly caught the scent of human. Alarmed, she looked around, and her eyes met with the children that had been born the same day she was. For a moment, the three quietly watched each other; then mother wolf called her pups and scrambled away, melting into the brush.

That night, Carrie and Mack told their parents about the wolves. That gave the parents much food for thought. When the children went to bed, the parents had a long discussion. They remembered how their parents and grandparents had hated wolves, even contributed to their extermination, but they also had listened to the scientists when they reintroduced the wolves to their lands. They had seen the effect of too many elk on the land; they knew that if there was no one to kill sick elk that might be a problem, so they had made a decision not to kill the wolves on their farm unless they became a problem. They were extremely careful farmers—using livestock guarding dogs, penning the mama sheep about to give birth, and riding the range. Thus, they had no losses. So they did not hunt the wolves, and they didn't allow trapping on their property. Their farm flourished, and the nearby elk grew wary, but strong.

Carrie and Mack's dad in particular hoped he was making the right decision to leave the wolves alone. His own father had hated wolves. Sometimes it was very hard to know when your parents have been right all along, and when it was time for a change. He really hoped he was making the right choice.

The life of a wild wolf is precarious and short. Although Raven was not with the pack much longer, the children watched young Imbo grow up. From the gangly eight-week old pup they had first seen, they caught glimpses of the strong wolf he would become. He learned to avoid the sheep because the dogs made it so difficult for wolves to approach. He watched some of his brothers and cousins caught in the painful traps, and learned to detect and avoid metal. He learned how to hunt the elk and feed his family and pass these lessons along to his own children. He learned to lie low or flee at the very sight of a human, except for the two young humans. Wild wolves can learn, their very lives depend on it, and Imbo learned to distinguish Mack and Carrie from the others, and he sometimes let them catch a glimpse of them.

Some four years later, in the fall, Carrie and Mack were at the edges of the farm again. They had grown into new flannel shirts, of course, but still preferred their blue and brown ones. It was during the fall rut, when the elk "strut their stuff" for the females, bugle warnings to each other, and sometimes are so caught up in the moment that they can be dangerous. Carrie and Mack knew this, of course, and were extra careful. Nevertheless, that day they were caught unaware, and an older bull elk, past his prime and thus pretty angry and worried, charged out of a thicket and straight for the spot where Carrie and Mack were sitting. The children scrambled up, but for Mack it was not quite in time. The elk caught Mack with the tip of his antlers and pushed and flung him away. Now the elk had a focus and started to go after Mack again. Carrie watched helpless.

Suddenly, Imbo and his pack appeared. Ignoring the boy, they circled the elk. They had detected weakness—that though this big elk could still hurt a boy, he was not quite healthy—a good target for hungry wolves.

The elk noticed the wolves and turned his attention away from Mack, who scrambled back painfully. Carrie moved to his side to support him, and they moved slowly away, but not so slowly that they missed the drama.

There were six wolves in Imbo's pack, and together they darted in, grabbing, working hard to avoid the deadly hooves and antlers. Finally one yearling wolf, just learning how to hunt, managed a fatal bite, and the elk was taken down. Imbo raised his nose and gave his signature howl song, summoning his family to eat.

Carrie helped Mack slowly walk home. Both were very quiet. In all the years they had been on the farm, their lives had never been in such danger, and they knew it. They would learn from this, and would have to give serious thought to how to walk about the farm during the rut.

That night, as they recounted the story to their parents, their father felt many things—fear at what almost happened to his son, apprehension about what they would face in the future, and a new feeling: gratefulness that he had made the right decision about the wolves, for without a doubt, the wolves' presence had saved his son that day. Times were changing, and one change was for certain—there would be room for wolves.

KRYSTAL O'BRIEN
TAKEN: TO THE STARS—BOOK ONE

Bio

Krystal O'Brien is a freelance fantasy writer, copy editor, and spare-time artist who lives within the Sunshine Coast area in Queensland, Australia. Holding a Diploma of Professional Novel Writing and a (Nationally Recognized) Diploma of Professional Book Editing, Proofreading, and Publishing, she writes online commissioned literature as well as doing small traditional and digital artwork on websites such as Fur Affinity and So Furry during her spare time. Though currently studying Graphic Design, 2014 has recently brought her short story "Through the Eyes of a Wolf" into publication within the anthology Lupus Animus: *an eBook and paperback print for the non-profit UK organization Artisan Rarebreeds.*

This story, to be the beginning of a novel, tells the tale of a world of wolves. Darkness is on the rise, and no one seems to be safe.

Not all things are ever as they seem to be, especially when what is being viewed is something so incredibly far away, it can only be guessed as to what that thing truly is, like the stars, as humans we believe that they are made up of a type of gas that burn for an incredible length of time before they burn-out or die. We see things as simple non-complex things, but if we were to look beyond all, look beyond and into the heart of all life...we see the truth.

Stars are more than we think we know they are; stars are the souls of all living creatures on earth who have passed into the Never-realm awaiting rebirth. That's why it is known that stars never live forever; they disappear, that is a soul being brought into new life. Each different type of creature that dwelled upon the Earth who did good in their life and followed the way of light would gather around one another forming bright galaxies, those who had done bad and followed the way of darkness drifted as empty stars gathering upon the edges of space; never allowed to be reborn once they've become stained and impure.

The Gods themselves feared that the hatred within those souls would never turn back to the way of light, and so they all agreed to bind such souls into an eternal purgatory to keep pure the lives of their mortal kin. And yet, as much as the light is always said to win, darkness will always gather, darkness will always live on...it prevails. But as with every end there must always be a beginning, and the beginning to this one, lies inside the cozy den of a small wolf pack.

Something invisible and light brushed against the soft fur of two squirming bundles that lay pressing against one another, ears instantly perked, and their heads lifted as they heard quaffing sounds of their mother calling them from outside of the den. They were old enough now to take their first steps into the great unknown: at six weeks old the two wolf pups peered out of the earthen hollow; dug by their mother while they were still within her belly.

All they had known until now was the feel of her fur and the dirt that kept them safe and warm when she went away; this was what they had become used to during the first few weeks of their lives. At first when they were yet to even open their eyes neither knew what she looked like, but her scent was distinct, and they knew the instant she re-entered the den to feed them, learning things by their scent was one of the first things the two pups learned. As they grew and the weeks passed, their eyes opened then saw her and the earthen walls about them, though nothing more than a blurry form through near blind, blue eyes but in time that too passed.

On the sixth week of their lives their mother began spending more time away from the den; each time she'd come back to them with a belly full of freshly eaten meat, and they would whine and lick and nip at her muzzle in order to make her regurgitate it. Once they had had their fill the pups would then rub themselves against her, sniffing at each new scent that she bore on her cream-black coat. Every time there would be a different scent, and each one they learned to be as part of their family, their pack. It was a ritual their mother had been through when she had been a pup herself, as did her mother and her mother's mother, generation after generation.

It was the way of the wolf, how from a young age each was taught to know family, whom to trust and who was safe outside the den, they would also learn the smell of dangerous creatures and plants, but that would only come once they left the den. It would be then that the world they knew would become so much vaster and much more dangerous than their mother could truly ready them for, and that day had finally come, and as the oldest of the two pups by mere minutes gathered his courage to peer out of the entrance, he immediately ducked back in whimpering. His sister pressed against his rump lightly and tilted her head in silent question as she took a step forward upon hearing their mother call to them softly again.

Always the more inquisitive of the pair the young wolfess strode from the den a short way with her head and tail lifted; it wasn't until she saw how big everything was around her did they lower, and she skittered toward her mother for comfort. Neither of the pups took notice of the rest of the pack until the male crept out slowly, gaining a lick of approval off them both as he finally plucked up the courage to trot out. It was only the murmurs which drew their attention to the five wolves half circled waiting with growing enthusiasm to greet them into the family.

With the slightest flick of an ear the alpha female gave permission, and murmurs turned into excited yips and a churning cloud of dry dust kicked up by over a dozen paws as the pups became drawn into a fray of welcoming tongues, tangled limbs, and shaggy coats. The excitement soon died down as another wolf appeared from a ledge above, the alpha male who had been keeping watch over them all from above. The pack moved aside, and silence fell over them. His mate who would protect them against even the strongest of forest creatures stood a few steps away; she gave him the room he needed as he lowered his head down and sniffed at his pups.

Having been the first scent they learned aside from their mothers, they knew his importance, and even though excitement still rang in their ears, their bodies rolled as if on their own accord showing the barely furred soft underbellies in submission. As their fathers nosed over their forms onc at a time, giving each a gentle hold about their throats in acceptance, he then flopped beside them, and once more the excited romping commenced. Both parents looked at one another, though briefly: it was to acknowledge the pride and love of their pups. Each wolf within their pack would watch over them, teach them and guide them from this day forth. For they would grow to be the future of their kind as would the next litter of pups the alpha bore, not just for this pack but as with every litter born within all others as well.

A few dozen miles off toward the west where the soft green grassy hills were beginning to show, and slowly flowing rivers turned to the rocky tundra plains and slate stone mountains. Not far after that another litter was just being brought into the world. Sadly however the mother was alone, her pack lost to the harsh blizzard storms of the winter just past, her sister the last to have been by her side until recent days when starvation took her last breath from her bone-thin body. She died giving everything in order for the birthing mother to have a chance to make it, the last of her pack now ready to greet the world anew, but exhaustion had already set its toll on her.

Barely able to make herself a sufficient den that was deep enough to keep her young safe from the elements, she kept her back turned to the far end of the den as she lay on her side, trembling with each wave of labor pains that wracked her frail form. Soft whines escaped her muzzle, and her upper lip curled as she gritted her teeth tight and pushed; when the pain subsided she lifted a back leg to see a tiny pup within the sack...she didn't reach for it to nip open and clean the pup, she could see it was stillborn. Three more were the same, though bigger in size than the first. She simply nosed them to one side and flopped her head down, panting heavily. One pup remained, she prayed to the Gods to let it be the same, knowing her chances of survival were slim.

As the wolfess gave one last push a squeak reached her ears, and she wriggled around; for a moment she considered a hard nip to the back of the pup's neck, saving it from whatever hardships she may face. But instinct overtook, and she broke the sack and nosed the pup close to her teats, lapping at it in an almost frantic manner to clean and warm her lone pup. Her emotions torn between hope that they could both somehow make it and guilt that if things went bad she'd not be able to protect her offspring much less herself, she looked over at the four lifeless forms and closed her eyes tightly. Her choice was simple: her pup needed her to be as strong as she could be, for that her own body needed nourishment. Without it they would both surely die before weeks end, and as horrible a thing as it was for a mother to lose a pup, what she did soon after was something unspeakable, something only the most desperate or maddened of creatures would do.

For days she remained in the small den, huddled to brace her newly born pup against the harsh cold winds that rushed in from time to time when it changed directions; hunger had begun to gnaw at her insides, and soon she would have to go and try to hunt. But she would have to first move herself and the pup to somewhere that was safer. Upon the open tundra plains there weren't many places, and most of the ground was hard clay-like dirt filled with stones that made digging painful. Upon the lower half of the mountains where her pack had lived they had a natural cavern, which they'd used as their den.

The entrance had been large enough for the pack to enter, yet small enough to keep out any predators--like bears--that would gladly chase off a wolf pack in order to hibernate in the safety of such a place. The inner part of the cavern opened up like an egg-shape; stalagmites and stalactites decorated their den, creating a spot for each of her family members somewhere to sleep if they chose to do so alone. Mostly they would sleep at the far end where the calcium formations created a copse, so herself and her mate slept together, and the rest of the pack slept in a semi-circle about them. Their shared heat and the enclosed placement of the cavern kept them nice and warm.

But that was all gone now, as was her pack...save for one; the wolfess gazed at her slumbering pup with gentle and loving eyes. She would do what she could to ensure they made it for the sake of those she had lost. She wriggled herself from about the pup, lapping its forehead when it gave a squeak in protest as the cold reached it. She took a deep breath, scenting the wind as it blew, testing to see if they were alone before she poked her head out to look around. She scanned along the tundra slowly, watching for the slightest sign of movement. When she was content nothing harmful was about, she withdrew back in to retrieve her pup. Ears pricked this way and that listening for the sounds of prey and searching for somewhere she could safely leave her pup so she could hunt.

The wolfess traveled as far as she could without exerting too much of what little energy she had gathered whilst lying in the den. The pup hung silently by the scruff within her jaws; the very same jaws that could easily crush bones and tear flesh carried that young tiny scrap of fur with a firm gentleness. A sudden movement caught her attention, and she stopped in her tracks, nose twitching as she sniffed at the cool air; her heartbeat quickened as a trickle of fear wound its way along her spine, but as she noticed a small mound of snow move, her fear ebbed away quickly. It was a snow hare out amidst the lesser snow drifts that edged the tundra plains. Her stomach churned in hungry protest, and her pup squirmed within her jaws: soon it would need to feed also.

Placing her pup within the crevice of some boulders to both hide it from the view of any predators that might be lurking about and also to keep it from the brunt of the cold wind, the wolfess then paced herself toward the left so she was still downwind of the hare and also so she had a clear line of view of where she left her pup. It was foolish of her to even think to capture such prey, not only was it faster than her, but it was plump and full of health, whereas she looked disheveled and resembled little but a ghost of her former self. Yet she had to try.

As she slunk along the line of boulders, thankful for her mottled white and grey coat that kept her partially disguised against the stark tundra around her, the closer she got to where she'd last spotted the snow hare, her pace slowed to a crawl. Every paw-step was carefully placed so that the snow and grass beneath them made barely any sound. Wind whipped up suddenly blowing white powder toward her, tussling her fur about but also carrying the scent of the hare to her. She moved her body almost stumbling on a hidden rock and alerted the hare before she was ready. It lifted itself up from grazing at a patch of moss and looked directly at her.

Both of them froze, eyes locked and hearts hammering hard within their chests. The wolfess had one forepaw lifted from the ground, her muscles were bunched and ready, and she knew with a single twitch her prey would be off. She sent a silent prayer to the Goddess of wolves hoping to have it answered, and as she let out a long breath the steam that came from her nostrils made the hare drop an ear, and the pair of them dashed off through the clumps of snow and across the open plains, weaving left and right as she desperately tried to keep up with the hare and it hoping to find a hole or crevice to disappear into.

A few moments felt like an eternity for her; the wolfess felt as though each breath was sending shards of ice into her lungs, and her limbs were growing stiffer with the seconds that went by, but it was as if the great Goddess had answered her prayer for just as the hare veered sharply to the right, chancing to go amongst a heavy thicket of sharp tundra grass its back leg slipped on a patch of ice, and she snapped her jaws around its mid-section before rolling her ankle on the same icy patch. Not wanting to release the hare she whimpered around the thick fur that muffled her muzzle; the hare had let out a loud shriek of pain as her jaws clamped about its body, and bright red spots quickly marred the pure white color of its coat.

The wolfess gave the hare a vicious shake breaking its neck before lying down, panting heavily, body shaking from having pushed herself as she had, but at least she had food and could ensure another few meals for the pup. However she couldn't rest where she was:she need-ed to get back to her pup before the cold took it or something else did. Tracing her paw prints back, only stopping to lap at a puddle of water, she kept going until she saw the boulders marking where she'd left the young pup to hunt her prey, but a dread filled her heart, and the freshly killed hare dropped from her maw when she rounded one of the vast rocks. Two wolves as dark as the night paced in front of the crevice where her pup lay curled up.

Back toward the East warmth spread over the forest as the sun reached its highest peak within the sky, pooling rays of light throughout the otherwise densely packed canopy above the pack. "Kirin, it is time," a gravelly voice called from above the den, the alpha male, whose coat was mostly black, with patches flecked of fawn-brown and white that marked around his throat and along three of his legs. His mate the alpha female rose to her paws and dipped her head in acknowledgement to him before nosing their two young toward the omega of the pack. A two-year-old once rogue, now watcher of the pups that happily romped over him without a care.

"We'll be fine Brenna, I will protect them as always." He promised his alphas, never once bringing his eyes above their shoulders, fearful to instigate an unwanted challenge. Neither replied to him, and his ears flicked back slightly as he lay his head on his paws and allowed the pups to nip and pounce upon his form. Drawn out howls filled the air about them as the pair called to the rest of the pack: the hunt was to begin without him joining. Not that he really minded: he'd been chased from his blood-pack when he was old enough to mate, his father not wanting his position challenged, especially from his own son.

Within a few weeks he'd found this pack, making himself known and yet keeping his distance until the beta had given him allowance to come near the pack. It wasn't a small pack, so when the alphas accepted him within the pack he was more than glad to do whatever was asked...even pup-sitting when his heart yearned to be a part of the hunt. He had a long way to go to earn a real place amongst them. Until then he kept alert and watchful of the swiftly growing youths that now had chosen to tumble with one another while their parents and the others were off to chase down prey big enough to feed them all.

Both had dark coats, the male, who had been named Skrei was the very image of Brenna, black fur covering his slim form, brown ringing his neck and donning his over-sized paws. His sister, Asha, looked more like her mother's mother. Her thick coat made her look plumper than Skrei, heavy brown flowing along her form from the middle of her sides down to her paws. Along the top, her fur tinted more toward black than brown, and in the very middle of the top of her head she had a single spot of white. The eldest of the pack said that she had been "touched" though he wasn't exactly sure what the old wolf had meant by that, but, by how proud the alpha pair had looked, he knew that the pup had an important future ahead of her.

As he kept vigilance over the alpha's pups, the pair themselves were leading the rest of the pack far out of the heavily grown forest and along the river that now rushed cold with clear snow-melt down from the mountains. Soon it would rise and become impassable for weeks until all the snow that would melt had finished doing so, so the pack took advantage of the low-set river and crossed where the water barely touched their bellies. Where the hills touched the outer edges of the tundra plains was where the border of their territory ended and the territory of the Mountain Pack began. This was where they'd find their prey, amongst the vast herd of shaggy coated caribou that now grazed on the newly sprouting grass that reached up from the cold powdery snow in search of the first rays of spring's light.

From here the pack split into two smaller groups. One group would take the higher ground up around slightly to the North, driving the herd down to those waiting. They knew that the bucks would be eagerly fighting between one another to show who was the strongest and would take the females as theirs to mate with. It was easy pickings but also dangerous as the males would fight off anything that crossed their path, but the wolves would use the fights to their advantage and pick out the weakest or most visibly hurt caribou. It was how nature went: the weak fed the pack, and the strong carried on their line, re-newing life in the herd for another year.

As Kirin and Brenna lay atop a rise that overlooked a gully where the main part of the herd milled around, already restless, as two bucks charged one another, a loud crack resounded about them all when they collided; horns interlocked, and muscled bulged as both pushed with everything they had in order to get the other to back down. Brenna never grew tired of watching such a scene; his mate however kept her attention on every other caribou down in the gully. She would choose which one to take down, and then they would cut it from the herd and chase it toward home.

There they would join with the other half of the hunting party, and as one the pack would work to bring it down, kill it, and feed until each of them could eat no more. Afterward, when their hunger was sated, the group would carry back large pieces to feed those left at the den. "Brenna," Kirin said sharply bringing his attention to where her golden eyes were locked: she had found their meal. Brenna stood, his dark fur brushing against hers in acknowledgement as he did, but just as they were about to start the hunt a piercing howl sounded from somewhere behind them, just across the borders into the tundras.

Not a single strand of fur lay flat on their bodies, for the pain-filled call made their coats bristle with mixed emotions. "Brenna...what..."

"Hush," the alpha male said, ears pricked toward the rocky plains.

No reply sounded, and now the caribou were warned of the wolves' presence. They thundered off south-ward away from them. Concern flickered across his narrowed eyes, and Kirin looked at her mate as a shudder went through her body. The elder pushed himself in front of them, both audibly sniffing at the blowing winds.

"...I know that call. It is Creeda, the alpha from the mountains!" he said looking back at the pair; his words gave necessary caution and need to respond. Brenna merely nodded and turned his head to the fourth wolf in their group.

"We go. The hunt must wait." His words were final, and they set off over the border at as fast a pace as their paws would take them. Back near the river where the remaining three wolves sat waiting for the herd to come down and their alphas to show them their target, but their ears lifted at the sound of a chilling howl moments before their eyes caught motion off to the south, their caribou trotting off with no sight of the others. Frowns marked all three faces, and they grew restless with concern about them.

The beta kept them together: if their alphas required their aid they would call. Until then she told them to remain alert and in position. As the four wolves raced across the tundra the sounds of a vicious fight and cries of pain became more audible, a small outcrop of boulders blocked their view, and as they rounded them each wolf stopped for a heartbeat to take in what they saw. Creeda the alpha female stood with her rear pressed close against a crevice, her frame was all but bones, and her gray and white coat was now jotted with bloodied wounds; they knew in an instant she was protecting something.

All their eyes fell on the two large dark wolves whose yellow and angry eyes locked upon them. Kirin didn't waste another moment: a growl left her muzzle, and Brenna launched from beside her clashing with the nearest wolf, the elder a mere tail-length behind him. Kirin and the other wolf moved to put themselves between Creeda and the second wolf that had made to attack the already wounded female again. Sounds of savagery filled the air, and time seemed to slow down as the Forest Pack fought off the offending, unknown wolves.

Finally the two had had enough; knowing they'd been beaten they retreated with snarls back enough to show the fight was over. "Luck was on your side this day..." one of them spoke looking directly at Creeda before his gaze drew level with the alpha pair. "As for you both, your turn will come. The darkness is in need of young healthy vessels...don't be so sure your own are safe!" And with that the pair of them turned tail and dashed off out of sight.

Kirin gave a puzzled look at her mate then turned to Creeda who had flopped down upon the ground beyond exhaustion and any further help from them. "Creeda...what did they mean?" the elder who knew the younger wolf asked lightly nosing at the female who merely whimpered in pain. Brenna meanwhile had not taken his eyes from where the two wolves had fled not long ago. Kirin touched his flank lightly, and the elder stepped aside.

"Creeda, my name is Kirin please tell us, if you can," she said her words seemed to bring the wolfess' attention back to them, and she lifted her head just slightly off the ground.

"It is the prophecy...they wanted...wanted to take my pup...my...is he?" Creeda barely had strength in her to form a full response, even as her head moved to look toward the small crevice where she'd left her pup. The elder padded over to where she indicated, snuffling and pressing his nose into the gap before withdrawing it, inside his grasp was her pup, wriggling in protest over this strange creature's grip upon him. "Thank the Goddess...they wanted to...to take him from me. They said he would become one with the soul-less shadow and grow..." she stopped coughing so harshly; blood flew from her muzzle and splattered on the dirt.

Kirin's eyes filled with sadness, and she lowered herself down level with the other female; though they came from different packs and neither wolfess knew the other, Kirin had always been taught to help those in need, no matter how important or unimportant a rank they held. "You are not alone," she spoke softly as Creeda closed her eyes for a moment.

"Those wolves told me my pup would grow and become a part of the never-fading darkness...the darkness is coming, and it cannot be stopped," the wolfess told them. "I know that I am dying. I am soon to join those of my pack amongst the stars of our ancestors. I ask of you as a mother...as an alpha, take care of my pup. Do not let him die too." Creeda pleaded with Kirin, whose eyes filled with unshed tears. She nodded to the dying wolfess as her last breath left her body, and the life in her eyes went out.

Kirin rose to her paws slowly and licked the tiny pup marking him as her own, and Brenna gazed back giving a slow blink of acceptance of her decision before pacing to them. He pressed his nose to the dead female then lifted his head skyward howling long and loud for the Goddess to take her soul safely to the starry heavens. His mate and the two others joined in their song carrying across the tundra by the winds, as silence fell upon them and each pressed their nose to the female. Kirin took the orphaned pup within her maw gently, and they headed back toward home.

It wasn't until they passed over the last slope just before the forest began that the scent left not long ago by the beta of their pack warned them of a new danger. The alpha pair locked eyes, and a silent realization struck them in unison. The elder wolf spoke their thoughts as fear drove their pace faster toward home. "The young ones..." When they reached the den, the scene that lay before them had Kirin's heart leap into her throat: the beta female Hiren and the two pack mates that had been with her lay bloodied and dead around the den. There were so many paw prints. None of them could take a guess as to the number of wolves that had been there. Brenna growled with a deep rage, his hackles raised in warning to anything that might still be around to pose threat.

"Asha? Skrei?!" she barked for them both, her tone filled with audible distress. The elder stood watch over the tiny pup they'd brought back with them, worry easily seen within his gray-brown eyes. The sounds of scraping paws and whimpers came from inside the den; hope washed over the wolves as they saw a muzzle poke through. However it was the omega who came out. His ears and face torn and bloodied as was his hind quarters, dirt clung to the wounds upon his ashen coat even as he lowered himself when Brenna and Kirin went to him sniffing and growling.

"They came from nowhere, in great numbers I tried to stop them...Hiren, she had heard and came with the others. We all fought, but there were just too many...I..." He closed his eyes and hid his wounded face ashamedly with one paw. A soft voice called from behind him: it was Asha. She came racing out of the den when she heard her parents had come back.

"Ma...Pa!" Her yips of joy where joined by those who remained in the pack about her. "Don't be mad at Layt. He fought bravely, just as bravely as Hiren, but...but there were so many dark wolves. Hiren told us to hide in the den. I went in, but they attacked Layt as he was protecting me..." She told them with such sorrow.

"What about Skrei?" Brenna asked gazing toward the den; the entrance had been dug around. It was clear the wolves that had attacked had tried to get to them meant business. Their fallen pack mates were proof of that. Layt rolled to one side and looked to the alpha male's chest, the one word he spoke shook them all to their very souls.

"Taken..."

KAYLA GRIFFIN
GUARDIAN

Bio

Kayla Griffin lives in Boise, Idaho. She has been working with wildlife for the past three years. She graduates college in May of 2015 with a Bachelor's in Communication. Kayla wants to become a lobbyist for animal rights and has been fortunate enough to accept a temporary position with Defenders of Wildlife. Kayla now does community outreach and teaches people all over Idaho that wolves are an important part of Idaho wildlife.

Guardian. Kayla Griffin. Oil on canvas.

SCOTT A. BLOCK
DENALI & LUNA

Bio

As a photographer, Scott A. Block wanted to capture images of wolves in their full glory and beauty, and that typically meant photographing them in the winter. Annually, he and his wife make a trip to the International Wolf Center, and he treasures his time with the pack, taking several photographs.

These images are of the current exhibit pack. Denali is a six-year-old male (145 lbs), and Luna is a one-year-old female.

Denali. Scott A. Block.

Luna. Scott A. Block.

PAULA JAKOBSSON
HUNTER OF HEARTS

Bio

Paula Jakobsson lives in Finland and is a traditional art student. She specializes in ink drawings.

Hunter of Hearts. Paula Jakobsson. Ink on paper.

ERROL ÉTIENNE
DAKOTA

Bio

Errol Étienne was a famous watercolor artist born in Scotland. He graduated from the Art Center College of Design in California. Throughout his career, he painted over 8,000 paintings, displaying his work at exhibits across the world, including Paris, London, and New York. For animation, he also won an Emmy. Unfortunately, Étienne passed away in 2011. His wife, Janice L. Étienne has granted us permission to print this work of his, which was donated by the owner of the painting Jaclyn Powell. Ms. Powell fondly calls the work "Dakota."

Dakota. Errol Étienne. Watercolor.

HANNAH VIROSLAV
HEMLOCK GROVE CREATING EQUILIBRIUM THROUGH METAMORPHOSIS

Bio

Hannah Viroslav is a senior at Vanderbilt University, majoring in English with a minor in Chemistry. She hopes to attend medical school in the near future, but for now, she enjoys writing, researching, and reading in her free time.

The following essay details a recent werewolf novel Hemlock Grove *and what it means to be a werewolf in this society: what is man? What is beast?*

In the study of thermodynamics, entropy can be defined as the measure of chaos and disorder of any system. In a system, a reaction must take place, either creating or dissolving different forms of matter by rearranging basic elements. Fundamentally, systems energetically favor increasing entropy, meaning that nature pushes toward a disordered state. While entropy exists as a relatively modern scientific notion, Lucretius' explanation of the movement of matter and elements between the boundaries of the clouds and the fragile earth, in his poem *De Rerum Natura (On the Nature of Things)*, mirrors this measure: crossing boundaries favors increasing disorder. Lucretius explains the rearrangement of matter and elements through clouds. The clouds represent a semi-permeable membrane, "neither.../so dense a body as stones and wood, nor again so/ thin as mist and flying smoke," but just leaky enough to hold "seeds" of fire and water and release chaotic thunderbolts and rain (Carus 6.102-5). The clouds simultaneously reinforce and transcend the boundary between elements and the earth. The systemic reactions in the realm of thermodynamics serve as an example of Lucretius' understanding of nature, invoking boundaries as permeable. Yet, while energy and matter mindlessly cycle between different forms, humans undertake an opposing understanding of their own nature, preferring to set and follow a strict order.

The human shape remains largely unchanged since the time of the Neanderthal—four limbs, opposable thumbs, large head, upright posture—a concoction that intimidates differences out of the gene pool.

Disfigured humans, perhaps sporting disproportionate limbs or missing one altogether, remain a spectacle to the point of being almost inhuman. But, what society deems disabled should rather be viewed as a chaotic misstep, a metamorphosis reaching a different form of order. Brian McGreevy's *Hemlock Grove Or, The Wise Wolf* indulges the metamorphic side of our human society, exposing the perceived outcast members as those who understand humanity the best. McGreevy uses two characters, Peter Rumancek and Christina Wendall, to hypothesize on the impact of the reality of werewolves; one could say the ultimate metamorphic triumph for a human form. Peter embodies the typical outcast archetype—separated from society due to his heritage yet embracing this role as safest—while Christina represents immaturity—impressionable beyond reason and too curious. Each character battles the confinement of their stereotype by attempting to further control their futures and fates; Christina mistakes lycanthropy as the answer to her adolescent chaos and Peter works diligently to separate his human self from his wolf form. I aim to explore these opposing tactics, following the entropic relations between each character and their wolf counterpart as the boundary between each form leaks, working against human nature and in favor of wolf nature to reach equilibrium.

Peter descends from gypsies, typically portrayed as dishonorable wanderers. Being a werewolf comes as naturally to Peter as his long black hair—it is simply genetic, a recessive gene to be precise, originally held by his grandfather. In other words, he had no choice. As a result, Peter was taught a code: how to contain the beast, how to separate his monthly wolf walk from his daily human conscious. "Don't hunt when you're not hungry; when you do hunt, go for the flank…; and when you are filled with the song of the universe…throw your head back and close your eyes and join" (McGreevy 73). These rules implicated Peter in upholding a standard separation. His grandfather passed along the boundary between humanity and wolves because it kept the chaos at bay, somehow managing to maintain lycanthropy as a clean business. While Peter is not particularly shy about his other half, often nonchalantly sharing his condition with near strangers, he clearly distinguishes between his human form and his wolf form. Both forms are outsiders, as Peter the human was also "not their kind," so the transformation was more so drastic in appearance than in action (15-6). Being a wanderer and a loner helped to smooth over the seam connecting Peter to his wolf form, but the code kept the seam in place, a seam Christina was drooling to rip open.

Christina becomes the first human aware of werewolves in her town, but rather than an appropriate response of disbelief, evolves an infatuation with the beasts. Christina, inhabiting the body of a thirteen-year-old girl, finds herself among influential sexual beings; most importantly her twin best friends rave about their apparently endless sexual encounters. Her adolescent age allows for an intense obsession to develop between her and her sexuality. She knows not whether to control it or whether to explore it, fearing her prude nature. The confusion grows so paramount that upon discovering a young girl's disembodied corpse, Christina "lowered her mouth to the dummy's," kissing her rotting lips tenderly (55). Christina's experimentation with her sexuality begins to mirror her obsession with her werewolf neighbor, Peter.

There is an unwritten boundary between neighbors that encapsulates both friendliness and distance. Christina's access to Peter was privileged, but her curiosity pushed her sensibilities to their limits. She "ask[s] [Peter] if he [is] a werewolf" based off childish superstition only to proceed to beg for him to bite her so she too can be a werewolf (14). She wants nothing more than to not be Christina the adolescent. By rejecting her position as a thirteen-year-old girl and determining Peter to be the key to a new role, Christina sets an entropic reaction in motion in Hemlock Grove. The town shrouded in the ghost of the Godfrey steel corporation already reeks of unnatural darkness, serving as a breeding ground for chaos. Her otherwise childish intentions are fed by this pull toward disorder, turning deviant. She manages to push the boundary of her self far enough to reach her goal: she metamorphoses into a werewolf.

The novel culminates in Peter's discovery that Christina is the "vargulf," defined as "a wolf that's gone insane," implementing Christina in a slew of murders (62). This climax creates a scenario where both characters reach their chaotic potential. The murders mirror Christina's obsessive relationship with sexuality; rather than indulging herself, she scolds the promiscuous women around her, including her twin best friends. She uses her werewolf form to discard of the trash. Speaking to Peter, she explains her disdain for Peter's girlfriend, Letha, whom she views as equally sexual.

"'Because when I saw you in here with your ugly little thing in that whore I wanted more than anything to feel her fear on my tongue and her bones crunch between my teeth and her blood run down the fur of my neck'" (290).

Being a werewolf allowed Christina the means to cross the boundary into her understanding of maturity—she was powerful, controlling her sexuality and the sexuality of those around her. Her metamorphosis culminated in a different state of order, turning her from the controlled path of humanity to the wild path of wolf.

Peter, on the other hand, reached a blend of his two forms, the only option to defeat Christina. Peter first discovers that Christina obtained her wolf abilities from him, sipping water from his tracks. His controlled wolf nature gave birth to a rabid, uncaged monster in Christina—"Peter had made her, he was part of her now" (290). The code of his grandfather breaks down, initiating an inward collapse of identity. While both of Peter's worlds were ordered separately, the moment he loses his human face to Christina's vargulf ignites a gravitational pull, strong enough to cause overlap between worlds and decomposing boundaries. The werewolf within Peter awakens without its human counterpart, as Peter the human has been mauled. However, the true evidence supporting new equilibrium is reborn with Peter's human form. "The wolf looked back and they were Peter's eyes" and it became clear: "...Peter's true secret" is "that there is no 'it,' only him, always him" (298). Both forms have engulfed one another because the amount of energy necessary to stop Christina from fully reaching her idea of equilibrium can only be found in Peter's cosmic collision.

The two types of werewolves studied in *Hemlock Grove* are ironically born out of natural chaos. Peter inherits his brown coat and Christina drinks up her white coat. The irony arrives in the backdrop of the novel: the White Tower. The White Tower symbolizes the Godfrey steel corporation's newest endeavor of biotechnology, perhaps the most extreme unnatural. Experimentation on humans for gene-altering drugs makes the metamorphosis of Peter and Christina less surprising. In other words, McGreevy aims to make commentary on the society of Hemlock Grove through high school students dealing with lycanthropy, a seemingly extreme manner except for the overarching tone of oddity set with these gene experiments. The boundary moves beyond the two werewolves into the universally distinguished nature versus engineered. While Peter and Christina literally fought tooth and claw to reestablish an order, the biotechnology residing in Hemlock Grove appears to already operate above nature. The question remains as to how long natural order would need to overrun the White Tower or if the White Tower will be a gateway into a new definition of natural. The settlement of the vargulf and the werewolf microcosmically shows that inheritance wins. Control and order must seep through a stage of disarray as the means to a natural end, but the ending has yet to be written regarding the fate of the town. The climactic rebirth of Peter in both human and wolf form along with the defeat of Christina's mutated wolf form spells a happier future for Hemlock Grove, perhaps won at the claws of a werewolf.

Bibliography

Carus, Titus Lucretius. *De Rerum Natura*. Trans. W. H. D. Rouse. Ed. Martin Ferguson Smith. Cambridge, MA: Harvard UP, 1992.

McGreevy, Brian. *Hemlock Grove Or, The Wise Wolf*. New York: Farrar, Straus and Giroux, 2012.

TRACIE KOZIURA
SNOW WOLF, SILENT WITNESS, THE MESSAGE, & NO GOING BACK

Bio

Tracie Koziura lives in Leicestershire, UK with her partner, Paul, and their (currently) 6-month-old Tamaskan puppy, Loki. While she has been a poet since childhood, she only began working with pastels in 2008. Since the start of her artistic career, her wolf work entitled "Winter Watch" was the winning entry of the Pastel Guild of Europe's October 2009 Juried Art Contest ,and she was awarded "Artist of the Year 2011" by The Artist In You for another wolf piece, "Silent Witness."

Snow Wolf. Tracie Koziura. Pastels on velour paper.

The Message. Tracie Koziura. Pastels on velour paper.

Silent Witness. Tracie Koziura. Pastels on velour paper.

No Going Back

As I look in your eyes, I see triumph and madness
Yet I long to tell you the pain that I feel
I long to understand the fear and resentment and
find a way for this rift between us to heal

I bear no ill will toward you or your brothers
I ask for no favors just to live life my way
Our world bears the scars of wars we have wagered
It's time to lay down arms and call it a day

I hoped for too much when our paths crossed this morning
I believed it was time to put an end to this war
But my biggest mistake was to have faith in your hearing
Not in my lifetime will I see a hand touch a paw

The darkness draws closer as my spirit grows weaker
looking up to the eyes of my brothers of old
the wisdom of ages gently soothing the trembling
Replaced by the deathly numbness of cold

Unable to run, I lie here at your mercy
and watch as my life blood runs through your hands
Realizing my sacrifice will make little difference
Your need to destroy can be felt across the land

Your eyes gleam with fire while mine slowly fade now
On the wind comes the distant call of my pack
Howling with grief and inconsolable sorrow
As they, and I, realize there is no going back...

ROB WILKINSON
ON THE PROWL

On the Prowl. Rob Wilkinson. Photograph.

KRISTEN CONANT
CANIS LUNA

Bio

Kristen Conant lives in Jacksonville, North Carolina. She is working on her Bachelor's in Environmental Studies at Brevard College. She already has an Associate's in Biology. Her major goals are to work toward conservation for both wolves and wild horses, her other lifelong passion.

Canis Luna. Kristen Conant. Ink on paper.

FRANCISCO SHOJI RAMOS
THE FOREST, THE RIVER, AND THE WARMTH OF THE PACK

Bio

Francisco Shoji Ramos is currently a student attending his senior year at Reseda High School in a suburb of Los Angeles. From an early age he showed a love of nature by taking up the hobby of growing orchids. He has since grown his interests to focus on global ecology and the conservation of nature, and he plans to study biology, conservation, and world cultures in college.

Here we once again enter the world of anthropomorphic wolves. This time, the Native American wolf Koba deals with coming out to his father as a homosexual with the historical backdrop of European colonists coming to claim their land.

Koba sat quietly by the river, his amber eyes scanning every ripple of the silvery water for the fish he knew were lurking just below. The half-moon shone silver off his fur, and he kept his bushy tail curled around his leg, making doubly sure to not cause any ripples. The young wolf saw a flash from under the water, and his spear became a blur as he released all the tension he had built in his arm; in an instant, a second later, he felt the forked point of his fishing spear sink into something fleshy. A smile crept up his muzzle as he pulled the fat wriggling form of a trout out of the water and with surgical precision. Koba took his claws to the head of the fish, decapitating it and killing it in the same moment, ensuring that his prey hadn't suffered for long.

After the young wolf cleaned his catch and placed the fillet in his sack, he padded slowly toward the camp, navigating swiftly through the moonlit pines. Koba took a moment to look through the trees and feel the soft breeze ruffle his fur, the simple pleasure of these sensations making the young wolf coo and close his eyes in enjoyment. The only thing that could add to this beautiful night was if he could spot the beautiful pink moccasin flowers that grew near Crow Hill. Koba made a slight detour and skirted the edge of Blue Meadow, feeling a slight pang of regret that he had missed the blue torch flowers earlier in the spring. The breeze was blowing toward Koba's right, and he enjoyed how it brought him the scent of pine from the woods and clover from the meadow; a scent then registered on the wolf's sensitive nose that made him bristle with fear and reach for his knife...human.

The lupine heard them before he saw them, two males tromping carelessly through the wood in heavy coverings that hid their footpaws, and Koba snarled with disgust as he spotted the digging point they carried, knowing without a doubt that they intended to take the moccasin flowers. Immediately he knew that communication was out of the question: the humans spoke in this low slurred mulling tone that Koba could not understand, and with the missing grouping of birches in mind, he wasn't terribly in the mood to be diplomatic. The wolf drew his knife and padded silently behind a group of ferns within sight of the delicate hooded pink flowers, becoming as tense as a bowstring as he awaited the arrival of the two intruders. Koba felt his breathing almost stop as he saw the shambling forms of the humans approaching not more than a tail's length away, but the wolf relaxed slightly as he heard a noise that seemed to indicate confusion come from one of the humans. The other imitated that noise, and they discussed something. Koba sat up slowly and got a good look as they seemed to not know that their object of interest was so close ahead. The wolf only dropped his guard when he saw both humans turn and move away. Koba's knife returned to its sheath, and he stepped around to see the soft silken pink blossoms, smiling and admiring their delicate beauty before he proceeded on his way back to the pack.

Koba's nose twitched as a familiar scent wafted over from a short distance away, and a warm smile crossed his muzzle as he saw a familiar red-furred pelt emerge from the fern fronds beside the river. "Hello my love," said the red wolf as he approached Koba and licked his mate's nose affectionately, "I see that fortune has smiled upon your fishing tonight."

Koba smirked and nipped at his 'love's ear playfully, ""Eavesdropping as always Ageni. It's lucky for you that you know better than to interrupt my fishing." Ageni responded by giving his mate a swipe to the cheek with the pads of his paw, turning and letting his tail brush over the silver wolf's calves.

"You're always so fierce with things Koba; I just love you enough that I let you take care of things before barging in"." He turned and faced his russet-furred mate, smiling softly but showing an unmistakable look of apprehension in his amber hued eyes. "You still haven"t talked to your father about us have you?" said Ageni gently, breaking the silence with the question that he already knew the answer to.

Koba shook his head and paused slightly in the midst of walking up the bank, "it isn"t that I don't love you sweetheart; it's just that my father is the alpha, and both of us know what it means if he says he does not accept. I know that he has other sons to carry his name on, but I just don't want to put us through that." The silver wolf looked at Ageni with a frightened, pleading look in his wide watery eyes, and the red wolf padded close to him and wrapped his arms around Koba's soft furred shoulders.

"Listen to me love," said Ageni softly in a voice that was was palpable in the cool night, "I know this is hard to deal with, but you mustn't worry about it: we have our love, and if the pack does not want to accept us, then it is a loss on them and not on us."

Koba took a moment to think and breathe, letting his leathery pads rub over the silky contours of his mate's back, resting his long snout against Ageni's shoulder. "You are right of course love. I know that the ways of nature also teach us that a being's first obligation is to his mate. I know you have gained acceptance from your parents, and there is no refuting how much my father cares for all of his pack. I will let him know for our behalf."

Koba's muzzle was then met in an affectionate kiss, and he gladly returned it, lingering for a few moments in the warmth of his mate's arms before gently breaking away. The young couple walked closely at each other's side as they padded softly up the spongy soil of the river bank. "It is a shame that the blue torch blossoms are no longer out," said Koba softly as the ground began to level out in front of the wolves, "I know how much you love seeing them." Comfortable silence followed this comment, and both of the young lovers noticed the soft fragrance of pine carried on the breeze, the gentle swishing of the river behind them and the twinkle of countless stars above.

As it happened, Alpha Quidel was the first soul Koba encountered as he entered the pack's quarters, but instead of being chastised, he was met with a sense of concern from his alpha. "Koba, we wondered when you would return. Were the fish more slippery than usual my son?" said Quidel with a soft deep rumble as he licked Koba over the ear caringly.

"I do apologize for the lateness of my arrival my alpha," said Koba with his head bowed slightly as he set his fishing spear on the rack with all the others, "I had been diverted to some activity near Crow Hill before I neared the pack grounds."

Quidel shook his head slightly and chuckled to himself before resting a paw on his son's shoulder, "You mustn't trouble with those humans. I have watched, and they have made mistakes there for years. I know what you have heard my son, but I can thank the great mother for giving us life upon safe ground. I have heard tales of other packs who had been forced to move for the sake of human invasion. While my heart grows sad at it, I knew what the warning signs were, and I see none within vast distances of our lands. It is not healthy for your heart to worry my son," the alpha added sweetly as he gave Koba a warm smile.

Koba sighed softly and looked back to his father, a bit of apprehension burning in his yellow eyes. "I know, I know, and I thank you for advising my happiness, but I merely wish to do my duty for the pack. I only wish to repay all of the wonderful chances I have had and times I have lived through..."

The older wolf stopped Koba as he raised a paw for silence, "I know that you and Angeni are mated my son. I know it is something that has weighed heavily on you because you are guilty for not providing us with cubs, but love for a mate is the deepest meaning any bond can have, and I will love him as a father as long as you love him as a mate."

Koba's muzzle hung slightly open for a moment, but then all the young wolf could muster was a delighted squeal as he jumped forward and knocked his father backward, covering the older wolf's face in loving licks. "Thank you father! Oh thank you so much!!" Koba beamed, forgetting his worries and his fish as Quidel sat up and brushed off his fur, readjusting the row of feathers braided into the fur around his neck and smiling at his son.

"It is as much my obligation as a father as it is my pleasure at seeing my son happy. I regret that you let stories of non-acceptance from the rock pack have made you wary. It is a shame that they starve and suffer this year, but I know that from judgment and intolerance rises suffering and hardship for all." Koba smiled and nodded in agreement and padded back into the pack's quarters, handing the pouch with his three fish to the cooks and moving around until he spotted the handsome smiling face of his mate.

Koba padded over and hugged the red wolf, smiling softly and letting his paws trace through Ageni's soft fur. "I suppose you heard the good news sweetheart," said Ageni affectionately as he held his mate close. Koba kissed Ageni on the muzzle in response, and others in the pack looked on without judgment of the young couple. It seemed that through its unity and support, Quidel's pack managed to withstand hardship and avoid internal misfortune, acting to show us all what love and acceptance can be capable of.

JULIAN NORWOOD
SILENT WATCH, THE BARD, & THE DREAMKEEPER

Bio

Julian Norwood is a writer and illustrator living in rural Connecticut with his spouse, two cats, and a small menagerie of pocket pets. He is the art director for Word Branch Publishing and has sold and displayed work internationally and recently published his first novel Forsaking Magic. *When he's not writing or painting, he's elbows deep in an engine, bottling the next home-brew project, enjoying a cup of tea, or traveling the countryside.*

Silent Watch. Julian Norwood. Acrylics.

The Bard. Julian Norwood. Acrylics.

The Dreamkeeper. Julian Norwood. Acrylics.

HANNAH CHRISTOPHER
HETANE AND HATOME & THE MAN WHO HOWLED

Bio

Hannah Christopher lives in Ohio, and she is going into her first year of college at the end of the summer in the hopes of becoming an English teacher. She takes inspiration from the blessings around her and is often seen at her desk with an ill-tempered Siamese cat on her lap and her favorite music on repeat. She publishes her stories often online under pseudonyms and is working on a trilogy of books in her free time. This is the first time her work has been chosen for professional publication.

"Hetane and Hatome" plays with the idea of "hunter" and "hunted." When a wolf, man, and deer come into the same picture, who will come out triumphant?

"The Man Who Howled" follows a young girl as she learns about the mysterious Rufus C. Paddington and his connection to the wolf-on-display Usdi.

A kill had just been made. Success among the tribe. In the camp in the field, smoke rose out of a triangular mass, and a massive bellow sounded out of the mouth of an ancient instrument. But, over the land, an immense storm was kissing the sky. The other hunters were waking.

He crawled over the ground on calloused, padded paws. Teeth bared to the bleak sunlight, drawing the tantalizing tastes and scents over his ridged pallet, collecting a myriad display brighter than any television screen, broadcasting or not. His blotchy fur mixed together in waves and hues of brown and gray, matted together near his joints, caked with blood near his mouth.

The fur around his ear twitched, and his ear followed after, batting the unwanted sounds away. Something wooded and heavy moved through the plains on the other side of the forest edge, on the other side of the underbrush. Its four feet fell pleasantly over the earth; its nostrils widened as it sniffed the air. It was looking for the hunter, and the hunter for it. The deer pivoted its head toward the woods, but only briefly. After a moment, it ducked down to the crackling grass again and softly nibbled at the fronds.

The wolf dared a few steps further. Its nose piped through the brambles, twitching. He closed his mouth. His midnight-black pupils dilated, focusing in like twin crosshairs over a moving target.

Prey froze. Hunter did, too. In fact, he stopped breathing entirely. He was one solitary unit in a vast plain of nothingness and deer. He stopped breathing. He stopped existing.

Across the open plain, a wordless and motionless signal fell over the darkened land, and a crack of thunder followed. The gray wolf darted out of his cover and screamed onto the field, a bullet out of a gun, a dog out of the gates. He took his breaths back in great gasps, hissing through his teeth. The deer loomed nearer and nearer, then farther and farther, bounding over the field; it fell prey to only lightning at first, the dramatism of unfortunately timed effects. Then to the others. The other wolves, they streamed from the underbrush like spirits from a ghost town, their claws clanking together, the air rasping in and out of their heaving chests.

They fell upon their prey together, all at once. One at the neck, two at the flank, another at the head, four at the haunches. And when prey fell, there echoed a great crash through the forest, heard by all the others but the ones that didn't care to listen anymore, the death of the mother under the mourning sky. The wolves danced around their dinner, legs thrown out underneath themselves and tongues lolling out. The hunter gave his brother a congratulatory nudge. It had been his first time on a hunt.

Faraway in the field, smoke rose out of a triangular mass, and a massive bellow sounded out of the mouth of an ancient instrument.

The Man Who Howled

The awful creature hardly looked like a dog, let alone a wolf. Fenced-in, sprawled out sleeping on smelly hay that grew like briars from a sticky concrete floor, the Mexican Wolf the fair called "Balto" seemed hardly alive. Yet, here it was, like some sick elephant at a carnival for children to gawk and throw moldy peanuts at. I sighed in disgust and leaned against the wobbly metal fencing. Balto flicked a fly away with his ear, otherwise unresponsive.

My best friend from college, Valory Mason, had dragged me through miles of hillbilly heaven to see the seasonal autumn fair; being a spoiled country-bumpkin herself, it was hard to resist the sparkle in her bright blue eyes when she had asked me to tag along. And when she mentioned the small zoo...well, I liked zoos, but I couldn't imagine a sadder excuse of a collection of animals. Valory, however, seemed perfectly content with its garish condition. She read over the information plaque hanging from the tent for the eighteenth time.

"Huh," she commented aloud, "raised in captivity."

I grunted boredly. She seemed to understand this, at least, because Valory soon had me by the wrist and was moving over to the other animals.

"I heard they have a tiger somewhere around here," she muttered, half to herself, half to someone who wasn't me. She stopped suddenly on her heel, and I collided with her right shoulder. She was asking a man in front of us—a volunteer, telling by the puke-green hue of his patched vest—for directions to an animal that was conscious. I furrowed my brow and blew a few black strands of my own hair out of my sullen face, falling into my usual spot at Val's right side. From my height, I could only make out the shabby volunteer's nametag, his full name: Rufus C. Paddington. Sounded a little suspicious to me, like a name a little girl would give her ratty stuffed-animal. I narrowed my eyes and looked up.

The first thing I noticed was that poor Rufus C. Paddington had probably been skimping out on a lot of sleep. His frumpy fair uniform was caked judiciously in splatters of mud and flecks of hay; his silvery hair jabbed every which way, unkempt and uncombed, graying despite the fact that he looked no older than I was. When Rufus smiled, the grin spread wide across his features, like some ill-modeled nightmare, all tooth and tongue.

I thought to myself that this Rufus C. Paddington character was probably not someone we should take directions from. Still, Valory was relentless—a true soldier of a girl.

She beamed. "Hello, Mister...er...Paddington! I was just wondering...uh...could you direct us to the other animals, pretty please? The tiger, preferably."

The man called Rufus paused in apparent thought. His horrid smile slipped into a more human-like and practiced frown. Mournfully, he brought his hand up to his nose and pressed his thumb to the corner of his mouth; almost as if, though practiced regularly, he were vaguely unfamiliar with the shape it made on his lips.

"Oh, you know, they're around," he said. His voice had a melancholic sort of timbre to it. I raised an eyebrow. I had been right about one thing: we certainly weren't taking directions from him if this was all he had to offer. He averted his pale eyes and spoke again, "You'll find 'em."

Val grimaced. "Mister, you're supposed to help."

He pointed to his nametag apologetically. "You can call me Rufus."

"Well, Rufus," I chipped in, standing up for the both of us because I knew Valory was a pushover when it came to speaking to people she didn't know, "you're not being very helpful. I'll tell your boss if you don't help my friend, so, can you be more freakin' specific, please?"

Rufus hung his head and gave in without a fuss, thankfully. There was no way I was going to report him to the boss of this ramshackle lot, but he didn't know that.

"Fine," he whistled through his teeth, "follow me. I'll give you the exclusive tour." We both hesitated when he started forward through the sluggish crowd. He snapped over his shoulder, "Well, come on! I have other things to do, you know!"

Val went first, pulling me along by the hem of my black shirt sleeve. Mister Rufus C. Paddington begrudgingly showed us to a group of boisterous lion cubs (probably illegal), a sick-looking tiger with hardly any stripes or fur left clinging to his skin (illegal), and a fly-bitten elephant in an ugly silver pen (*definitely* illegal). He made very sure, with each increasingly illegal and exotic creature, to explain in great detail how each was supposed to look and how disgusting each one was in its current condition, using great sweeping hand gestures and stretched, Disney-like expressions. When Valory had had enough depression, she urged me to go ride the carousel with her.

"Come on," she pressed, "I want to ride on the peacock. How about you?"

I made a face. "No thanks, Val. I think I'll sit this one out."

"You're no fun!" she stuck her tongue out at me with her words. I rolled my eyes.

"We're almost adults, Val. I don't wanna be seen riding a dumb carousel," I shot back. "Besides, I'm kind of tired. I think I'll just find someplace to rest for a while."

"Ugh, fine. You're so boring!"

She was pelting away before she could get the last word out. I called after her, "Hey, meet me by the entrance when you're ready to leave!" but I don't think she heard me. I turned and walked back around the animal enclosures with disinterest. It was getting kind of gray and cold outside, and I wanted to stay as close to the tents as I could.

By some series of unfortunate events, I ended up back where I started, at Balto the Emaciated Wolf. I leaned forward against his flimsy metal fence and closed one eye wearily. He was still sleeping.

"You know," a familiar, mournful voice called up from my left, "not all wolves are like that. It's not her fault, her owners—if you'd call them that—they just...they don't know what they're doing."

"Are you defending them?" I muttered.

His voice dropped. "No. Not really."

I paused for a moment and decided to change the subject. If Rufus C. Paddington was going to stick around, I might as well let him talk about something he actually cared about. Maybe then I could get some shut-eye.

I half-turned. Rufus stood rigidly next to me, eyes cast to Balto as if ashamed.

I sighed, "It's a girl?"

He seemed to relax at the statement, and nodded. Moving stiffly, he joined me at leaning on the fence. "Yeah," he said in his slightly, awkwardly accented tone, "she's a girl. They only say she's a boy because the males gather more attention. You know, like the great lone wolf, and like the real Balto. Though, I don't think Balto was really a wolf. That's just a cartoon. He was domestic, and they have him stuffed in some museum in Cleveland, I've heard. Not that it makes him any less of a creature, but there's little dignity in that, I think."

I laughed uncomfortably. "Wow, dude. You're kind of a downer, aren't you?"

He wasn't listening. Rufus rambled on, "I'll get her out of here one day. That's my current dream: to earn enough money to buy her. The guy's selling her for two thousand dollars."

I sat up straight, giving him a scrutinizing look. He pressed his lips together and tore his light amber eyes away from the flea-infested she-wolf.

"How long have you been working?" I asked.

"Uh, not very long," he answered with quite a bit of nervousness, "I just started at the fair again."

"Again?"

"You may not believe this," Rufus began.

"Shoot," I dared.

He scratched the back of his head in contemplation. "I travel the country, buying them off of their neglecting owners. Spent ten-thousand on the last one, a pretty Gray in Montana. Broke my bank."

"Buying what?"

He answered simply, "the wolves."

I turned back to Balto, suddenly very keen to observe if she had any beauty left in her. As sure as I thought, there remained a certain luster on her coat, underneath all the hay and mud, an undeniable dignity in her resting. She shifted her muzzle over her paws and suddenly winked open her eyes; beautiful creamy orange, like the moon set on fire. They flicked over to us. We were the only ones left to watch her, until a pair of suits sidled up to the fence next to us in hushed voices, pointing, but we paid no mind to them.

"You're an awful pretty girl," Rufus crooned. I startled, but he wasn't talking to me. He had reached his fingers into the low bars of the fence and was calling out to the wolf. In his face and in his eyes, I saw the same kind of dignity I saw in her, the same kind of wildness. A depth that no other man, no matter his passion, could have ever hoped to obtain. He continued to beckon her forth, "Balto is such a silly name. Poor thing. What have they done to you, Usdi?"

I blinked. The she-wolf sniffed the air curiously, then sank back into the grime. Rufus sighed and stood up again.

"What do you do with them after you buy them?" I asked.

"Huh?"

"The wolves," I repeated, "where do they go?"

"Oh," he said through a smile better than anything I had seen on him so far, "you know, around."

***

Valory called after me sooner than I thought she would, and Rufus C. Paddington vanished into the ether. I didn't think I'd ever see or hear from him again, though I took the liberty of giving him my home phone number and asked politely for an update on his quest to buy Balto back into freedom. Not that it interested me, I was simply curious on how far his plights would go.

Valory dropped me off at my house, a squat little brown thing tucked into the corner between the grocer's and the dentist's office, and she sped off into the late-night hours, off through the hills and back-roads, in long pursuit of her family's estate.

I slipped my shoes off at the entryway and fell onto my couch without changing. My feet ached, I smelled like manure, and every muscle in my body pulsated with new tension. I grabbed the remote and turned on the antique television. It flicked to life, tuned to a half-over crime drama. Somewhere between midnight and three, the channel changed to Animal Planet and I didn't change it back.

The plastic, wall-mount phone clanged like a broken fire alarm close to five in the morning. I must have fallen asleep sometime during the show about meerkats, because I jumped back into wakefulness and nearly rolled right off the couch. Groaning and sore, I shambled into the kitchenette and yanked the phone off the receiver.

"Yeah, hello," I moaned, "you've reached—"

I was cut off by a very frantic voice. It was Rufus the Volunteer, and he was in overdrive mode. "I am so sorry for waking you, but this is an emergency! You're the only person I could call, I'm so sorry..."

"Rufus?" I yawned, "What's the matter? Why the heck are you calling me at dark o'clock in the morning? You should be sleeping."

"I don't have time! It's Usdi!"

"Uz-what?"

"Er...I mean, Balto. Two guys made an offer and the owner couldn't refuse. They're going to buy her and either send her off to some horrible breeding camp or turn her into a coat! That can't happen! I mean, er, she's an endangered species and it's very illegal!"

Leaning up against my wallpapered wall to support my dead weight, I mumbled, "I don't think you should jump to conclusions, Rufus. I mean, just talk to them. They might be good people."

"If there's one thing I've learned over the years," he responded darkly, "it's that men in suits are never good people, especially at county fairs."

"Wow, geez," I breathed through my teeth. "Well, what are you going to do about it at...five o'clock in the morning with not enough money, little sleep, and no warrant papers? You can't expect—"

Rufus cut me off again, urgent. "Do you have a car?"

"Yeah," I nervously said, spinning the phone chord on my pinky finger, "if you'd call it that. The old junker hardly runs. I don't even know if it has gas in it, and it's parked a few blocks away."

"That's great! Listen, I have enough to pay you for gas money if you'd just—"

This time, I was the one to cut him off. I glanced at the still-broadcasting television screen. "Yeah, got it. Rufus, don't worry about the money. Where do you need me to be?"

"The fairgrounds."

"Alright. It'll be about thirty minutes."

"Hurry," he said desperately, and the line went dead. I hung up the phone and ran a shaking hand through my coarse hair. Well, there went my college scholarship. If this didn't work, I was as good as dead. My parents probably wouldn't listen to reason if the cops showed up on their doorstep saying I had committed Grand Theft Wolf.

I grabbed my rusty key ring off the coat tree by my front door and was outside before I could pull my coat on. I didn't even bother to lock the door—the dentist worked early hours and kept a good eye out for me. Like a bullet on a mission from a pistol, I streaked down the uneven sidewalk and past the closed storefronts, aching legs screaming in protest with each lurching stride. The things I would do for a strange kid I barely knew amazed me in that moment. The cold autumn air bit at my cheeks and I regretted not changing into warmer clothes. But, before I had the chance to decide to turn back and pull some on, I had reached my nasty, mystery-brand, four-door beast and threw open the passenger side door, crawling through there to get into the driver's seat. I gasped over the steering wheel and jammed in three keys before finding one that fit. Old Nasty sputtered and growled to life. I patted the dashboard.

"Sorry, old guy," I panted, "I promise never to drive you again after this, okay? Just cooperate with me tonight and I'll set you free forever. Please, please, don't break down. Not tonight."

Surprisingly, Old Nasty listened to my bartering desires and stayed running until I pulled into the gravel parking lot of the turned-down fair and pulled out his keys. Luckily, the horn had broken long ago, so he didn't bleat when I locked the doors. The carnival music had been silenced hours ago, when the fair closed, leaving only soundless fireflies and bristling grass. I briskly ran to the fair entrance and peered into the almost-darkness; the carousel lights still blinked despite the quietness, illuminating a creature that lurked near the front gate. His eyes reflected in the alternating patterns, and his shadow danced over the earth. It was Rufus, and he fidgeted where he stood. I met up with him wordlessly.

"Good, good," he spoke fast. "You're here, finally. I thought you said thirty minutes. You only took twenty-three. Great timing."

"Thanks," I tried to say, but my mouth barely emitted a sound. Still, he managed to hear it and nodded knowingly.

"Alright," he said, "I hope you don't mind dogs in the car."

"My car will be mad, but we made a deal earlier so he's not allowed to complain," I pointedly returned. "So, how do we steal this thing? Do you have lock-picking experience, or can we just waltz in and—"

Rufus moved aside. Now in better lighting, I could see him in his entirety, muddier and more hay-coated than before, with pricks of yellowed wheat heads sticking from his clumpy hair. His nametag was gone, but his uniform was otherwise the same as before, only grubbier. Where he had been standing a moment ago, a rather lively Balto basked in the half-moon's flooding glow.

He admitted uncomfortably, "Sorry, but I couldn't wait. I took your advice, though, and checked the purchase papers the two men left on the owner's desk. One of them's a taxidermist, just so you know."

"Okay," I blinked, in awe. She looked so much better already, out of the pen and stretching her legs in the grass. "I have to hand it to you, Rufus, I didn't think you could do it on your own."

A defensive look crossed his face for a moment, but then the carousel shut down and his expression was gone. We both turned to the sound of metallic clanking and footsteps from the fairgrounds.

"That's our cue to get the heck out of here," I hissed, "we better get going. Grab the—grab Balto."

I started off at a quick run to Old Nasty; he blinked to life as I jabbed at the unlock button on my key ring and I cursed under my breath. I hopped into the driver's seat seconds before Rufus, with Balto, surprisingly enough, over his shoulder, clambered into the back. He deposited his precious cargo on the bench seat and slammed the door closed with slipping fingers.

"Go, go, go!" he yelled.

I turned the keys three times, still cursing, and the car groaned to relative life. I adjusted the rearview and saw thick black smoke trailing from its backside, but I was tearing out of the fairgrounds too fast to care, burning too much rubber to smell much else, focusing only on the small silhouette of a portly man brandishing his fist as the darkness left behind by my singular taillight swallowed him up. I sent up a silent prayer that he hadn't seen my plates. This was *by far* the most illegal thing I'd done in my life. I vaguely recalled, when I was younger, stealing a candy bar from the convenience store and being so eaten up by the guilt that I went back and left ten dollars and an apology letter on the counter. The same protocol probably didn't apply to my current situation.

To calm myself down, I kept an eye on the speedometer. If I went any faster than forty miles an hour, Old Nasty was likely to cough up his engine and die. I turned on the radio and John Denver buzzed through the speakers. Rufus told me not to change the station and I laughed; not because it was a ridiculous taste in music, but because it was exactly the taste I had expected someone like him to have.

Balto was whining lowly and pressing her paws to the side-door, eyes so wide the whites showed. Rufus, meanwhile, gave her a brief pat on the ears and sighed in relief.

"I owe you so much," he said.

"Yeah," I agreed. "By the way, where are we going?"

"Since you probably don't want to go to New Mexico," he sighed again, "I don't know. The nearest forest. We'll walk the rest of the way."

"You're going to walk?" I gawked, "You and a smuggled wolf are going to walk from Northern Utah to New Mexico?"

"I've gone longer," he shot back, defensive again.

"Whatever," I grumbled. I leaned forward, against the upper portion of my steering wheel. The road was long and straight and seemingly endless, only visible under my flickering white headlights. I didn't have to move at all, the car drove itself, murmuring along the bumpy way. Miles and miles of wheat and grass, and nothing more.

"Hey," I muttered tiredly. I needed to make conversation to keep my eyes open. "I've been wondering, what are you planning on doing with Balto, anyway? She's almost completely domestic, right? Bred and raised in captivity."

Rufus frowned in his reflection in the window. "By the time we get to New Mexico, she'll know everything she needs. I just hope there's a pack that's willing to take her in. Otherwise, I suppose she'll just join mine."

"What?"

"Er—I own a lot of land up north. It's a long journey, but whatever happens, it'll be worth it."

"You're really something different, you know that?" I said.

"Not particularly different," he sighed wistfully, "just...not domesticated yet. You know, the whole wide world is spinning and spinning and no one really gives a crap about the things that have been here longer than they have, like me. I've seen a lot, and I've seen this world grow up, and I've seen it get violent and I've seen it destroy itself over and over again. But, I've also seen a lot of good things, too. Like, in World War One, they stopped fighting on Christmas day. Of course, they fought again at dawn, but just the thought that people could work together like that and set aside their differences...the world hasn't been domesticated yet, and that's a good thing. When you're domesticated, the emotion is bred out of you. And I'm glad it's still there."

"You sound like an old man," I scoffed.

"I may not look it, but I am. Stop looking at me like that, like I'm crazy."

"I didn't say anything," I chuckled.

"Well," he started, but he never finished. Balto had moved over in the car, still panicking, and now took up all the space available on Rufus' lap. He sat still for a good ten minutes, with me perpetually dozing off at the wheel, and stared out the window at the grains passing by. He probably knew each and every one by name.

Just wait until Valory hears about this, I thought to myself with great humor. It was not in my heart to tell her, though. This was something that was best kept to myself.

"Say," Rufus finally said above the drone of the car. I peered through the chipped rearview to see his expression, plaintive and wondering. "What's your name, anyway? I don't think we've been properly introduced."

"We haven't," I sheepishly admitted, "and, my mother's black, just so you know."

"I didn't ask," he plainly stated. "I just wanted to know your name. I'll bet it's not as weird as mine. You guessed a while ago, I think, Rufus isn't my real name."

"Well," I started with a sigh, "my parents couldn't decide on what to name me, and my dad wanted a boy."

We waited.

"It's Layla-Sean," I chuckled nervously. "Weird, right?"

He shook his head, and his messy hair shook out with it, gathering back together in matted clumps. "Not really. Mine's Chibiabos."

I laughed, "Rufus *Chibiabos* Paddington, eh? Quite a pseudonym. I think I'll stick to calling you Rufus, no offense."

"Most people do."

Despite the scathing comments, I could see that he was smiling.

Thirty minutes and a lot more small talk later, Balto's nose was propped out the window and I was pulling into a vacant field that edged up to the most daunting patch of woods I had ever seen. The trees seemed to extend forever, dipping and rising into hills and rocky valleys, giving way to a small stream. The sun was peaking over the horizon, casting everything in a pleasant pink color. I opened the back door for my two strange passengers and, no sooner than I did, the wolf Balto was hurtling out of my car and into the grasses, prancing and rolling in the cut grain stalks, bounding with purpose alongside the barrier of the forest, ears flattened, too frightened and excited to head in by herself. Rufus stood next to me with a delighted, serene look on his face. The whole moon shined through his eyes. He glowed underneath, like Balto did, with a hidden and wild mysteriousness that could never be fettered. In that moment, I felt eternally enlightened and unburdened. I didn't shut the car door.

"*Canis lupus baileyi*," Rufus announced aloud, closing his eyes as a perfect breeze wafted over the field. "The Mexican Wolf. They released eleven back into the wild recently, and I do hope they're still there."

I nudged Rufus's shoulder. "What are you? A walking dictionary?"

He smiled his garish smile at me. "Not quite. Hey, Layla?"

"Yeah?" I asked curiously. He looked down at me with the mournful expression of a once-captive animal. Yet, somehow, I knew he was abundantly happy.

"Do me a favor, and don't change your phone number, okay?" he begged, "It'll be a long while until I'm back again, but I haven't had someone to talk to in a very long time, and I could use some more help out there every now and then."

"Of course," I joked, "as long as you don't interfere with my exam schedule."

He laughed, husky and cheerful. "I wouldn't dream of it." Then, looking at Balto and at the woods, he smiled again, and it completely took over his face when he said, "Alright, I'll be seeing you, Layla-Sean. I've got a lot of ground to cover this winter, it seems."

Before I could ask where or how or what he was doing, he was sprinting off toward the cusp of the woods, fluid and wolf-like, and to the best of my memory, nobody would have believed what happened next. I stood at my car, the wind picking up and the smells of the country billowing over me, the doors still open because I was in too much shock to close them. The sun had risen, and the darkness of night had been banished, even if the moon lurked up there somewhere, huddled in daylight and clouds; there was no possible way to mistake what I had seen.

I take myself as a very critical and skeptical woman. Yet, for all the world, there was a man who howled running into the woods on four paws, and the she-wolf from the fair hesitating only for a hardly noticeable moment before diving in after.

I drove home in silence. The car seemed to work better than it ever had before. Or, maybe, I just wasn't in the mood to yell at it anymore. When I got to my house, there was a paper on my doorstep. One of the side articles read: THEFT AT THE FAIR, with a subtitle of, RARE MEXICAN WOLF STOLEN BY VOLUNTEER. There was a picture of Rufus's nametag sitting where he had abandoned it in the wolf pen. The news showed the same picture when I switched the television channel, along with another one which I hadn't seen featured in the *Morning Trumpet*, a photograph of two sets of paw prints leading out of Balto's cage. Something they didn't have hung on my coat-tree: Rufus's mud-stained vest, with a few of the same paw prints on it, perfectly preserved, as if he'd left them there just for me.

"An expert has identified the tracks as Balto's and another wolf's, leaving us with only one question," the broadcaster lady said in her high-strung voice, "who busted the docile canine out of his pen? And where in the world did Mister Rufus Paddington go off to?"

"That's two questions," I muttered to myself on the couch.

An expert came on next. "The tracks look to be of *Canis lupus baileyi* and of *Canis rufus*, or the Red Wolf, a species indigenous to the South-East."

Then the newslady came back with, "the mystery may never be solved. At the moment, the director of the county fair is being investigated for illegally keeping endangered animals, so the fairgrounds will be closed today. Back to you, Clint."

***

Five months later, the phone rang.

ELAINE BROWN
NOSTALGIA

Bio

Elaine Brown is a short story author and poet who grew up on the volcanic soil of Northern California and now makes her home in Oregon's Willamette Valley. In her writing, she explores the juxtaposition of the physical and mystical realms and seeks to understand the interconnection of all things. She recently had two poems published in the Denali Literary & Arts Magazine. *When she's not developing her own artistic voice, she is likely helping others find theirs; she regularly leads families in art projects with a spiritual twist and guides adult learners to writing success.*

then
lush snow
shrouded Mt Shasta in silence
magically
You'd appear
silhouetted
amongst the rocks and sagebrush
the earth held her breath
in awe
as you sang
Your solo became a chorus
Your golden eyes
sacredly perfected
the moon's light
now
Mt Shasta is in rocky silhouette
You are shrouded in silence
the earth whispers her prayers for
Your golden eyes
to once again
sacredly perfect
the moon's light

SAMANTHA DUTTON
WOLF: A SHORT STORY

Bio

Samantha Dutton lives in the South West of England with her husband and two children. She has a Bachelor of Arts degree in English Literature. A compulsive reader, she likes to draw and write whenever she has the time. She also loves to spend her time in both Cornwall and Devon, both of which provided a backdrop for her childhood and are often present in her writing.

In this heart-wrenching story of a wolf in a world ruined by humanity, a rain-storm quickly approaches. Can the old wolf find food and shelter in time for the imminent danger?

It was particularly dark and quiet that night. The air was warm and humid, taking on a claustrophobic quality that took a stranglehold upon all of the residents of the forest. The wolf stood quietly observing the campsite from the shadows, his eyes flicking warily across the scene that he surveyed. People sat around the fire, laughing and telling stories. A row of low tents lay beyond them flapping and swaying slightly in the barely present breeze. The wolf narrowed his eyes and considered his options briefly. He could skirt around the camp and continue on his journey now, or he could wait until the residents of this community turned in for the night and scavenge a meal from whatever morsels they would leave scattered around. It was an easy decision to make. The hunger had been growing in the pit of his stomach for days now and without food it was unlikely he would be able to go on. He would wait.

One by one the people filtered away until all that remained was a charred pile of wood, the embers still glowing dully. Taking a final, cursory look around, the wolf tentatively made his way across the clearing. He dodged the paraphernalia from the revelries of the night until he reached an open bag, its contents half-strewn upon the gritty floor. Cut steak and a soggy chicken wing would be the meal that he consumed, although what was left for him was minimal after the over-consumption of the humans. Their excess left him with barely two mouthfuls, which he bolted down rapidly. It would not be enough to quell his ravenous hunger for long. He walked to the edge of the camp and took a final glance over his shoulder. The camp looked like a desolate, ghost town. Litter was dotted all around and moved lazily in the breeze. He shifted his tired body into the thick tree line and was gone.

It was almost half an hour later that the wolf decided to rest, if only briefly. He slept fitfully, whining and wheezing constantly. Upon waking, he dragged himself to his feet, yawned widely and resumed his journey. Heading for the plateau his body ached and creaked, but still he pushed on. Age and hunger had ravaged his once proud countenance, and his head and neck sagged to a level that coincided with the height of his emaciated shoulders. Food was scarce these days, with hunters culling the ready food source of deer and smaller animals until there were few to provide the strength to make it through the day. Hence, the raiding of certain populated areas. It was a risk, but one he must take to survive. The trees dipped and swayed, their leaves rustling loudly in the increasing breeze. Through cracks in the tree tops he could see faded stars winking through the wispy clouds. The moon shone a sickly yellow, providing barely enough light to guide his way. It was a pale and jaded reflection of how it had appeared to him less than a decade ago. Slowing slightly, he sniffed the air to check for danger and finding none he passed noiselessly between the rocks that marked the entrance to the place where he was born all those years before.

Shivering slightly from the cold that now engulfed him, the wolf continued onto the plateau with a sense of purpose. The entrance to this little Eden was concealed from the prying eyes of men. Yet even if they had known of its existence it was unlikely they would have been able to navigate their way into it. Before him lay a large, grassy clearing, surrounded by trees that reached far into the night sky. Unlike his previous haunt, this clearing was no man-made affair. Trees lay scattered and rotting from the elements that had become increasingly erratic over the years. He picked his way among them, stepping carefully to avoid the splinters that would surely follow should he catch one with his paw. It had now been an hour and a half since leaving the encampment, but the wolf had no sense of the human concept of time. He breathed in the perfume resonating from the flora that was prevalent in this unsullied landscape, and as he did he felt a droplet of rain hit his nose. Suddenly the air was alive with the sound of rain splattering on the ground, the rocks, and the leafy trees. The torrent of rain that descended on him was as sudden as it was unexpected. It drenched his matted coat, weighing him down until he appeared to be cowering in fear from the water that poured from the skies. He had not noticed the cloud thickening overhead, had not realized that the breeze had now become a wind. That wind had now whipped itself into a gale that drove the rain in sheets that seemed to penetrate him to his very core. He headed for a rocky outcrop, knowing that he would find shelter from the tempest that was brewing. As he climbed the rocks to the mouth of the cave he slipped and stumbled his way to his destination. Once inside the familiar surroundings, he slid to the floor and rested his head upon his paws. As he slept the wind and rain persisted in their attack of the night landscape.

A loud cracking and fizzing sound disturbed the wolf from his self-induced coma. The air smelled of burning and the dampness of the earth. Yet, the wolf was not afraid. Not even when a loud, ominous bang signaled a new bout of lightning which tore through the night sky in shades of silver and purple. Electrical storms were becoming a more common place occurrence in these parts as man ate into the remaining countryside with their homes. The wolf shook with cold and hunger. His journey had weakened him considerably, and the storm had broken the humid heat of earlier, leaving in its place an icy coldness. He could view the awesome destruction from the entrance to the cave where he lay exhausted, his glazed eyes barely reflecting every flash that occurred like lariats through the blackened night sky. It was a sight that evoked strong memories for him. The stormy night when he had been born and the night during which he had slunk away from the pack to wander aimlessly through the then unpopulated forests. Those events seemed to be a lifetime away now. Many things had changed, and not for the better. As years had passed, the world in which he lived had shrunk considerably. There were fewer and fewer places that could be safely navigated. Man had hunted, cleared, and littered the once magnificent landscape into a shadow of its former glory and in doing so had gained a strangle hold upon the dense flora and fauna that had occupied their new surroundings. Some species had been whittled down to merely a handful, and some had been unable to survive in the altered environment at all. The wolf knew that many of his kind still occupied the forest, but he also knew that it would not be long before they died from malnutrition or a hunter's stray bullet. Or perhaps even worse...perhaps they would be hit by a speeding man carrier and left for dead by the side of the road to be picked at by carrion in a horrific and painful death. Yet all of the options were painful ones. It was likely that in no time at all there would be no possibility of a natural death from old age, as man pushed further into the microcosm that the inhabiting wildlife called their home. He sighed deeply and tried to stand. He would need to venture out soon to locate water and maybe an abandoned carcass if he was lucky. He was aware that the weakness he now felt made him vulnerable and also that his ability to hunt live prey would be severely diminished. He managed to prop his haggard body to a half-sitting position, but as soon as he applied what little strength he had left his legs folded under him. He persisted in his efforts, but still could not stand. The storm that had been so fascinating previously, now seemed ominous. The wind howled forlornly through the tree tops, the lightning ripped into trees causing them to burn like funeral pyres, and the thunder provided a macabre soundtrack to all that the wolf surveyed. The rain poured like bitter tears, ricocheting up from the rocks in an eerie mist. With one final effort, the wolf tried once again to pull his exhausted body into an upright position. He failed. He whimpered helplessly at his misfortune. He could do no more than watch the tempest through drooping eyes. More than ever before, he felt the need to sleep. As his eyes closed one last time, he drew his final breath. He felt peace at last. He would no longer feel the effects of a brutalized, degraded world. Now, for him, there was only an eternity of darkness.

COLETTE KORVA
TWO WOLVES, HOWL, & WOLF AND ANTLERS

Bio
Colette Korva is twenty years old and lives in Minnesota with her husband. She has won numerous awards at the St. Louis and Itasca County Fairs.

Two Wolves. Colette Korva. Graphite.

Howl. Colette Korva. Acrylics.

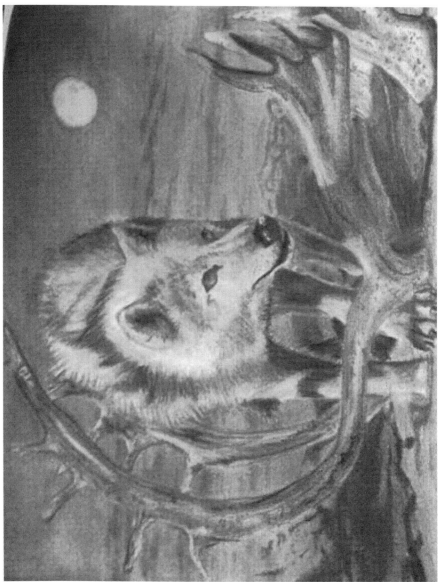

Wolf and Antlers. Colette Korva. Colored pencils and sandpaper.

BERNADETTE BURGER
CRYING WOLF

Bio
Bernadette Burger is an artist from South Africa.

Crying Wolf. Bernadette Burger. Fine liner.

CONNIE SPARKS
THE WILD

Bio
Connie Sparks is a mother of five and grandmother of one. She hopes to someday finish her degree in wildlife biology, and her major passions include God, wildlife, and her family.

The city lights, they blind my eyes
The noises, they are deafening
I miss the silence of the woods
The songs of grey wolves howling
I long to dance in the cooling rain
Underneath God's great canopy
And sleep deeply in the earth
At the roots of His oldest trees
The wild calls my very soul
The mountains hold my destiny
For God intended all of man
To live with nature peacefully

WILLIAM HUGGINS
THESE WOLVES ARE OUR WOLVES

Bio

William Huggins is an avid father, husband, reader, hiker, camper, and wilderness and animal advocate. He lives, works, and writes in Las Vegas. His work has appeared in Studies in American Indian Literatures, Critical Insights: Louise Erdrich, Another Realm, Third Flatiron, *and monthly blogs for* We Are Wildness. *One of the few things left on his bucket list is to see a wolf in the wild.*

The following essay talks of the connections the wolf has with American history and culture. It was originally published in the blog We Are Wildness.

"Of all the wild creatures of North America, none are more despicable than wolves."

–William T. Hornaday, 1914

While crossing the north Atlantic, the forefathers of America not only brought with them the desire for religious liberty but also many of the cultural attitudes with which the Continent had imbued them. Some of these dealt directly with nature, especially wild nature, which was a fearsome place to the medieval Christian mind and continued to be so in poems and stories from Chaucer to Shakespeare. From a Biblical perspective, Christ's biggest test was in the wilderness, Matthew 4, and one of the Old Testament God's ways of punishing wayward peoples was to eradicate their fertile lands. The message was clear: God's people would tame the wild places to prepare for the kingdom to come, or be cast out with the beasts.

The early colonists landed with this embedded doctrine and quickly set about correcting the perceived imbalance they saw all around them. Of their many environmental sins, and perhaps most molested of their victims, was the wolf. The war they began against *Canis lupus* resonates through our culture to this day. Wolves historically roamed the entire continental US, besides small coastal portions of California; and by 1960 they had been completely wiped out, except for Michigan's Upper Peninsula.

The change in attitude toward wolves has taken time. Aldo Leopold's story from *A Sand County Almanac* on shooting a wolf should be required reading for anyone interested in wolf studies, as should Barry Lopez's *Of Wolves and Men*, which traces the long history of wolf-hatred through many cultures, not to mention the works of Rick Bass, Renee Askins, and others. But Leopold's influence went farther than that, as the first writer to set ecology as a benchmark. Because of his realization of species interconnectivity, and with a lot of work over four decades, reintroduction programs began in the 1980s with the red wolf in North Carolina, the Mexican Wolf in the American southwest, and the gray wolf in Yellowstone National Park in the early 1990s.

Predictably, there was an outcry from voices in the localities where the wolves were reintroduced, with a small but vocal minority in opposition. Ranchers have little to complain about as organizations such as Defenders of Wildlife have compensation programs in place. For those who can stomach it, check out Kill ALL the Wolves on Facebook, currently at 57 likes, with tips on trap-setting and enough graphic photographs to keep even the most rabid wolf-hater happy. The cultural bias of these voices looks remarkably similar to the same vapid pre-Renaissance rhetoric of medieval bestiaries: wolves can strike a man dumb with their gaze, a horse stepping in wolf prints would go lame, wolf-bitten meat is poisonous and if a pregnant woman ate such meat her child would have teeth scars in its flesh.

Perhaps it's time to listen to science. Pick up something by Rolf O. Peterson or L. David Mech. Having a top predator in ecosystems, sometimes called keystone species, plays toward a balanced ecology. Since the reintroduction of wolves in Yellowstone, forests are recovering: deer and elk that enjoy eating small trees move into deeper cover so saplings have time to grow. Recent studies also show that wolves are helping Yellowstone's grizzlies, as well, by preventing other species from eating berries which are vital for bear hibernation. Herds pressured by wolves are healthier as the young, infirm, and ill are culled. As much as hunters' groups like to say so, wolves do not have a negative impact on deer and elk populations—if anything they are a benefit. In Minnesota, a disease moving through deer herds might be spreading more quickly because the 150,000 to 200,000 animals taken each year by hunters are the ones in prime condition, leaving weaker ones remaining to get and pass on the disease, potentially to cattle, which would lead to trophic dispersion which could ultimately affect us. A new documentary *Lords of Nature: Life in a Land of Predators* effectively demonstrates the value of keeping wolves and other four-legged hunters in the wild where they belong.

The quote that begins this blog is from a well-known early 20th century naturalist. Most of his experience with wolves came from those in cages, as he ran the New York Zoological Park. He was a contemporary of Frederick Jackson Turner, whose 1893 paper at the Chicago World Fair claimed the American frontier closed. But the frontier is not closed: with the Wilderness Act of 1964 and Endangered Species Act of 1973 we reopened it, and those who care about our wild heritage have the chance to correct the wrongs our ancestors committed. With all the work that has been done over the past century to put these animals back on the land, individual states should not be allowed to cull wolves just because they fear them. Take action: organizations around the United States that fight for wolves need our help. Choose one or several or all and get involved. The lands these animals freely roam belong to all Americans. Before we set about another extermination pogrom, perhaps we should look at an example our wilderness-hating Puritanical founders could have chosen: St. Francis and the Wolf of Gubbio, enlightened co-existence, a *Pax Lupus* we could be a lot prouder of than a picture of something so vital and essential in the crosshairs.

Bibliography

Askins, Renee. *Shadow Mountain: A Memoir of Wolves, a Woman, and the Wild*. New York: Anchor Books, 2002.

Bass, Rick. *The Ninemile Wolves*. Livingstone, Montana: Clark City Press, 1992.

Leopold, Aldo. *A Sand County Almanac*. New York: Oxford, 1949.

Lopez, Barry Holstun. *Of Wolves and Men*. New York: Simon & Schuster, 1978.

Mech, David L. and Luigi Boitani, eds. *Wolves: Behavior, Ecology, and Conservation*. Chicago: The University of Chicago Press, 2003.

Peterson, Rolf O. *The Wolves of Isle Royale: A Broken Balance*. Minocque, Wisconsin: Willow Creek Press, 1995.

Stolzenburg, William. *Where the Wild Things Were*. New York: Bloomsbury, 2008.

SARAH HUANG
A STUDY IN CANINE CRANIAL MORPHOLOGY: WOLF PORTRAIT & A STUDY IN CANINE CRANIAL MORPHOLOGY: SKULL OVERLAY

Bio

Sarah is currently a Painting major at Florida Atlantic University in Boca Raton, Florida. When she is not supporting Wolfwatcher, she enjoys drawing everything she sees, adventuring, practicing martial arts, video games, and spending time with friends. Personal interests include taking as many photos as possible of her dog, Neo.

A Study in Canine Cranial Morphology: Wolf Portrait. Sarah
Huang. Graphite and ebony on Bristol vellum.

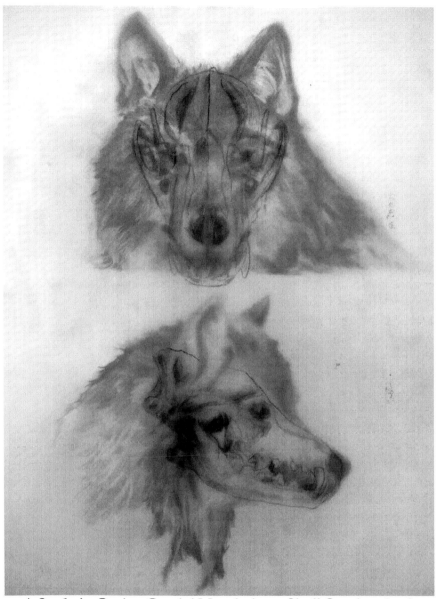

A Study in Canine Cranial Morphology: Skull Overlay. Sarah Huang. Graphite on drafting film.

MURRAY BROZINSKY
TWO FABLED WOLVES TELL THEIR TALES OF WOE

Bio

Murray is an entrepreneur, start-up company advisor, dad, open-water swimmer, passionate student of science, and author. His literary pieces been published by numerous journals, including: 3711 Atlantic, Ascent Aspirations, Brink, Business 2.0, Danse Macabre, decomP, Defenestration, Duck & Herring Pocket Field Guides, Laughter Loaf, Opium Magazine, Peeks & Valleys, Prose Toad, Rumble, Science Creative Quarterly, Shine Journal, The Big Jewel, Wired Magazine, Word Riot, Yankee Pot Roast, *and other wonderful literary magazines. Murray has undergraduate and graduate degrees in philosophy, economics, and engineering from the University of Pennsylvania and Northwestern University. He lives in San Francisco with his wife and 10-year-old daughter who is also crazy about wolves.*

The tales that follow the most despised of all the wolves in folklore and tell the stories anew…from their *points of view. This change in perspective gives them intelligence, wit, and, most of all, a sense of humor.*

"Sure, sure, I gobbled up the First Little Pig after I blew in his house of straw and the Second Little Pig after I blew in his house of sticks. But in no way did I fail to eat the third little piglet on account of his prescient decision to use a stronger building material, as is common lore. The moral folks draw from this story—that whatever you do, do it best you can; or don't cut corners; or some such thing—might be a fine lesson but false in this account.

You see, a wolf of my stature should easily be able to blow down a house of brick; especially one erected by swine with no special training in masonry. Truth is, I suffer from emphysema. I have been smoking ever since I was a teen wolf, running around with the wrong pack. Of course, we did not know how deleterious smoking could be to fable characters Once Upon a Time. The TV ad featuring the old she-wolf puffing a 'ciggy' through the tracheotomy hole in her throat was years off. Big Tobacco buried the evidence linking smoking to pulmonary disease and relentlessly targeted young pups like me as part of their 'Little *Canis lupus*' campaign.

Only much later did the Doc diagnose my emphysema, and I recently joined a pack-action lawsuit against Big Tobacco. But the damage is done, and it is irreversible. Time was when I was like the wind, howling as I blew a house in, and we ate bacon aplenty. Now I huff and I puff just to fill my lungs with enough air to blow in sticks and straw. The inhaler Doc gave me helps a bit, but it is only a temporary fix. This disease is progressive. To add insult to injury, my pork belly investments are going belly up as a result of the increasing pig supply. My days are numbered, but my dying wish is that my plight forces change in legislation regarding Big Tobacco. Unfortunately we are battling some serious pork-barrel politics in opposition."

—The Big, Sad Wolf

"You know the story: A wolf—that would be yours truly—found it difficult to get close to a flock of sheep. So one day he found the pelt of a sheep that had been flayed and put it on over his own skin. Donning his new clothes he joined the flock and through this deception was able to pinch some easy meals. The moral of my story— Appearances can be deceptive—is dead on.

However, owing to lazy readings and straight interpretations I have been unfairly labeled. More than that I have become a rallying cry to persecute others. To call someone A Wolf in Sheep's Clothing is to expose a bad person, someone who willfully deceives others for his own gain. Nothing could be further from the truth. I should be pitied, crying out as I did for acceptance. I tried to fit in with the pack. I lowered my head in the presence of the Alpha Male and tried to follow the complex social order that made no sense whatsoever. Deep down I felt different, and it was not deep down enough to go unnoticed. I was ridiculed by the others and ostracized.

I retreated to the solitude of the steppes—a Steppenwolf, if you will—to find myself. I came down one day for a walk and saw the flock of sheep. I felt drawn to them, identified with them, longed to be among them. That's when I came across the sheep's skin. I loved the feel of its soft texture on my fur, and my esteem shot up like a roman candle as I saw my reflection in the watering hole. I finally found myself, I thought. I was a sheep in wolf's clothing.

Unfortunately, life is cruel. Another biological imperative overrode my feelings for an instant; the next thing I knew I brought down a calf, and the flock fled from the cannibal among them. I am forever des-

tined to be outcast by wolf and sheep alike. They call me names—
Transpecies, Animal-bender, Cross-skinner, yet this is the way Nature
made me. It is not my choice, but who I am. Please believe me when I
tell you, I have tried to deceive no one."

—The Sheepish Wolf

MICHELLE KNOWLTON
GREAT MOTHER WOLF

Bio

Michelle Knowlton is a scientific curator who enjoys writing genre fiction from erotica to horror under the pen name Nikko Lee. Born in Canada, she moved to Maine after completing a Ph.D. in Zoology and her post-doctoral training. She resides with her husband and malamute, who both enjoy getting visitors whenever possible.

Here we find a creation myth told from a very interesting and unique perspective.

Eons ago, a pup was born from the dark inferno of chaos. Nurtured and cared for by the unseen, the pup's eyes were first opened by the light of a distant sun. It called to her in a language she could not yet understand. When she was strong enough, the pup left the safety of her den for the vast unknown.

On a trail of starlight, she traveled many lifetimes. The echo of a far-off world was her only playmate and companion. She learned to hunt. She learned to survive. She saw stars born and die. She learned the balance of the universe but not her place within it.

The song of the far-off sun sang to her of a blue-marbled world waiting for her. So the pup continued her journey through the galaxies and the voids between them until she came upon the spiral-arms from which her companion's voice rang out.

In the yellow-light embrace of her one true mate, the pup became a mother. Her first pups were small and looked nothing like her. Over millennia, she bore many pups in different shapes and forms until the seas swam with life and the lands crawled with green.

They grew so fast and reached out so far that they forgot the warmth of Great Mother Wolf's embrace and the sound of her silvery voice. When they became so numerous that she could no longer see them all, Great Mother Wolf took her place in the sky. Before she left, she gave birth to one last line of pups in her own image. Their lives echo the balance of life and death.

Ever watchful, Great Mother Wolf circles the earth along with her sun lover. Her voice still sings in the howls of her earth-bound pups.

ADRIAN LILLY
WOLF HOWL

Bio

Writing from America's North Coast, Adrian W. Lilly is the author of the novels The Devil You Know, Red Haze, The Wolf at His Door, The Wolf in His Arms, *and the collection of poetry,* Childhood and Other Traumas. *His short stories and poetry have been included in various publications, including* 69 Flavors of Paranoia, Hello Horror, Dead But Dreaming, Nervehouse, *and* The Weekly. *When not thinking of ways to scare people through writing and practical jokes, Adrian likes to hike, camp, and garden. Dedicated to Matt.*

your call rises up from your throat and slips past the full moon
of your lips. into the night, unanswered.

a backlit silhouette against the moon, a voice at once tremulous
and brave. your cry

is your own. your voice speaks for many. cascading
octaves, tones of hunt and lust and ecstasy
within a banshee wail of sorrow. you seek
companionship. hunted

without reason, you move in silence, a specter unseen, save
the echo of your voice.

I answer your call. and it echoes
through the valley, as I follow you through the dark corridor
from this life to the next
my footfalls are far behind, yet I will one day glimpse you
beyond the trees as you chase new prey. And I
will join you in the sport
as I did in this life. my companion, I am
still at your side, as I
feel you at mine.

CHELSEA DUB
FUN IN THE SNOW & HOWLING PRACTICE

Bio

Chelsea Dub is an artist from Indiana and is currently studying animation and painting at Ball State University. Being autistic and having learned to draw before she could speak, art was—and continues to be—both a mode of escapism and expression for her. She enjoys working with various media, including drawing, printmaking, painting, sculpture, digital photography, and computer graphics. Along with being an autistic self-advocate, she is vegan and often addresses issues such as human rights, animal rights, and environmental sustainability through her art. She also explores the relationships between neurodiversity and biodiversity, ableism and speciesism, and animal agriculture and the decimation of wildlife. Through visual media, she hopes to effectively communicate these ideas, and change society's perceptions of marginalized communities, including other animal species. Her art has been exhibited in the Cannon Tunnel in Washington, D.C., and in local art fairs and galleries. When not in Muncie, she lives in Noblesville with her family, including her rescued dog and three cats.

Fun in the Snow. Chelsea Dub. Oil on canvas.

Howling Practice. Chelsea Dub. Watercolor.

TIMOTHY BRUNO
LUPUS ARCANUS

Bio

Timothy Bruno is a former U.S. Army field artillery meteorologist. He currently resides in eastern Kentucky, and is a strong supporter of the Red Wolf Coalition. Dedicated to the International Wolf Center's Shadow and Malik.

They all begin with Birth
And end with Death.
What lies between, however,
Humans, for some reason, find mystical.

We build statues dedicated to them;
Tell wives' tales regarding their ferocity.
We jump and shiver at the sound of their howls
Or tremble when one is near.

Stories pass down from generation to generation
Of how one wolf attacked a village.
Another was a human transformed.
The full moon their friend
And silver bullets their mortal enemy.

Their fur is wanted for coats or rugs.
Their pictures hang from walls
Or plaster blankets, mugs, videos.
Others consider themselves one on the inside
A spirit trapped within a human body.

We make videos of them howling,
Or trying to eat humans.
Sometimes we show them
Befriending a lonely human

We keep them pinned up in parks
For us to see and wonder
What life would be in a wolf pack?
Would it be fun?
Dangerous?
Achieving?

Maybe one day we will
Have the chance to find out
Until then, all we can do
Is sit and think about
The Wolves.

Marla Fasano
Sainted Wolf 1 & Sainted Wolf 2

Bio

Marla Fasano creates modern, nature-based icons with animals as divinity. When she works with illuminated icons she is reminded that nature is unpredictably wild, yet always present. She begins a piece of work by cutting panels of wood, sanding them, and applying gesso. She enjoys using traditional methods such as working on wood panels and gilding with gold leaf, much like a traditional religious icon painting. Her first layer is usually a pencil drawing that she then paints with oil paint. When the first layer is dry, she adds another layer of detail with walnut ink and finishes the piece by gilding with genuine gold leaf, which she finds adds a reflective and ever-changing aspect to her work depending on the time of day, the light, and the nuances of the room.

Her home in upstate New York is surrounded by rural farms and rolling mountains. There is a large parcel of woodland behind her home, and she often hears the yips of coyotes, the hoots of owls, and even the occasional bear wandering through the backyard.

Sainted Wolf 1. Marla Fasano. Oil and ink on wood panel with 12 white gold leaf.

Sainted Wolf 2. Marla Fasano. Oil and ink on wood panel with 12 white gold leaf.

SKY DIAMOND
STORM

Bio

After reading The Twilight Saga *in 2009, Australian author Sky Diamond began writing and reading at age fifteen. From reading the saga, it became evident what her true passion in life was meant to be—writing. She became well-known through writing fanfiction for* The Twilight Saga *over several websites.*

Her Christmas story, "An Aussie Christmas," was accepted into Firefly and Wisp Publishing's the anthology, A Home for the Holidays. *The following year, Sky's short story, "The Angel I Belong To," about a mysterious EMT and a troubled young girl, was accepted by Write More Publications in their spiritual anthology,* Angels Among Us. *The anthology has since become an Amazon Best Seller. Then in 2013 Firefly and Wisp Publishing accepted, "Curse of the Witch," into their bewitching anthology,* Thirteen.

In the past year, Sky has studied Creative, Short Story and Romance Writing with OpenColleges, and is now in the process of self-publishing her paranormal romance, Ghost Wolf.

Here a young girl discovers inner strength through protecting wolves from an animal-hating father. When the tumultuous forces above tear at those she loves, she will find her newfound strength tested in more ways than she could have imagined. The storm is coming.

Rain pelted against the earth. Lightning flashed violent streaks across the night sky cloaked with clouds. Thunder rumbled the atmosphere as gusts of wind forced their way through trees and their branches. They rocked to and fro as the wind ripped the branches bare of their fresh, springtime greenery.

Crystal lay in the center of her mattress, staring outside the window just above her bed. Lightning lit the dark room—the loft that had been an attic and remained to appear like an attic—as it flashed and flickered on the horizon of hills, lighting the lush green fields. The wind blew a ghastly, cold howl through the crack in the window.

The sound of the wind reminded her of the wolves she had often seen in the area, running wild and free as they should be. She longed to be like them—free and happy, with family and friends. That is, until her step-father killed them to be sold and made into coats for the rich.

She sighed at the thought. She couldn't really hate her step-father; he'd given her a home and continued to care for her after her mother's death. Though it wasn't much of a home, it was a roof over her head, clothes on her back, and food in her stomach. But what she did hate about Brian though, were his beliefs of hunting and killing animals for money, especially the wolves.

He despised the beautiful creatures, believed they were nothing but vermin, pests to dispose of. He loved hunting them, especially when he was double paid: from the farmer whose livestock would be spared from the animal and then again when selling the pelt.

As she had such young and steady hands, he made Crystal clean the pelts. He said it was a way for her to pay for the privileges of staying with him, and if she did a perfect job on the pelts, he would give her a quarter of the profit. She shook her head clear of the thoughts. She hated the jobs he gave her to do with his killings.

All she had to do was wait another two years, until she was eighteen, and then she'd inherit the money her parents had left her. Then, she'd be free. She could leave her step-father behind and find her own place in the world.

Crystal's eyes shifted from outside to the corner of the dusted windowsill, where a small brown spider was weaving a web to join to the other hundred webs that clung to the many cracks, corners, nooks, and crannies in the attic.

From the draft of the window, each time a gust of wind howled, dust and dust-bunnies crept a little farther along the floorboards as though they had a life force of their own. The wind changed direction, forcing the rain to hammer against the window. Something cold dripped on Crystal's long chocolate hair. As she levered her head to the ceiling, a drop of water hit her cheek.

Sighing, she slid from under the warm blankets, and dressed into a coat and jeans. From under her bed, she produced her gray ugg boots and pulled their fluffy helms above her knees. She bent further under the bed and found the old rusting cook pot. She placed the pot on her bed, under the leak in the roof.

While padding across the attic, her boots left their print over the dusty floorboards. She stepped down the steep wooden stairs leading to the hallway.

The hallway didn't look much different from the attic. Most of the house looked much like the attic—old, dusty, and cold. The floorboards beneath Crystal's feet howled as the wind blew beneath them. She wrapped her arms around herself.

The narrow hall led into the lounge-room where the room opened into a wide, open space. Cream carpet covered the wooden floorboards beneath its seams. The walls were cream, like the rest of the house. In front of her was a wide window with a large windowsill-bed below it. Pink cushions sat in each corner of the bed. Apricot curtains hugged the window that faced the dark front yard. On Crystal's right was a fireplace. White lounge chairs surrounded the dying, rich orange, and red flame.

This room held memories of her mother, Libby. Crystal felt closest to her here, because her mother had decorated the place with what little money Brian had at the time, just for her daughter. Libby had wanted to give Crystal something for her daughter to remember her by. The warmth of the room alone made Crystal think of her mother, because it was so cozy—just like a mother's hugs.

Crystal crossed the room to the windowsill-bed, where she lowered her weight to the soft mattress. She stripped off her coat and left on her top, woolen jumper, and jeans. She laid the faux coat over her legs and body before turning toward the window where she stared out at the dark sky. Lightning lit the clouds. The intensity of the electric bolts outlined each and every individual line and shape of the thick blanket covering the night sky.

Crystal's eyelids began to weigh heavy as they eased closed. White and gray colors swirled and passed over her closed lids before forming actual colored pictures.

Icy wind whipped and whistled through the atmosphere. Paws hammered against the white blanketed earth, leaving large paw prints in her trail. Crystal lifted her head to the icy flakes fluttering to earth and released a piercing howl. The wind carried the sound of two more howls back to her.

Her ears pricked forward. She took off, howling as she raced in the direction of the howls—free—with the wind blowing through her toasty pelt. She leaped over a small, frozen river and rocks. She left her worries behind as she raced forward; clueless to what was in front of her or what was behind her. All she had was now. There was no past, no future, and no how in a wolf's life. They didn't question things—what they'd do tomorrow or think what they did yesterday. They lived for now, and the current weather helped to make it so. The wind and ice made it impossible to see any farther than three feet ahead. Crystal didn't know where the wolves were or how she was going to find them; she just knew she was going to find them. She had to find them, to secure her own safety.

The sound of the welcoming howls grew louder before two wolves appeared up ahead. One a dark gray and the other, white. But as the wind strengthened and the ice blew thicker, they disappeared as though she had been drawn back from her hopes and dreams.

Then, a shotgun went off. A howl of pain ripped through the atmosphere. Crystal jumped around to see Brian standing behind her with his long, deadly hunting gun in hand.

"Choose them, and you'll lose everything," his voice echoed.

Crystal gasped awake haven dreamed that exact same dream for the seventh night in a row. Her heart raced inside her chest. Her breath caught in the back of her throat. A moment later she heard exactly what she had in her dream—the piecing sound of a howl of pain.

Not again... she thought, shaking her head. Brian had yet again killed another innocent animal.

She jumped forward with her coat in hand, wrenching her arms through its sleeves and pulled on its hood. She hoped to God the wolf had just been caught in a trap instead. At least that way there was some hope she could release the animal before Brian found it.

Racing from the lounge room, Crystal snatched the flashlight from beside the door as she flew outside and down the stairs of the old wooden verandah. Lightning lit the front yard. Thunder cracked like a whip. After being inside, the violent weather seemed deafening as she kept her head down. Rain hailed against the coat's fabric. Crystal had never been so grateful that the coat was waterproof.

To her left, a small shed sheltered her car from the weather. Farther down, in a straight line stood several old and unused feed bins. Beyond the bins was a wooden gate that led out onto the road. Lightning reflected in the silver metal of the feed bins as headlights traveling along the road caught Crystal's attention. The light of the lightning revealed Brian's blue truck coming up the road.

Ahead, Crystal could hear a low whimpering howl being carried by the wind. She held her coat close to her body and forced herself forward, against the wind's force. She kept the flashlight low in hope her step-father wouldn't notice. If he saw the light, he'd come home to investigate.

The rain soaked her skin, almost having her hand frozen in place around the base of the flashlight. Crystal's jeans clung to the skin of her legs as they shivered under her, threatening to give out at any minute if she wasn't careful.

Numbly, she climbed the wooden fence and looked back over her shoulder to see her step-father's vehicle pass the gate that would have led him into the house yard. Once he was out of sight behind her, she elevated the flashlight to see farther up the grassy field, toward the low whimpering howl. She passed the glow of the flashlight over the field. The howling stopped the farther out the light shone.

Crystal gasped upon finding a patch of grass that had been pressed down by a large gray-russet wolf, lying on its side, bleeding from the chest. She waited for the animal's blood-stained creamy chest to rise. But the wait was futile.

She stiffly jumped from the fence and raced toward the animal, only to be stopped in her tracks when a little scruffy gray-brown pelted wolf raced from around the bigger wolf and began snarling. Greenish-yellow eyes stared back at Crystal. She lowered the flashlight, noticing cream fur splashed his chest, front legs, and lower body.

The pup lowered his body. His lips pulled back. His little white teeth glistened in the brightness of the flashlight.

The girl lowered her light farther onto the little wolf to see that on the side of his shoulder, a small fleck of cream fur formed a heart. He stepped back, still growling though not acting on his threat.

Crystal leaned forward and touched the larger wolf, feeling all heat had left her body. Her lower body and front legs were also splashed with cream fur. In the center of her left shoulder, her cream fur also formed a heart. Crystal's fingers touched the wolf's neck. Crystal exhaled a held breath and looked to the pup, no longer growling as he stood beside his evident mother, staring between the two females of different species.

"C'mon," Crystal breathed, sadly, "we're both loners now."

The pup's lips pulled back again as she gently picked him up by the scuff. Gray and russet fur stretched over the upper half of his body. The cream fur was a real contrast against the darker.

The pup whimpered in evident defeat as he was placed inside her coat. Hearing the subtle beat of Crystal's heart and the warmth of her body, he curled into her before continuing to howl.

"Shh you have to be quiet," Crystal cooed as she stood with her hand around the pup. He wiggled and squirmed inside her coat as she clasped a thick clump of grass from the earth and laid it over his mother in hope Brian wouldn't find her until it was too late to use her pelt.

She looked down at the innocent pup, snuggling into her, that'd surely suffer a slow death without his pack or mother. It angered Crystal that he believed this was right. "It's our God-given right to hunt animals, "Brian had stated every single time she questioned him. She agreed to a point, but not when the animal was already endangered and needed on this earth to keep the balance of life. It was hard to protest with him, especially when he drilled it into her that the wolves were beasts that'd kill any human they spotted without a second thought. Crystal knew it wasn't true, but she also knew it was pointless to try and talk him into believing anything he didn't wish to know.

Crystal had studied wolves for years and knew wolves only attacked when provoked. And further proof to her studies was in her arms, drifting to sleep beside her chest as every now and then, tiny howls escaped the orphaned wolf.

The rain eased to a drizzle, and the wind dropped. The storm was passing though still lingered on the near horizon as flashes of lightning and grumbles of thunder were still present.

Crystal turned toward the house and ran into the building's direction as headlights flashed over the field. She knew what this would mean—it was Brian or the wolf pup. But she had had enough of him and his cruelty.

The thought of running away, underage and with little money, scared her. But she knew it was the best. For both of them. They would find some way to live.

As she raced inside, the warmth of the lounge room greeted her. Crystal craved the warmth and the thought of watching the fire's flames die out after getting so wet and cold, but she couldn't. She couldn't stay. If Brian caught her with a wolf inside his house, there'd be little glance he would let them both live. He'd take the pup from her and do away with it. The mere thought of anyone harming the innocent sleeping pup in her arms brought a tear to her eye.

She left the temptation of the lounge room behind and quickly entered the kitchen. From the microwave, she found a small bag of warm mincemeat and ripped it open for the pup. Smelling the scent, he perked his head out of her coat and leaned down to lick at the mushy meat inside the bag while Crystal supported the bag on her leg while holding the pup back from jumping down. She smiled watching him down the meatball proportion. Once it was gone, the pup licked his lips as Crystal flew up the stairs to her room. She couldn't afford to lose any more time.

Standing before her closet, Crystal stared at herself in the mirror of the wooden door. Her chocolate brown hair was hidden inside the hood of the coat. Her gray eyes were wide with adrenaline and glistened with tears. She pursed her plump, pink lips together as she threw open the doors of her closet and found her new black and pink school bag, that had been waiting to be used next week when school resumed.

With one hand still around the now sleeping pup, now sleeping against her chest, Crystal awkwardly took out her clothes, jackets and shoes before stuffing them inside the bag while holding it open between her legs. She collected her precious wolf books her mother had given her for her sixth birthday and grabbed the piggybank that contained all her savings. On top of the already large pile of items, she rolled up the thickest blanket she owned. She crossed the room to her nightstand and opened a drawer. Inside the drawer was a pair of keys. They had been her mother's final gift to Crystal, for when she wished to move out and live alone. Hesitantly, she reached down and pulled the cold metal into her palm. Memories came flushing back:

"Mom?" Crystal called from the doorway of her mother's hospital room. Sun shone through the floor to ceiling window. A dull apricot curtain was partially pulled around the bed.

"Come in baby," she whispered, smiling.

"You wanted to give me something?" Crystal murmured as she crossed the room to the bed. Tears streamed down her cheeks with seeing a noticeable difference in her mother overnight.

Her mother leaned over to reach into the nightstand drawer beside her bed before sitting back in the center of the bed as she coughed. She smiled upon her daughter as her hand brushed the tears away and ran the length of her cheek.

"Open your hand Crystal."

She nodded and did so. Her mom placed something icy cold in her palm and closed her fingers around it. Crystal withdrew her hand from her mother and looked down at the keys. She tilted her head to the side.

"For when you wish to move out baby and make all your dreams come true."

She breathed in a deep, jagged breath and gripped the keys in the palm of her hand. It had been like Libby had known what was in store for her daughter's future, her destiny. Everything from the past—from Brian paying her for doing a good job on the pelts, as much as she hated the thought, to her mother giving her the wolf books at such a young age and then keys to her old house—everything seemed like it had been placed perfectly in order, leading up to this day. That alone increased Crystal's beliefs that she was meant to do this. She was meant to save the wolf and live out her goal, her dream, of raising the awareness that wolves weren't the vermin they had been known to be.

Placing the keys inside the bag, she zipped it closed and threw its weight over her shoulder as the front door slammed shut. Her heart leaped in panic.

There was no way out of the attic apart from the window that was too far from the ground to jump. She'd have to pass through the lounge room or sneak through the kitchen, but first, she had to get out of the attic before Brian came to check on her.

Crystal quietly but quickly raced down the stairs, two at a time. Sensing the increase in her heartbeats, the pup woke and began howling just as Crystal got to the last step and came face-to-face with Brian. His black-bearded, dry, wrinkled face hardened, and his green eyes narrowed the instant he heard the howl.

He ripped the side of her coat open n to see her holding the pup. "What the hell do you think you're doing?" he snapped.

Her eyes welled with tears as she stared into the cruel-eyed monster that stood before her. "I'm standing up for what I believe in!" she cried. "You," she snapped, pressing her finger into his chest, "are the monster. Not this." She looked to the pup. "This is innocence. You're the dirt of mankind! You are what is wrong with this world."

Crystal shoved past Brian and ran down the hall as he stood gobsmacked by what she had said. His step-daughter had normally been a quiet girl, who did what she was told without question and never spoke much or said what she thought. She had the odd comment or protest against what he did for a living, but apart from that, that was all he heard from her.

The door slammed shut behind her. Brian followed.

Crystal was halfway down the front yard, on her way to the shed, when she heard her step-father yell, "If you choose that vermin, you'll lose everything, Crystal! Don't come crawling back when you're starving, hungry, and cold!"

Tears were streaming down her cheeks, and for what reason she didn't know. Maybe it had to do with the memories she was leaving behind. But by leaving, she had little to lose and everything to gain, even if she didn't see it that way right now. Crystal had been getting those dreams—where she ran off with a wolf pup and Brian yelling after her that by choosing the wolves she would lose everything—for a week, so it wasn't like she didn't know what she was getting herself into.

Lightning ripped through the sky above their heads and lit their surroundings like the light of day as Crystal slid into the front seat of her old white Ford car and locked the doors. The pup kept up his howl while she stroked her shaking hand over his thick coat, waiting for her breath to ease and her heart to calm. He fit perfectly in her arms.

"It's okay little guy," she cooed, wiping her eyes while glancing down at him as another lightning strike lit up the wolf's eyes. He yelped and ducked back into the cover of her jacket. A smile pulled at the edges of her mouth. "It's okay, Storm."

***

Two years later

Storm walked down the corridor of the hospital with his head and tail high, despite the fact he hated the metal muzzle the government had ordered he wear in public. He was a proud, social wolf that behaved more like a loving family dog due to his upbringing with Crystal, but he had his wild side too.

After Crystal had driven both Storm and herself thirty miles from her father's property, she turned right and traveled down an old, dumpy dirt road before finding her mother's old, country home with the rotting wooden gates. They stood already open, stretched out toward her like her mother's arms were open, awaiting for a hug.

Crystal smiled as she blankly stared out at the window screen. They had both once lived here, before Libby needed constant hospital care. Crystal glanced up to the sky, giving herself a moment before driving forward. The storm had long passed, but still a light breeze swayed the old trees that were planted on either side of the gate. Their leaves had yet to grow back. Storm whimpered awake and poked his head from under her coat. She brushed the feather-like softness that covered his tiny gray and brown ears as she drove forward.

The full moon and the headlights of her car now lit her way toward the one-story house she now had to call home. In what little light the car's headlights and the moon provided, the house looked like it had all those years ago—a simple white country home with a gray tilted roof.

Crystal used the key her mother had gifted her and unlocked the front door. She found the house almost as she had remembered it ten years ago. The only addition was a mass of dust coating the furniture and cobwebs occupying the corners of almost everything. Apart from that, everything had stayed pretty much the same. The walls were still papered in light-mauve-blue marble wallpaper that hadn't peeled even the slightest over the years. Under all the dust bunnies Crystal picked up on her way through the house, the carpet was still the cream color it had always been.

That night, with being unable to check for bugs and mostly spiders, Crystal stripped the mattress and used the blanket she had brought from Brian's house to make a bed for both her and Storm. The next morning, she woke to him yelping and howling. When she opened her eyes, she found a gray-brown wolf with a matching lower body pelt, much like Storm's, pawing and licking at the window. He was taller, older, than Storm, but not by much. He could have easily been a big brother for how their eyes—greenish-yellow—features—strong, powerful legs and large paws, and markings matched. He even owned the small white heart on the side of his shoulder.

Upon seeing the girl, the other wolf bolted for the shelter of the forest behind the house. But every now and then, he'd sneak back up to the window to see Storm.

After thinking and observing the two, once she was sure, Crystal opened the door for Storm to join the other wolf, while full well knowing it was likely she'd never see him again. He bounded outside and howled at the edge of the forest line. A second later the larger wolf appeared, and Storm disappeared with him.

Crystal sighed at the bittersweet moment before retreating back inside. She had work to do. It took her half the day to clean up the kitchen alone, and once done there, she went back to her bedroom to sort the blankets, bed, and pillows. It seemed the house had been vacant for so long, even the spiders had moved on. After sorting the two main rooms, she headed into town and bought some food. All the while she dusted, cleaned, and shopped, her mind was on Storm.

Upon saving him, she hadn't thought how she'd care for him. Going by her studies, she guessed him to be about ten weeks old, when he'd need to be fed by the other wolves from their kill. The only way she could care for him is if she mashed the meat up into a gooey constancy—like the mincemeat last night—but then, he'd never be taught how to hunt. Crystal signed at the checkout, realizing she had been in over her head to begin with.

On the drive home, she thought back to all the times she had seen wolves around her mother's house, in the forest and around that area when she was little. Her mother often photographed them as they raced out of the forest once in a while after a rabbit or deer. Libby's house was so secluded, they both often wondered if the wolves even realized they lived there with the animals. But of course they would—they would smell their scents there, surely.

But when she got home, the headlights shone on a small brown and gray pup, curled into a ball at the front door, asleep. Tears of joy came to Crystal's eyes as she stared at the pup. *Maybe this will work after all*, she thought.

The very next morning, the older wolf came back, and the day before repeated itself. While Storm was away, Crystal went back into town and explained herself to a park ranger, Rick.

At first Rick wanted the pup to be brought in immediately, but then Crystal told him what she had risked and that another wolf had found him. The ranger took sympathy on her and kept in contact while keeping a watchful eye on the pup. Rick had been worried Storm would be rejected by others with having a fresh human scent on him, but none of the wolves seemed to have been bothered by it. Maybe they knew that this human was different?

Through the past two years, Rick and Crystal worked together to make sure Storm was happy living with the other wolves also while being with Crystal. They also came up with a plan to raise awareness about wolves and how important they were to the ecosystem. Crystal often got paid to take Storm into schools and hospitals not only to raise further awareness but to also brighten the day of students and patients. Everyone loved him, and he loved everyone.

"Good-afternoon, Crystal," a nurse with long, dark brunette hair said with a smile as she passed them in the hospital's corridor.

"Afternoon Ms. Roselyn," Crystal said and smiled before being halted to a stop as Storm paused between the two women and made the sound of "Arrarr," as if to say, 'what about me?'

"And good afternoon to you too Storm." The nurse laughed and petted him. Storm raised his paw to his face, like he was wiping away a tear which earned him another round of laughs. He howled out in pleasure of the sound and stood.

"Bye you two," Ms. Roselyn said with a smile.

Storm pulled up the corridor like he knew exactly where he was going. "Storm will you wait up?" Crystal complained as the wolf turned into a room where a teenage boy with black shaggy hair lay back in bed watching TV. A green cast was wrapped around his left arm as it rested on his chest in a sling. He perked up and turned his head as he smiled seeing the wolf.

"Storm, not here," Crystal stated, trying to pull him from the room. "I'm sorry, he never does this."

A smile pulled at the edges of the boy's plump mouth. "He's fine.

Storm right?"

"Yeah, how'd you know?"

"He's kind of famous."

"So I guess I don't need to tell you what an amazing animal the wolf is?"

"Nah. My mom was Native American, so there's no need to convince me how incredible animals are."

"Was?" Crystal tilted her head to the side. "I'm sorry, I shouldn't have asked. I'm not exactly used to being around people." And it was true. Crystal spent most of her time with Storm or alone in her house.

He shrugged his good shoulder. "She gave me up for adoption. First time I seen her was last year, and she doesn't want anything to do with me." He smiled. "Forget it. It's a common question."

He stared at the wolf without making eye contact. Crystal tilted her head to the side when the atmosphere thickened as Storm looked over to the boy, having eventually sensed his gaze. It was like a connection, a bond, had formed between the two.

"Can I pet him?"

"Sure." Crystal stepped forward. Storm sat beside by the bedside. The boy leaned over to the side of the bed and ran his hand over the wolf's chest and back. Storm bent his head back, loving the attention.

"He likes you," she murmured, lowering her weight to the blue material of the guest chair, smiling while watching them.

The boy glanced up at Crystal. His eyes shimmered a dark brown, almost molten black color as his mouth formed into a crooked smirk. "I think he likes everyone. I'm Kyson, by the way. Just call me Kai."

"Well you have that right, but, there's something different between you two. I'm Crystal."

"Pretty name, but I already knew it."

Crystal's heart flickered and her cheeks reddened as she tried to hide the smile dawning on her face. "My mom named me. How do you know us so well?"

He tilted his head to the side. "Do you not watch TV, read the newspaper, magazines, or go online?"

"Um, no..." she said awkwardly, suddenly feeling out of the loop. "What do they say?

"Just how you saved Storm, took him in, and are now raising awareness. That is amazing alone Crystal. What do your parents think?"

She sighed. Obviously the media didn't know everything nor told the whole story. Crystal had always tried to keep most of her life a secret, and clearly she had achieved that, but if that's all they said, they made her life sound so simple and easy, when really, it was anything but.

Tears were streaking her cheeks, having not thought about her mother in the time she had looked after Storm. He and his care had been a full time program.

"Hey, are you okay?" Kyson asked. The warmth of his hand embraced her own. His tanned skin was a contrast against her own paleness. After realizing what he had instinctively done, he withdrew his hand back.

She nodded and pulled her hand away to wipe away the tears as she forced a smile. Storm turned away from Kyson and laid his head on Crystal's knee. He whimpered a small howl. She ran her hand through his thick russet-gray pelt.

"Yeah I'm sorry." She shook her head. "My parents died. My father was a soldier and died before I was born, and my mom had Cystic Fibrosis."

"Oh, wow. That sucks. I'm sorry." Kyson sat back in the bed and remained silent for a moment, absorbing the information. "But don't you have a step-parent or guardian or something?"

She nodded, still petting Storm. "My step-father was my guardian, before he shot Storm's mother. He hated wolves. He hunted them, got me to skin them, and then sold the pelts. The night I found Storm, I ran to the house Mom had left me." She took in a shaky breath. "It's strange through..." she trailed off, wiping away more tears. Kyson looked at her. "It's like everything was set in place for me to do what I have done."

"What do you mean? Go on," he encouraged.

"Well, I always loved wolves, and my mom was a hippie at heart." She laughed through glazed eyes. "For my sixth birthday, she gave me heaps of wolf books, on their pack life, behavior, hunting, breeding, living habits, everything to do with them. Then when she was dying, she gave me the keys to her old house—I mean why not leave it to me in the will like the money she and dad had left me? And then after she died, Brian, my step father, got me to skin his killings and gave me a quarter of the money he'd make. I hated the job, but through that alone, I had enough money to live without a job until the past year. It's like everything has been put in place for me to live this life, before I had even realized this was my dream—to raise awareness about wolves and how they're not such cruel creatures everyone makes them out to be. Do you know what I mean, or do I sound like some crazy, lonely kid?" She chuckled while turning her head toward Kyson.

"I am a huge believer in destiny, and with what you've just said, I think you're right. You're in the path you're meant to be on Crystal. Both of you." He smiled, looking down to Storm, who lifted his head toward Kyson like his name had been spoken.

Through the years, Storm's coat had lightened and changed. More creamy fur now flecked through his pelt than brown. His ears had grown fluffier. Their backs were still russet but dark gray fur lined their insides. Light brown fur now flanked his sides and the marking that had been identical to his mother, had grown but was cut in half like a broken heart by his gray fur. His eyes were still greenish-yellow but now they were more yellow.

"Ugh, enough about me," Crystal sniffed after a moment, drying the tears. "What about you Kai? Why are you in here? What happened to your arm?"

He shrugged both shoulders and winced. His free hand lightly gripped the middle of the cast. "I gotta get used to that," he mumbled to himself. "Car crash. My uh… foster parents were killed."

Crystal's mouth parted to speak her sincerity when Kai lifted his hand in protest. "Forget it, Crystal. They were just after the money. I didn't mean anything to them, and they didn't mean anything to me. At least now I'm a legal adult, and I don't ever have to see the walls of the agency again."

"I thought you said you were adopted?" she breathed.

"I was, until at the age of ten, when I was deemed a Satan worshipper for believing in the Native American spirits."

Crystal raised a brow.

"They were deeply religious and scared of any other belief but their own." He smirked. "I was happy to see the backs of their heads."

"That bad huh?"

"There's nothing worse than having another belief pushed on to you when you've already found one—daily mass, Sunday school, oh and the exorcisms." Kyson waved his hand like it was no big deal. Crystal stared at him, wide eyed. "Joking."

She laughed, feeling her cheeks redden again. She wondered what caused the feeling of her cheeks suddenly feeling hot. They had never done that before.

"But now at the age of eighteen, I'm free. I'm being discharged to-night."

"Then what will you do?"

"For tonight, probably stay at a hotel, tomorrow, search for somewhere to stay, maybe get a job, and stay around here for a while. I think I like this little town." He held her gaze while speaking.

Her face lit up pink as she looked away. Her heart flickered and skipped another beat. Her hand rose to her chest in wonder of all these new feelings. Butterflies were fluttering inside her stomach.

"Well," she started hesitantly, hoping she wasn't about to make a mistake, "I'm looking for a housemate now that *someone* is disappearing more often, for longer periods." Storm looked up at Crystal, knowing he was being spoken about and howled. Both Crystal and Kyson laughed.

"He might be searching for a girlfriend," Kyson suggested, smirking, but Crystal didn't notice as she shrugged.

"If he is, that's fine, long as she doesn't take him completely away from me … And, anyway, it'd be nice to have the company of a human for a change."

"All right, tell me where to find you," Kyson said, smiling so wide his eyes were sparkling.

***

Crystal jumped awake to the sound of Storm's doggy door flapping in the sudden gusts of wind outside. She sighed and turned over to see if the wolf still lay in his bed that was pressed against the wall. But it was empty, and Crystal came to realize that he had been absent for a long time as she swept her hand over his blankets to feel they were cold.

"Where are you Storm?" she whispered, looking back over to her alarm clock sitting on the nightstand to see it was 3AM.

Outside, the wind whipped and howled through the night. It was at times like this Crystal wished she had some kind of real connection to the outside world, just to see if there was a storm or tornado watch. Lightning flashed through the window.

The doggy door bashed louder as the wind strengthened. Crystal groaned and flung her legs over the side of the bed. To her surprise it was a warm night. She walked down the narrow hallway to the front door and opened it.

"Storm? C'mon! It's time to come inside," she yelled, looking left and right in wait of seeing him come bounding around the corner, having come from the forest at the back of her mother's house.

But he didn't come.

"Storm?" Crystal yelled again while wrapping her arms around herself. "Where is he?" she mumbled.

He always came or howled when called. Fear and worry gripped her nerves as she waited for Storm inside the door. When he didn't appear after ten minutes, she called his name again. *Maybe he's too far away to hear me*, she thought, biting down on her lip. *No, he's never done this before. Something is wrong. Wolves can hear up to six miles away.*

In the short two years she had known Storm, she knew this was out of character, and maybe if there wasn't such a server storm brewing outside she wouldn't be as worried, but she had to find him.

Crystal headed back inside and up the hall to the phone sitting on a coffee table against the wall. She dialed in Kyson's cell number he had given her at the hospital, and waited. On the final ring before the line would go to either voice mail or drop out, he answered. Sleep coated his voice.

"Crystal? What time is it?" he yawned.

"I'm sorry for ringing, but I-I ... Storm's missing, and I don't know what to do. He's not coming when I call him—and he always does or howls out to me—and there's a serious storm coming. I'm worried he's been hurt or something."

The line fell silent for a moment. "Kyson?"

"Yeah, I'm here, just looking up the weather. Can you pick me up?"

***

"I'm sorry, it's probably nothing—"

Kyson cut her off. He raised his hand as he shook his head from side to side and turned on the car's engine. "But nothing Crystal," he said and glanced to the passenger seat. "It may be nothing, but we're finding out even if it takes us until dawn." Lightning flashed, showing her the silhouette of his face as she looked at him. The jagged lightning bolt reflected in his eyes.

She exhaled a deep breath she hadn't realized she had been holding and nodded. "Thank you Kai." Crystal stared at the horizon, trying not to allow her mind to take her away on a path of panic and worry. She had been grateful he offered to drive and that her car was an automatic so he could with his broken arm.

"We'll find him, and he'll be fine."

For a long silent moment, Crystal stared at the silhouette of Kyson's face, wondering how he cared so much for Storm to be out in this weather so late at night when he barely knew the wolf. But then she wondered: was he doing it for Storm, or both of them, or her? Relief washed over Crystal. For the first time in what felt like decades, she had someone who truly cared, who was there for her that also saw eye-to-eye with her when it came to wolves and Storm. Though she had only known the boy for a few hours, she could see that he understood, and he cared whether his care was just for her or Storm or both of them. She had someone to share the load with.

Crystal laid her head on Kyson's shoulder. Another flash of lightning revealed a smile pulling at the corners of his mouth.

Earlier, back at the hospital, Crystal had said to him to meet her at her mother's house the next morning. She had drawn him up a map on a serviette and left it with him. As the house approached, Crystal sat up straight until they bypassed the turn off to the house. She looked back at the house disappearing in the taillights.

"Where are we going?" she asked.

"I heard some hunters talking about an old cliff where they saw a pack a few days ago, so I thought it'd be best to check there first."

"*The* Old Cliff?" Crystal exclaimed.

"I guess so. Why?" Kyson glanced between her and the road.

"There's a grizzly bear that lives around there. It used to be a campsite before they marked it off-limits to the public."

"Then we'll just have to be careful."

Heavy drops of hail battered down against the Ford's windscreen as they drove into the storm while driving along the straight road. Lightning flicked every few seconds, lighting the sky purple as thunder rumbled in the atmosphere.

Kyson turned right and onto a dirt road after seeing an old rusting sign marked: *Old Cliff Park*. A thin, one-car dirt road led up through a thick forest of pine trees lining the roadside. The greenery was so thick it almost blotted out the heavy drops of rain. Kyson followed the road until it and the pine trees disappeared behind the car and opened up into a large campsite that could have been a mile long.

As they pulled up, the car faced the horizon of the storms and ocean. Lightning reflected in the choppy waves as they smashed against the cliffs opposite to them.

"Whoa," they gasped in unison.

"It's breath-taking," Crystal whispered.

Kyson's seatbelt snapped into place as he slid out of the driver's seat. "We have to be careful here. Lightning is more likely to strike higher up places."

Absently, Crystal nodded and sighed. She slid from the car and looked around. Outside, the rain was deafening loud.

"It doesn't look like anyone or anything has been here for weeks," she shouted, while blinking back the raindrops blurring her vision.

"Let's look around first." Kyson's dark hair was plastered to his skull. Unlike Crystal, he didn't wear a hooded jacket.

Crystal and Kyson wandered off in opposite directions. Lightning provided sudden bursts of light that gave the flashlights great competition until their surroundings rushed back into oblivion again. The rain eased to a patter.

"Storm?" Crystal yelled through cupped hands and waited. "There's nothing here," she announced and threw up her arms. She turned toward Kyson. He was leaning down, looking at something she couldn't see from the distance.

"Yeah, there is, just nothing fresh enough to be helpful," he sighed, standing straight after observing some old wolf prints. "Do you know where the pack is that he stays with or where he goes?"

He looked over to Crystal as lightning struck down from the sky. The bolts' intense brightness forced Kyson to look away and cover his face with his arm as he turned away. Crystal leaped from where she stood. Her scream was blotted out as the bolt sliced down the center of a dead pine tree that was sent to splinters.

Kyson lowered his arm a moment later. Lights flashed and flickered over his vision as his eyes quickly darted left and right in search of his friend. "Crystal?!"

"Kai! Help, I'm over the ledge!" she screamed, clinging to the earth of the ledge for dear life. She could see him bent down, hunched over until he turned around with hearing her voice. Crystal's fingers dug farther into the muddy earth that was slowly giving way. A slight edge held her footing, but it was crumbling under her weight.

"Crap!" Kai scrambled to his feet and ran to the other side of the campsite. He dropped to his stomach and winced as he pressed his weight on his broken arm.

Kyson clasped her wet wrist so he could slide his hand into hers. "Take my hand on three and I'll pull you—" But his wet hand slipped from around her wrist.

She shook her head. Tears glistened in her eyes. "You couldn't do it with one hand anyway. We'd both end up falling. We need a rope— someone else. "

His mind raced with useless thoughts. Kyson thought that maybe he could use the car to bring her up, but they still lacked rope. "I can't leave you."

"You have to," she whimpered. "My hands are going numb cold. I can't keep holding on. Please Kyson."

He groaned and pulled himself to his feet. "I'll be right back. I'll get help. You'll be okay Crystal. " He held her beautiful light gray eyes so she knew he meant every word. "I promise." He turned and ran back for the car. In another flash of distance lightning, he spotted a fence lining the ledge where it fell away without any warning. From where he stood, farther down, through the thickness of the pine trees, Kyson could see the vehicle's headlights disappear around the corner of the road where it bent around the mountain.

Kyson sprinted down the hill, making sure to keep close to the fence line so he wouldn't end up lost. He dragged out his cell phone from inside his jacket and dialed 911.

"911 what's your emergency?"

"A friend is gripping the ledge of The Old Cliff campsite. She can't hold on much longer."

"Is she injured sir?"

"I don't know. Maybe. I just need help," he panted.

"Help is on its way sir."

"Thank you." Kyson hung up before anything more could be said as he hit the roadside. His chest rose and fell in labored breaths. The headlights of a blue truck flashed from ahead. He ran into the center of the road and waved his arm above his head while yelling, "Help! I need some help!" The closer the truck came, the clearer he could see that a teenage boy about his age sat in the passenger seat as a black-bearded man drove.

"I need help, now."

***

"Help! Somebody please help me!" Crystal cried repeatedly in hope someone nearby would hear her. "Help"— she paused, seeing movement ahead of her. "Storm?" she whispered, but her heart leaped into her throat when a flash of lightning revealed something much larger and aggressive. A grizzly bear lurked farther back around the pine trees, not too far from her.

"Oh no... oh no." Crystal shook her head from side to side, momentarily forgetting where she was and what she clung to as she tried to duck further down the ledge in hope of somehow hiding when she scraped her leg on the ledge. "Ow!" She grimaced, catching the bear's attention. Its head rose to the sky and sniffed the air before turning, stepping forward in investigation.

In the short distance, echoes of howls covered the forest.

Sudden headlines of a blue truck drove up the dirt road and halted just behind the bear that turned in response to the vehicle. The truck reversed back before halting. A black bearded man emerged from the truck with a shotgun in hand. He pulled the trigger but nothing happened. The man swore—he'd forgotten to reload the gun. He fumbled around reaching for the cartridges from his back pocket as Kyson jumped from the back of the truck and ran for Crystal's side, distracting the bear from the man as he moved.

"You okay?" he asked, breathless.

"Apart from still stuck here, and almost bear chow, yeah... How'd you find my step-father?"

Kyson's eyes narrowed at Crystal. "What?" he groaned, hearing her worlds repeat inside his head. "He was driving along the road. Crystal if I had known—"

"Forget it, Kai. We have bigger problems."

He carefully watched the bear as it stepped forward and snarled. Kai's eyes went wide as a russet-gray wolf leaped from the roof of the blue truck followed by two others.

Brian spun around in time to see the wolves, fearlessly racing past him. "What the—"

"Storm!" Crystal cried as Storm leaped at the bear, biting its back leg and forcing the bear farther away. "Don't hurt him Brian! Please don't hurt him."

The other wolves worked with Storm as two more wolves joined in, snarling and snapping while forcing the bear back. Brian lowered his gun, no longer being threatened. He leaned back inside the truck and flung a long rope over his shoulder.

The bear snarled and swiped a paw at the wolves, pushing them back as he broke away from them and approached Brian. Storm darted forward to leap on the bear's back and bit into its throat. The bear roared and rolled with Storm as the other wolves snarled and attacked the bear. Brian remained clueless about his savior.

Crystal looked away, whimpering and crying in fear that Storm was hurt.

"He'll be okay Crystal," Kyson cooed, rubbing her hand as he gripped the back of it in case the earth gave out from under her.

Brian tied a rope around the nearest tree before tying it around himself. He backed toward the ledge.

"You got her?" he asked Kyson.

He nodded and tightened his grip. "Yeah."

Brian slipped his fingers under Crystal's hand and hauled her up over the ledge with the help of Kyson.

The wolves took chase of the bear retreating into the forest.

"Oh thank God," Crystal gasped as Kyson helped her to her feet. Their mouths met as she wrapped her arms tight around the boy's shoulders. In shock, Kyson hesitated before his warm, gentle lips moved against Crystal's in a tender and sweet kiss. He raised his hand to cup the side of her face. His hand was warm against her skin.

Her heart picked up its pace and skipped as the butterflies in her stomach came swarming back. Her icy cold cheeks warmed. It was then she realized what made her experience all these foreign sensations—there was a spark between her and Kai. She smiled against his lips. For once, she felt like a normal eighteen-year-old girl.

Surprised by her own actions, after a moment, Crystal pulled back and stared into Kyson's dark eyes with her own being wide as a deer's in the headlights of an oncoming car. Her cheeks flushed redder. Kyson smiled shyly, glancing to Brian and wrapped his good arm around her.

"You okay? You're shivering," he whispered

"Just scraped my knee—wait, where's Storm?"

Crystal turned. Her eyes darted left and right while standing in the hold of Kai's arm now around her, before she found Storm standing across the campsite on three legs as he held up his left bleeding paw.

Crystal burst into tears as the wolf came hobbling over. Brian tilted his head to the side as his step-daughter and Kyson gathered around the wolf and petted him over. Storm whimpered and leaned into their touch.

"Would have made a damn good pelt, that wolf," Brian commented.

"Don't you dare even think about it!" Crystal's wrapped her arms tightly around Storm's shoulders as she glared at her step-father with narrowed, tear-filled eyes. The wolf lowered himself into her lap, as though sensing she was cold as Kyson kept close.

A smirk pulled at the corner of Brian's mouth. "Kidding Crystal. I had to say something to make you look at me. That wolf risked his life for you."

"And you," the boy from the passenger seat said as he slid from inside the truck.

Brian turned into the boy's direction. "What are you saying?"

"That bear was going to have you," he clarified and nodded toward Storm. "If it wasn't for that wolf, he would have had you. Everyone online says so."

Brian and Kyson's eyes narrowed in question upon the boy with shaggy brown hair. "I filmed it on my phone. Already on Youtube— one thousand hits."

"Who are you?" Crystal asked.

"Nevell Kingsly. I work for Brian."

"Good work Nevell," Brian said as he walked over to the boy and petted his back.

Red and blue lights flashed as two large vehicles made their way down the dirt road and stopped behind Crystal's car and Brian's truck. Kyson stepped forward to talk to the firefighters getting quickly to work.

"She's already safe guys," he said as the paramedics came over with a large bag in hand. Crystal groaned—she had always hated being a center of attention, for any reason but talking about wolves. From the moment she had recused Storm, she hadn't realized it until now, but she had dedicated her life to saving them.

With hearing her groaned, Storm looked up at Crystal. She petted him and forced a smile. Dawn was setting in as the dark night hue lightened to light blue on the far horizon where the dark storm clouds were breaking. Purple lit the sky above them. Orange and pink high-lighted the light of mountains in the distance.

A male and female paramedic came rushing around Crystal's car before they halted, seeing the wolf lying on their patient's lap. The woman looked over to Brian, sitting back against the side of his truck, lighting a cigarette. His shotgun lay on the truck's hood, now unloaded.

"We need to get rid of this animal, sir," the woman said, looking over to Brian.

"I'm not leaving him," Crystal cried.

"He's keeping her warm," Kyson explained, staring the woman in the eye.

"We need to treat her," she replied impatiently.

"Let me take care of it," he said and made his way around the paramedics to her. Kyson bent down to Crystal's side and rubbed her shoulder. "I'll care for him. You trust me right?"

She nodded and wiped away the tears with the back of her hands.

"I'll take him back to your house and treat his leg. He'll be fine. C'mon, you're freezing."

"Thank you," she whispered, handing him the keys as he wrapped his arm around Crystal and eased her to her cold, numb feet as Storm stood with his front paw still levered and resting against his chest. The wolf sadly watched as Kyson took Crystal toward the white vehicle where the paramedics helped her onto the stretcher.

Kai leaned down and pressed a kiss to Crystal's forehead as he whispered, "Storm will be okay. I'll see you later or tomorrow."

She nodded. "Okay."

Storm howled as the blue truck followed the white down the road.

Finally, Kai turned toward Storm and petted his head. "C'mon, I'll take you home." Kyson smiled and unlocked Crystal's car. Storm hopped over, but jumped into the backseat where he settled on the floor.

***

The Next Morning

Kyson and Storm walked down the hospital's corridor before they turned into a room with a floor-to-ceiling window and blue curtains pulled around the bed. Crystal sat back in the middle of the bed, staring up at the TV until movement caught her eye. Her face lit up seeing Kyson and Storm at the door. She noticed the neat white bandage around the wolf's front leg. Storm pulled at the chain as he whined and howled.

"Well, come on. Don't stand there all day Kai!" Crystal shouted with a grin stretched across her face as she reached her arms out.

A smirk pulled at the edges of Kai's mouth as he was dragged across the room by the wolf. Once at the side of the bed, Storm jumped up and into Crystal's arms.

"Eh, Storm." Kyson scowled. The wolf howled at him, causing both teens to laugh.

Kyson lowered his weight to the side of the bed and leaned over the wolf to kiss Crystal as his arm wrapped around her neck. The wolf decided to join in and lick his master's cheek until she broke away from Kai and pushed Storm off the bed.

"Yuk! Storm!" Her cheeks reddened as she laughed and wiped her cheek with a tissue.

Kyson grinned, laughing. "I believe he's trying to claim you as his."

"After the trouble he caused, I'm lucky to still be alive, let alone for him to claim me."

Storm whimpered and lowered himself to the floor like he understood every word spoken.

"I think he's been a little preoccupied," Kyson whispered, looking down at the sulking wolf as he stood and began howling. Crystal's eyes narrowed as she glanced between the two of them.

"I think that was wolf for, 'I have a pack to guard now.'"

"Really?" Crystal's eyebrows shot up.

Kai nodded. "Yep, ten wolves came around the house last night after he began howling."

"So that's where he's been disappearing to..." she trailed off, thinking.

Kai piped up at the news he had heard on his way in. "Did you hear the good news?" He grinned.

"That I'm being discharged tonight and I only had stage one hypothermia?" She waved her shoulders from side to side as she leaned closer to Kyson.

Kai rolled his eyes. "Storm has saved wolves state-wide, because of Nevell's video. It will be illegal to hunt or kill wolves in this state. But here's the thing," Kyson paused and slowly took in a deep breath, "It depends on you setting Storm free."

"What? I-I can't do that."

"You have to, or the wolves won't be protected."

"I can't Kai..."

Kyson sighed and shook his head. He understood the point, but he also knew what she had to do for Storm and the other wolves statewide.

That night, after Crystal had been released and gone home, it was as though Storm knew what had been said—he knew what he needed to do. Through the night, Storm woke in his bed of cuddly, warm polar fleece blankets, and looked up to a sleeping Crystal. He rose to his strong paws and nudged her hand that hung over the side of the bed before leaving the room behind as he hesitantly snuck down the hall. He opened the door of the spare room, where Kyson slept in Crystal's old room. Storm gave a low howl that caused Kai to turn in his sleep as the wolf backed out of the door. He continued down the hall and through the doggy door.

Storm stepped down the wooden stairs leading into the front yard and made his way around the back of the house where the forest concealed his lands. He turned back toward the house where Crystal slept in her room and Kyson slept in his own. The wolf levered his head to where the moon shone down over the house. A low though deep howl echoed through the night before he turned again and for the cover of the forest.

The next morning, Storm made his decision known when he appeared outside the kitchen window with a pack of ten wolves, while Crystal and Kyson washed up after breakfast. Crystal had wondered if he had ran off for the night again, like he had the other stormy night, but she hadn't expected that'd be the last time she would see Storm.

***

Four Years Later

The day was warm and sunny with drifts of clouds blanketing the sky for short periods of time. Small storms and showers threatened the area with dark clouds looming on the horizon. Birds sang in the warm spring breeze.

Crystal opened the honey pine door with a basket of washing in her grip. A golden metal band wrapped around one of her left hand's fingers. Looking up and out into the lush green yard before her, she stopped mid-stride in shock.

Kyson was behind her, dressed in a dark navy uniform and a medical bag at his side. He turned and groaned.

He went to take the over-full washing-basket as he said, "Eh, the doctor told you, no heavy lifting—"

"Kai," Crystal murmured, cutting her husband off midsentence while nodding toward the front yard. "Look."

Kyson took the washing-basket and shifted his eyes from the side of her face. He followed her gaze to the front yard, where a small pack of four wolves were warily crossing the yard.

To anyone else, they would look like typical wolves: brown-gray pelts with cream fur stretching across their lower bodies and tails. But Crystal saw the wolves differently. She saw each of the markings. Where the fur flecked cream through the gray and where the brown mixed with the gray.

And then, one wolf walked up to meet the others. Crystal gasped, seeing the broken heart mark on the side of his shoulder, where gray fur had cut off the once full heart.

"Is it him?" Kai whispered, wrapping his arms around Crystal's shoulders.

She nodded, biting down on her lip in case he didn't remember her. "Storm?"

The wolf stopped mid-stride and snapped his head around to see the young woman standing in the doorway of her home. His ears stood up straight, alert and aware before he looked back to another gray wolf as she nudged him.

He stepped forward, wary, while taking small steps toward the woman, and the man standing behind her. Crystal bent down, offering her outstretched hand. Storm hesitantly sniffed the skin of the palm of Crystal's hand before tilting his head to the side and howled.

She and Kyson burst out laughing as Storm began wagging his tail and leaned into Crystal's side. His paws wrapped around her neck in a hug as Crystal ran her fingers through Storm's thick coat. Tears of happiness glinted in the corners of her eyes.

After a moment, Storm withdrew from Crystal and leaned into her side as he nudged the small bump in her stomach. He howled, and two little brown and gray wolf pups came running around the side of the house and went to the gray wolf's side. She petted their heads.

Kyson smiled, brushing the tuffs of fur over Storm's ears. "He remembers you," he whispered. "And he knows you're pregnant."

Crystal nodded and held Storm as Kai wrapped his arms around both of them. "All my dreams have come true," she murmured.

RICHARD LOPEZ
SHADOW EYES & MEXICAN GREY WOLF

Bio
Richard Lopez is a photographer residing in Vancouver, BC.

Shadow Eyes. Richard Lopez. Photograph.

Mexican Grey Wolf. Richard Lopez. Photograph.

ALEXANDER CLARK
THEY HUNT US TOO

Bio

Alexander Clark is a cross-genre writer of fiction and creative non-fiction living in central Pennsylvania. He is a student at Penn State studying English, philosophy, and art. When he isn't writing, he practices Pai Lum Kung Fu, herds cats, organically urban farms, and blacksmiths.

In 2011, Alexander received Second Place in Harrisburg Area Community College's student honors show for 3D Design. In 2014, he won the Penn State Harrisburg Outstanding Undergraduate Creative Writing Award and From the Fallout Shelter's Best Creative Non-Fiction Award.

Here is the story of a wolf who has had to eke out a living for itself in the world of man, under bright lights and tall buildings.

A meal. That's all I want. Something simple and uncomplicated and filling. Not too heavy. I'm not greedy. Something small. Something big would be too much for me anyway. I wouldn't be able to stop from gorging myself. If it's too heavy I'll be sick, then eating will have been a waste. It's been five days since I've eaten. I would give anything to eat.

I can't fall asleep on my own. My stomach hurts the whole time I'm awake, it throbs slowly, numbing down to an almost forgettable ache and sharpening to a thought shattering blindness. For sleep, I have to wait until fatigue knocks me out.

It's too busy to sleep here anyway, too many people come through this alley, drunk or angry or just mean. It isn't safe to stay here. The boxes aren't that comfortable anyway. They swept away all the leaves.

I usually don't mind the alleys or the hard ground or even the lights that never go out. Sometimes there are bins in alleys, and sometimes they'll have food. Lately there has been none. The cats and the rats and the squirrels get there first, they can camp and wait and hide in plain sight, they get there first and take everything, then disappear. Some even get to go inside to eat again and be fed deliberately. No one gives me hand-outs, and I'd be afraid to ask.

The cold isn't so bad in the city. I miss the trees and the streams, but there was no way to support myself at home. Cities keep getting bigger, and the rural areas keep moving farther out or disappearing. You have to come to the city if you want to make a living. There was supposed to be opportunity here, I thought. Decent, respectable work, meat with every meal. There had to be. That's what I had before. You can't take away a thousand livelihoods building into the country without replacing them with something in the city, right? There has to be some equivalency, or why do it?

There's another alley a block away that I sleep in sometimes. I don't like it but my legs are shaking, stiff. It's too cold, and I've eaten too little to go far. I need to sleep and to hope that tomorrow is warmer.

In the wind that causes my eyes to squint and tear, the city almost looks like home. With eyes nearly shut the street could be a stream, the sidewalk its shore. The shadows on buildings could be gaps in the trees; the lights could be the moon over every shoulder. The glint from the windows could be stars. There are even puddles in the street to trick my other senses.

I step in one and regret it. It's nearly frozen and all the fun of pretend goes away. I look to either side, and no one is watching. The water looks mucky and disgusting, a multicolor film ripples in and out from where I'd stepped. It smells worse than it looks. I'm so thirsty, and no one is watching. I drink what I can stomach, cough and gag, and drink more until I'm worried anything more than that will make me sick. I can't throw up, I can't afford to waste anything.

I try squinting again, but it's no fun anymore. The city isn't the woods, and no matter how hard I try I can't pretend it is. My foot is so cold I have to limp, so now my gait is loping and awkward. Frost's beginning to form, making my leg numb, every other step is a limp. I can't be seen, I look sick. Someone might put me away.

The alley is farther away than it should be. I'm walking very slowly. My stomach is squeezing so hard against my spine it's hard to breath, hard to walk. I'd eat anything. I wish I could eat. I wish I'd never come here. I miss my home. It's a pointless thing to miss, it's gone, and I'm here, and my memory of it is fading, and that's all that's left to say it even existed.

A rat runs across the sidewalk in front of me, but I'm too slow to start. He's there and gone, a fat, well-fed streak of brown. The alley is still ahead of me. My feet don't hurt anymore, they're nearly numb. The wind is biting past my coat, through my skin, into my bones. I feel hollow and crushed at the same time. All I am is the thin membrane between the exploding emptiness of my stomach and the squeezing bitter of the cold outside.

The alley is here, but it's too bright. The blinking orange lights of a detention van blind me. An open door from the warehouse spills more orange light as two smoking men watch the authorities setting up before they all turn and look at me. I'm too tired to run. I'm too slow to get away.

I'm sorry. I didn't want to be here. I won't stay. I'm sorry. I promise I'll be better, I'll hide better. You won't have to see me. I was hungry, but I'll go away again. I never wanted to be here, but you tore down my home. I don't blame you, but you have to understand, I had no place else to go. I thought I was supposed to come to the city, I thought that's where I was supposed to go after. There are no deer here, there's nothing to eat, there's no ground to burrow. I'm sorry.

"Good shot."

"Thanks. Big sucker, wasn't he? See how he was walking like that? How he was all off balance? That means he had rabies. Don't even need'a run a test. It's a good thing you guys called."

"Yeah, man, we come out here on our smoke breaks, and there's this freaking wolf. Like, what the hell, you know? I thought it was just a dog or something, maybe it'd go away if we made a lot of noise, but he's been coming back a lot. Why doesn't it stay on its own land, you know?"

"Ha, well he won't come back now. You guys have a good night."

"Yeah, man, you too."

EUNICE C. ENGLISH
A WOLF IN THE FOREST

Bio

Growing up in Scotland and England, Eunice spent 34 years in Australia after she married, where she was a member of Newcastle Poetry at the Pub. She returned to the UK to look after her elderly parents and now resides in Nottinghamshire (Robin Hood Country!).

Eunice's poems have featured in seven anthologies, plus magazines, newspapers, and online in her own blogs. The latest blog is called Eunis World 2014. *Her own anthology* Inspirations and Influences *is available as an e-book.*

He moves
between the trees
Sleek
as a shadow
Soft
as a breeze
His eyes
Looking
far ahead
His ears
Listening
all around
His senses
Tuned to listen
For the cracking twig
The smell of death
That warns him
Man is on the hunt
Again

KELLY WALFORD
"CALL OF THE WILD. THE MAGIC OF WOLVES.," "WHEN THE SNOW STICKS…THEY WILL COME.," & "THE WISE ONE"

Bio

Kelly Walford is an artist who resides in Taupo, New Zealand. Her passion is horses, and she tries to capture their beauty and character within her art. Recently she has started drawing wildlife, big cats, and wolves.

Call of the wild. The magic of wolves. Kelly Walford. Graphite with color pencil.

When the snow sticks…they will come. Kelly Walford. Color pencil. Photo reference permission Denis A. Jeanneret.

The Wise One. Kelly Walford. Graphite on bristol board. Photo reference permission Denis A. Jeanneret.

LINDA ROBERTSON
THE LOOKOUT PACK

Bio
Linda Robertson has lived in the Methow Valley, Washington for the past 28 years. Her work has been published in The Methow Naturalist, Methow-Grist, The Methow Out My Window, Fishtrap Anthologies, Visions of Verse, The Far Field, *and other publications and websites. She is currently an MFA Candidate at Chatham University, Pittsburgh. Her chapbook* Reply of Leaves *was published in 2002.*

Exiles or emigrants,
the breeding pair left their northern den
to enter a broad valley thick with grouse,
marmots and mule deer.

Wary strangers, they roamed above the sage-heavy hills,
prowled through stands of Ponderosa
and Lodgepole pine, thickets of wild rose—
toward the granite mountain they would be named for.

Beneath the craggy Sawtooth Range
the wolves settled the slopes like citizens,
raising two litters of pups
alongside generous spring-fed streams.

The packs' howls stalked the wind, pursued
the night birds five miles east
towards paddocks and pastures,
roan-coated heelers, sheep dogs, and ranchers.

The paths of wolves are purposeful.
Their broad four-toed prints as easy to read as pavers
impressed in the forest's loam.
They left their bone-scattered dens to silence.

(continued on next page)

Down valley, snares waited for the wolves.
Men waited too, those with an eye for clumps
of fur rubbed onto puzzle bark,
and apparent patterns of passage.

On the scree-covered slopes of the North Cascades
ravens know more than most—
two grey males remain.

JENNIFER SELZER & DANIEL HUBER
WATER COOLER WOLVES

Bio

Jennifer Selzer and Daniel Huber are a writing team based in Los Angeles, California. Together they have a sci-fi/fantasy series, Destiny's Kingdom, *as well as the upcoming Urban Thriller/Paranormal Romance,* 30 Silver, *which will be released later this year. In the works are several other novels, including one that will be heavily wolf-themed. They currently like to describe this story as* "The Jungle Book *meets* The Lovely Bones." *Though Jennifer and Daniel are both animal lovers, it is Jennifer who is particularly passionate about the survival of wolves in the wild and is an advocate of the return to their historic range.*

In this humorous flash fiction piece, a group of wolves meet to discuss the recent changes to their habitats and the struggles they now must face.

Snow still clung to the mountaintops in the distance, but down in the valley, the golden blooms of daffodils popped through the sun-kissed earth. The quiet newness of spring rustled and warbled on the dissipating fog that rose above the lake, whispered through the swaying cattails that sprung up in the water. A splash broke the peaceful calm of the glassy water; a beaver, surveying the newly melted landscape, surveying for trees and potential wayward currents.

From the north, giant, heavy paws sunk into the soft soil, making their way toward the water. He paused, raised his great, furry head, nose to the sky, sampling the air. Eyes scanned the tall grass as his head bobbed, identifying who approached. His tail wagged, and he continued toward the water.

From the west, long, powerful legs carried a juvenile wolf, his black coat dusted with white. He trotted, following this familiar path. His mouth opened as he quickened his pace, panting and tasting the scent of the freshly thawed lake.

The gray wolf reached the shore first, dipped his nose deep into the frosty water and lapped to his contentment. When he looked up, amber eyes met his, steady and curious.

"Well come on over, Indigo," the gray wolf said. "Haven't seen you for weeks."

The juvenile trotted to the wet shoreline, dunking his tongue again and again.

"It's always so much better when the water's cooler," he said. "Have you seen the others?"

"Here come Running Wind and Mystique," the gray wolf answered, gesturing his large head toward the south. "Oh, and will you look at that!"

As the other two wolves approached, Dakota, the gray wolf, opened his mouth in a smile. Running Wind, a four-year-old gray wolf himself, dropped his head slightly as they met with the others.

"Oh, no!" said Indigo. "What is that around your neck?"

"It was terrible," Running Wind grumbled, punctuated his distaste for his new radio collar with a full-body shake. "The humans came in a pack. They rode on screaming, noisy beasts that spewed clouds of foul smelling air, and I ran through our whole territory. Suddenly I fell and couldn't move. I woke up and saw them all around me. Their naked, smooth hands were on me, but I could barely move away! Then they retreated, but they left me with their mark. I rolled on the ground for days, but I can't get it off!"

The other three wolves watched, water dripping from their mouths as they stood, captivated by the story.

"How long ago did it happen?"

"Two sunrises," Running Wind said and hung his head. "How will I tell my pups? I'm not ready to let them know that humans are real!"

A collective groan passed between them. Indigo dipped his nose into the water again.

"When Alpha told me about the humans, it was sure scary."

"I guess your time has come," said Mystique, the wolf who had arrived with him. He was the oldest and the largest at six years of age. His fur was tawny brown, and he had deep golden eyes. "You must explain man to your pack. I, too, had to do that many seasons ago."

"You have no mark of man," said Running Wind. "What happened that made you have to tell your pups?"

"The humans came and brought with them many fallen trees," Mystique drank long and deeply, then looked into the distance, remembering. "They cleared an area and began to lay the trunks on top of each other, constructing an above-ground den. My mate and I watched in wonder. What were they doing? Is this what they do when they raise their young? We did not know, until one day the logs stood strong and tall and complete, a shelter within the woods. We never saw any small humans, but the alpha and his mate stayed until the first snow, and then they left. We taught our pups to never go near that part of our territory."

"Humans are strange," said Dakota, and he snapped at a fly that buzzed past him. "In the coldest days of winter, I heard them flying over, riding inside their metal birds that rain down fire." He shivered at the memory. "I was running. I thought for sure it was chasing me. I was coming up to the mountains, and all the caves were covered over with fallen snow and ice, and the trees had stopped growing there, so it was just open snow, then the mountains. I had no place to go! Then suddenly, a human jumped out of the metal bird—on purpose! He had a flat tree branch strapped to his paws. When he landed on the snow, he slid down the mountain, riding on the tree branch."

"What kind of tree branch?" Indigo asked, water dripping from his jaws.

"I don't know: it was all kinds of bright colors, not like any of the trees I see here in the woods. It was flat and shiny. And the human was laughing and howling like he was enjoying himself! I've never seen anything like it. But I didn't stay around very long; I didn't want the metal bird to come back and find me."

Just then a coyote scampered up, appearing from an outcropping of tall reeds. He dipped his mouth into the cool lake, not looking at the wolves. A collective growl passed between then.

"Get out of here Carl!" said Running Wind.

The coyote drank quickly, ignoring them at first. The growls turned to snarls.

"Go on, get out of here!"

"Hey come on guys, the watering hole is a communal place!" The coyote drank hastily, but this time he watched the wolves with a sidelong glance. All four wolves had their hackles up, so Carl decided it was time to go, and he scampered away from the lake at top speed, snaps and snarls issuing from behind him.

"So, I'm looking for a mate," Indigo said offhandedly, shaking his body to calm the nervous energy of the coyote encounter.

"Really!" said Dakota. "Thinking about dispersing, are you?"

"Well, yeah." Indigo's eyes shone brightly as he looked at the older wolves. "I caught the scent of a female a few weeks ago, and I followed it for days. I finally found her. She was beautiful, gray fur, long fluffy tail. So I chased her around for a long time, and she ran right past a camp where there was a pack of yearling humans! I was so focused on following that female that I tripped! I saw the humans, and they freaked me out, and I fell right over a tree root!"

The three older wolves laughed and wagged their tails.

"You were always all hind feet!" said Dakota.

"Shut up, no I wasn't!" Indigo trotted nervously around the other three. "I'm not going to tell you guys anything anymore!"

"Didn't smell the humans, can't run without tripping," Running Wind said, an unusual lightness in his wise voice. "Sounds as though you are getting old, Indigo."

"No I'm not! I'm only three!"

The deep, bellowing sound of a nearby howl cut through the air, immediately silencing the friends. The three older wolves turned to Indigo. Without a pause, he tipped his head back in response.

"Uh oh," said Dakota. "Alpha's calling."

"He's close," Indigo whispered. "Don't tell him the story about the girl! He'll be really mad if he thinks I might leave the pack!"

"He might be more concerned about how you represent your pack," said Running Wind. "What with the tripping and the not noticing the humans…"

"Stop it!"

Soft, heavy paws tread across the tender grass, the large head and bright focused eyes of the Alpha shining as he approached. He stopped several feet from the others, and Indigo walked up to him, head lowered, tail wagging slowly. He licked his face and walked a circle around the elder wolf in reverence. A low growl issued from the Alpha's throat.

"Fellow wolves," he greeted cordially. Dakota and Running Wind, alphas of their own packs, both stood tall, staring steadily at their peer. Mystique, lower in rank in his pack, moved a few feet away, fighting to keep his hackles from raising. "That will be enough socializing for Indigo. I trust all is well in your territories?"

"Drink some water, Alpha," Indigo prompted hopefully. "It's so cool and clear and delicious."

"All is well," said Dakota, looking away nonchalantly.

Alpha stepped to the water's edge and took a long drink of the clear water. When he was finished, Indigo drank once more.

"I see you've been cursed with the mark of man," Alpha said to Running Wind. The other wolf replied with a growl. "That is unfortunate. I had hoped our area would not be touched by this monstrosity."

"There was little I could do to escape." Alpha raised his nose to the sky, sampling the air.

"Last year, they built a den in our woods," Mystique said.

"I saw them as well, in the middle of the deepest snow," Dakota concurred.

Alpha turned, and Indigo walked alongside him as he walked away, giving a backward glance and a smile to his friends as he walked. Suddenly Alpha stopped and looked back.

"You must be aware of the connection," he said. "The humans are moving in." He turned then, howling deeply, and in the distance his pack responded.

The three remaining wolves watched until they disappeared, then Dakota yawned.

"So the humans are moving in," he said. "Great. There goes the forest."

J.R. MILLER

Bio

J.R. Miller lives in coastal Maine. He has worked various jobs from commercial fishing, seasonal harvesting (apples, blueberries, oranges), and landscaping to computer programming and carpentry. His hobbies are living simply in the back woods of Maine, while staying connected with the world. He prefers to communicate as much as possible in as few words as possible, allowing the poem to quietly, but inexplicably, share the intent.

Through the brush
She wolf returns to her lair
Her warm breath fogs
before the remaining cubs

AMBUJA RAJ
WOLFE

Bio

Ambuja Raj is a 19-year-old Psychology student from Delhi, India who spends most of her time reading, painting, and playing with dogs (and reprimanding her own). She has been painting since she was three, making the wall her canvas. Her fascination with wolves roots in her reading The Call of the Wild *and having a deep-seated love for the animals.*

Wolfe. Ambuja Raj.

DEBRA ROOK
INVASIVES

Bio

Debra Rook lives, teaches, and writes in Hertford, North Carolina, next door to red wolf country. She loves kayaking through the Alligator National Wildlife Refuge on research trips for her work in progress, howling during Red Wolf Howling Safaris and listening for responding calls. Ms. Rook's fiction and poetry credits include "Miguel The Terrible," "Half-Moon," and "Sins of Omission" in The Lyricist, *"Curious Tandi's Secret" in* Doors and Windows: Stories for Children, *and "Where Things Comeback And The Land Reclaims Her Own," a short story involving red wolves, slated for publication in* Hunger Mountain *in Winter 2014. She also writes and edits educational material for ClassScape, Curriculet and Educators R&R. She has been a member of SCBWI Carolinas since 2007 and attended a novel-in-verse Highlights workshop in 2012. She is a third semester student at Vermont College of Fine Arts in the MFA Writing for Children and Young Adults program. She is currently researching her thesis on the history of the wolf archetype in children's literature.*

In the land between the Sounds
—Between the Albemarle and the Pamlico—
(Names pulling toward to a history—lost)
Red wolves howl—yelp—bellow
Songs ripple down the bones
Claw at the Milky Way Sky
Lurk in tannic bog waters—Slide
    through protruding cypress knees

There are some human wanderers
    who call the red wolves ***invasive***—
Weeds—trespassers—killers
Labels applied before (and again)
    to tribes—migrants—children

History proves there are those who build false connections
    between tradition—and intolerance

Many human wanderers on the Earth—on this land—
    exist only for an instant in time
Still—they proudly sport the football portrait—
—a red-skinned warrior in profile and feathers—
Still—they plaster the red wolf's silhouette
on red team t-shirts claiming ***This Is Our State!***
(They know it is easier to capture a mascot
    choked with attempted annihilation)

Before them—before us—the red wolf claimed this territory
In the land between the Sounds
—Between the Albemarle and the Pamlico—
She whelped and mothered generations
She ghosted through forest and swamp
She licked the mud and gnawed the bones
She dozed in thickets thrumming with cicadas
    warmed by a midday sun

She did not recognize invisible boundaries
    Carved into her frontier
She could not hide her existence enough
    to satisfy the ones who clubbed her pups in their dens
She sought refuge in the swamp—but even there
Her genes entangled and twisted like burrs caught in fur
Until she vanished from nightmares—banished
From memory into myth and legend and folktale
    —almost

She returned to sliver
of her once hunting grounds
She whelped and mothered and expanded her range

Still—there are human descendants claiming land long established
Who cry the big bad red wolf invades their State
They say Big Brother invades their privacy
And maintain the red wolf is the invasive species—

But we must stop—'member—ask—
Who invaded whom?

ILISA WALTER
WOLFWATCHING

Bio
Ilisa Walter is an artist in Kaneohe, Hawaii. His hobbies include leatherwork,
computer games, drawing, and painting.

Wolfwatching. Indi Walter. Digital.

JACQULYN MCGLYNN
PEACEFUL SOUL

Bio

Jacqulyn McGlynn is a photographer in Tyler, Texas. She studied Business Management as the University of Texas and Radiologic Technology at the Memorial Hospital of Radiologic Technology. She has participated in numerous photography shows, and she has published a photography collection called I Am in the Garden.

Peaceful Soul. Jacqulyn McGlynn. Photograph.

BEVERLY RAY
YELLOW EYES DANCING IN SUNLIGHT

Wolf eyes dance
With the light of the setting sun---
Lit golden before its fall.

Yellow eyes dance
Like sunflowers
Turning lovely faces to greet their God.

But Wolf eyes dance
strongest when bellies are full.

SELAH GAYNOR
DOGWOODS

Bio

Selah Gaynor is a fiction-writing damsel—formerly known as "in distress"—who lives in Littleton, Colorado with her dog Ben. This is her debut print story.

The following story details what happens when you get lost hiking. Always bring a buddy, and never, ever get too far ahead. There are beasts among the trees.

She had just been right there, I was sure of it. I turned around and called out in the woods, but the silence that greeted me was my only reply. I shivered as a creeping dread began to fill me. I could have sworn that I had only walked a little ways ahead of her. Summer had been on the path right behind me, but she had been walking too slowly, pausing to take pictures and examine flowers where they bloomed in the Earth. These things were all fine, and any other hike of the year I would have stayed right there with her the whole way. Not this hike though. This was the first good hike of the season. It was finally warm enough to get high up on the mountain without having to bundle up.

After the long winter it had felt fantastic to be able to stretch my legs. Summer had called out for me to slow down, but I hurried ahead recklessly, knowing that she would catch up eventually. The minutes had begun to add up, though, and she had not called out to me for a long time. I had assumed that she was being petulant and sulking because I had left her in my wake. It took me longer than I am proud to admit to realize that something was wrong. I turned back and hurried along the trail, but Summer was nowhere to be seen.

I tried to convince myself that I was worrying needlessly. People were always saying that I was a little high-strung. Taking several deep breaths, I tried to settle down, to not work myself up into a fit, but my heart refused to obey me. Surely she was just a little further down the trail. I called out for her as I went, but if Summer heard me, she did not respond.

Nothing looked familiar.

Shouldn't I be able to recognize something by now? I wondered. Shouldn't something along the trail serve as a reminder that I had already passed it? The sun was beginning to set beneath the high peaks of the mountains. I began to shiver, as much from the quick cooling night air as from my worries. Had I really been out here alone for so long already?

I heard the trickling sound of water and I stumbled headlong toward it. Summer had our gear in her pack, and I was dying of thirst. I drank first—long gulps of spring water. Refreshed, I eyed the running water warily, wondering what the likelihood was that I had just contracted some form of waterborne parasite.

I found a large river stone, still heated by the slanted rays of the setting sun that peeked between the tall pine trees and warmed myself in the light while I contemplated my next move. I knew that Summer and I had definitely not passed running water on our way up the mountain. I had to accept the inevitable; I was hopelessly, irrevocably lost. I had no way to let anyone know where I was, and Summer—oh, Summer—she'd be so worried. All the programs I had ever seen said to stay put and to wait for rescue—but it had been a long drive up the steep mountain, and not very many others were attempting the hike this early in the season, or this far north.

I dipped my head hopelessly. I was on the verge of tears when there was a loud crack like the snap of a branch underfoot. I looked up, startled, at the wolf across the creek that eyed me with unmasked suspicion. Tall and well-muscled, his tawny coat gleamed golden in the twilight sun, and his eyes shone like polished amber.

I scrambled to my feet, and the wild animal across the water tensed on stiff legs. Cautious but curious, he stepped fearlessly into the water toward me. In return, I stepped back. For every step the wolf took I took another until I had backed myself against a tree.

Don't come any closer, I pleaded silently. *Just stay away.*

Something about the way that I had held myself, stiff and still and frightened, must have made my thoughts clear to the wolf because he sat on his haunches just my side of the spring. When he made no move toward me, I turned my head to meet his gaze.

I would have suspected that a wild thing like him would have been matted and dirty, caked with mud and goodness only knew what else, but his coat had a soft and well-groomed appearance. A part of me ached to reach out and feel that fur for myself, but a larger part—the part that I had disregarded when I had run so far ahead of Summer—screamed at me to remain very, very still. Uncharacteristically, I obeyed the voice of reason, and stayed motionless against the rough bark of that tree.

The wolf lifted his lip to expose sharp teeth, but his ears remained alert, swiveling behind him as more wolves came to the water through the brush. A dark-coated female with swollen teats nosed a litter of cubs to drink from the river. Her eyes were wary when they met mine, but I did not move, not one muscle, as the young wolves filled their bellies with cool water.

Having drunk their fill, the largest and bravest cub splashed toward us. He bounded like a rabbit in the water, and the wolf who watched me loosed a rumbling growl from deep within his chest. The cub spared me a lightning fast glance before yipping twice and retreating. In his haste, he tripped over his own too-large paws returning to his littermates. He tumbled without grace over one of his siblings and ducked between his mother's legs. She lowered her snout to lick the cub dry but kept her yellow eyes fixed on me.

A pack of wolves! I did not know that there were any wolves in Colorado, even this far north. I assumed they must have wandered down from Wyoming, driven south by man or natural disaster or even by their own instincts, following the game trails as their prey migrated to less populated areas. The pack studied me with bewildered expressions, as though they had never seen anything like me before. I had certainly never seen anything like them before, other than on TV or in the movies—no, not even then. I often had the television playing in the house, tuned to an animal channel as background noise as I went about my day. The wolves on TV were shown as wild things with snapping, hungry jaws. Depicted as vicious scavengers and hunters, as far as I had been aware they should have killed me just for being near their cubs! From their powerful forms it was easy to see that they would have made quick work of me.

This was nothing like TV.

Two full grown wolves flanked the cubs and watched them—and me—in equal measures. They were as curious as I was, and I sensed no aggression from any of them.

The tawny wolf that had crossed the water waded back, tossing glances over his shoulder. He shook off on the other side and stepped over two of the cubs to lean his shoulder into the belly of the dark, female wolf. Eyes still fixed on me, the larger wolf licked the chin of the female in a clear sign of deference. A single velvet ear twitched as though he was flicking off a bug. She lowered her head and raised the bristles on the back of her neck, tail erect and angry as she stared me down.

I stepped back and around, putting the tree between her and me for what little good it did. To me, the tree felt as transparent as glass. I peered around it, knowing better than to flee. I knew I could never outrun her strong, agile legs.

The tawny wolf nipped her chin, and she lowered her tail and turned, puffing a deep breath and shaking her shoulders as she dismissed me. The other four wolves followed her lead, but the wolf from the water remained behind. He watched me with unblinking eyes, as still as a statue. The young cubs clambered to keep up, the smallest wolf stumbling until the older male righted him with his snout.

What now? I wondered, and no sooner had the thought crossed my mind than he had crossed the river toward me again. *Oh no*, I thought. *Oh no no no.* I scrambled backward as he trotted toward me, tail low and unintimidating. He lopped at a friendly gait, but I still backed away frightened.

I think I had seen this special once, I thought as I tumbled into a bush and squeezed my eyes shut. "When Apex Predators Attack, the Luring You into a False Sense of Security Edition." Heck, it may have even been TiVo'd. Summer was really into that sort of thing.

The wolf continued toward me. Unlike before, he was not satisfied to stop a distance away. He came right up to me, scenting me heavily, as he pressed his wet nose into my hip.

Personal space! I almost cried out as I pushed against him. His body was unyielding and climbed out of the bush and righted myself on unsteady feet. The wolf pushed into me again, herding me down on to the path back the way that I had come from. I looked back behind us, half expecting to see the other wolves following, but it was just the two of us, alone in the woods.

Do you want me to follow you? I had no way of asking. He paused, looking back at me before shaking his shoulders with his nose low and pointed in the dirt, and I sensed my answer. Perhaps I was just being delusional or looking for answers where there were none to be found, but my gut told me to follow this wolf. So, stepping carefully, I walked alongside the wolf.

The wolf was surefooted, even in the fading light. He walked the edge of the path, where the grass was higher and softer on padded paws. Initially, I tried to step where he stepped as he guided me along the path, but I kept stumbling over upturned roots and unseen snake holes.

The wolf huffed at me, either in laughter or irritation; I couldn't be sure which. He slowed down, obviously on my account. I had no way of gauging how long we walked along that path, but I was hungry, and I was tired, and I was beginning to shiver from the cold. Most danger-ously of all, I was beginning to doubt myself. Why was I following this wild animal? Nothing seemed familiar. In the dark, the trees loomed overhead in foreign and frightening shapes. They looked twisted and angry and I was so preoccupied with scanning them for something amiss that I didn't realize that the wolf had stopped until I plowed right into him.

I jerked back immediately. The muscles under his muzzle had jumped and clenched when I ran into him, but he shook it off after a moment and gestured toward a rock outcropping before padding to-ward it.

Oh, no, I thought as I tracked his movements from the trail. He paused at the mouth of a small cave before disappearing into the dark-ness. I looked at the cave in disbelief. No. No way! I had a thing about small, dark spaces—the thing was this: I didn't do them. When I was much, much younger, I had gotten separated from my family in the woods near where we lived. I had taken shelter in a small burrow under a large tree and had remained there for days. Frightened and alone, I had been unwilling to leave the safety of the tree roots even for water. I had been weak with dehydration and hunger when a firefighter had rescued me. Since that day, I had struggled with anxieties—particularly when there were small, dark places involved. I had no desire to sleep in a cave, no matter how cold it got on the mountains at night.

Long moments passed though, and the wolf did not reemerge. It was getting darker along the path, and I shifted my weight from foot to foot. I called out to the wolf, trying to get him to join me outside again, but he did not come out from the cave. It became apparent that he was not going to be coming out no matter how long I waited. I made my way to the cave, hoping with every step that the wolf would poke his head out, and we could keep moving.

I came upon the entrance after what felt like eons, and I steeled myself. *Just like old times,* I thought with a shuddering breath. I allowed myself one last superfluous glance up the trail, searching hopelessly for signs of human life, before I followed the wolf into the darkness.

I had to crawl on my belly to get inside, but after only about a foot or so into the room the roof raised to make a small cavern. It was hard-ly big enough for the two of us to move around without touching, and I could not stand up without hitting my head, so I crouched low to the ground as he circled back to the mouth of the cave. The darkness was suffocating. I could hardly catch my breath as I was overwhelmed with memories from long ago. I closed my eyes shut and held my breath, willing my anxiety to go away. *This isn't then*, I reminded myself. *I am not alone.*

More calmly, I opened my eyes. They had adjusted to the poor lighting, and I saw that the earth had been overturned in the rear of the cave by the wolf and was much softer and warmer than by the mouth of the cave. I could smell mildew and moss, but I was warm, and I was tired, so I rested my heavy head on my forearms as I curled into myself for warmth. The stress of the day caught up with me, and I cried then, quietly and childishly.

I wanted to be home. I wanted to be in my warm bed. I wanted Summer to know I was safe, and to know that she was safe as well. The thought of her alone on the mountain was almost worse than my own overwhelming sense of isolation. I was scared in the dark, and I felt completely alone, and I was afraid—I was so afraid—that I would be alone forever.

The wolf lay down beside me, and my breath caught in my throat as he pressed his body against mine, blocking me from the cold chill that seeped into the cavern through the mouth of the cave. He moved his mouth at my neck, clicking his teeth against my bare skin without piercing, and I smiled. It tickled. An unlikely mirth bloomed warmly in my belly as he nibble-groomed the sensitive skin beneath my ears and in the face of my pleasure, my worries seemed much less daunting, and in no time at all, they faded away entirely.

Exhausted, but not hopeless, I fell into a deep, dreamless sleep.

A soft white light slated across my eyes hours later. I blinked awake, confused and disoriented. Briefly, I wondered where I was, and then with a lurch, I wondered where my wolf had gone. The moon lit the cave through the mouth, and I inhaled sharply as I realized he was no-where to be seen. My heart was pounding. I crouched down, careful to avoid cracking my head as I crawled out into the forest. What would I do if he had left me? At least before, when I had found him, there had been water, but now I didn't even have that! I scrambled out of the cave, and I saw him then, backlit by the smiling, sleepy moon.

The long lines of his strong neck were exposed, and he was howl-ing, his voice a deep and sonorous melody, to his distant pack. His breath billowed in white puffs as he called to them, eyes closed. My breath lodged in my throat and choked me as I watched him in awe. He howled until all of the breath had escaped from his lungs. Only then did he bow his head beneath the moon. I remained on my belly with my mouth agape, and he turned to me, eyes bright and wild, and I thought to myself, *This is what we should all strive to be.* Loyal and brave, he was helping me at his own expense with nothing to gain. He didn't know me; we weren't even the same species. Everything I knew about his kind, everything that I had thought that I had known, was wrong. He'd kept me warm and sheltered, and I was humbled by his majesty.

On a distant mountain peak, a choir of howls echoed down the valleys and the hills, but he remained unblinkingly as he watched me. Slowly, our gazes steady, I rose to my feet and moved to stand by his side. Swallowing any shame that rose within me for acting silly, I tilted my head back and joined the wolves in their song.

The sound that I made was unpracticed and broken and completely unlike his rich voice. Even in this I lacked his elegance, but my inexpert howl was not without meaning. As I answered the howls of the other wolves, I was flooded with both gratitude and humility.

The wolf joined in beside me. My cracking tenor was supplemented by his rich baritone. The vibrations rumbled out of his chest, and I leaned into him, to feel connected in every way I could: they filled me as well. I was so filled with emotion that it overflowed from my mouth, in my howl, and from my eyes, in the wetness that cooled my face.

This simple freedom was not only the birthright of the wolf. It was the birthright of every living thing: to be proud and free, to have a family, and to love and be loved. My thoughts turned to Summer, and I wondered if she was still in these woods, searching for me in the cold night. I wondered if she had gone back down the mountain to get help. I wondered what she would think of me, howling in the forest as though I was a wild animal, and I wondered if, out in the darkness, she could hear me even now.

I liked to think that she could.

If she did, she did not answer. Why would she? Loneliness overtook me once again, and I bowed my head in anguish as my calls went unanswered.

She and I were not like the wolves. We did not have to worry about finding shelter from the ravages of the world; we had soft beds, and pillows to lay our heads down on at night. We never had to fear where our next meal was going to be coming from; we had good food easily and readily accessible to fill our bellies with. We had entertainment and pleasures, both simple and complex, but in spite of all of these things, we were not free. We were trapped by the very things that kept us safe and satisfied.

I wanted to be so much more than just satisfied.

The wolf seemed to notice as I fell into despair and leaned his body heavily against mine in a comforting movement of solidarity. I smiled. At least, if I had to be lonely, I didn't have to be lonely alone. We could be lonely together, on that waning moon night.

My wild wolf and I.

When I woke again, it was in the early dawn, and the wolf was nosing my face with his snout. I pushed him away and rubbed at my face, only to realize I was marked with something slippery, and wet, and hot. I yelped as I realized that the wolf's snout was covered in blood and now, so was I.

The wolf huffed deep and panted breaths of amusement before he lifted a dead-eyed rabbit and laid it on the ground by my feet. If I had had anything in my stomach I am sure that I would have lost it. The rabbit stared at me with empty, black eyes frozen forever in fear. I wondered what had killed it first—the wolf's jaws clenched around its neck or the heart attack that the poor thing obviously endured. I blinked at it. The rabbit did nothing. The wolf pushed the warm corpse toward me again with its nose, looking at me expectantly, his tongue lolling out of the side of his mouth as though to say, "I brought this for you because the cubs in my pack are better hunters than you are. You're welcome."

I wondered how you could possibly say "thanks but no thanks" in Wolf. I turned my nose away from it, trying to convey my message even as my treacherous stomach growled in defiance. It was true that I had not eaten since lunch the day before, but I was a long sight from being hungry enough to eat a raw rabbit. It probably had worms.

The wolf seemed to understand my meaning: even he did not share my scruples, and dug into the soft underbelly of the rabbit. His sharp incisors sliced into the belly and spilled its still-hot viscera as easily as a warm knife slipping through butter. Nauseous, I left the cave and wandered back to the trail. After relieving myself, I looked around. In the daylight, things were much less frightening. More familiar. In fact—yes.

Yes! I was sure that this was the way that I had come the day before.

I turned around to try and express my gratitude to the wolf, but he was already sauntering past me, licking his bloody maw as he walked down the path past me. Hungry but rejuvenated, I followed, certain now that he really was leading me back to civilization.

As we walked, I wondered about the wolf and the life that he led. He had a similar appearance to the other male, though he was slightly larger in build. The other two were obviously a mated pair with a litter between them, but what about him? He had provided for me—shelter, food, and comfort; was the wolf population hurting so badly that a creature as healthy and well-fed as him couldn't find a mate?

I thought back to what little I had actually known about wolves in the wild and knew—yes. As far as I was aware, wolves weren't even supposed to come down as far south as Colorado, preferring to stay north, but something must have driven the pack down here. Without other wolves, he would eventually be forced to choose between leaving his pack and traveling great distances in search of a mate of his own or a life of quiet solitude.

He huffed at me and scratched his hind legs in the hard-packed dirt as though he was telling me to hurry up. His tongue rolled out of his mouth, and he panted heavily, a facsimile of laughter.

No, I thought, knowing that idea wasn't quite right. He was not going to be alone. Though I did think that he'd be a prime example of an alpha, he obviously was just as capable of providing from his established position in his pack. He would take care of his own, and his pack would be there to take care of him in return. While it was possible it would never rear cubs of his own, he would never know one moment of loneliness. It would be enough; no, it would be more than enough.

He picked up his pace, and I hurried after him, but I could barely keep up. He was practically running, racing down the sharp decline. I had been about to cry out for him to slow down and wait for me when suddenly I heard what he must have heard first: the sound of boots on gravel. The sound of Summer, cupping her hand to her mouth as she called my name.

Single-mindedly I raced for the sound, overtaking the wolf in an instant as I turned the bend. There she was, looking as relieved as I felt as our eyes met.

"Willow!"

Summer kneeled down as I bulleted toward her. The ground raced beneath my paws until I was in her arms. Her fingers latched in my thick, matted fur, and I licked the tears from her cheeks. She mumbled wet and incoherent words of joy as she squeezed me, just a little too tightly, but I didn't mind at all. I was home.

I pulled out of her arms and bounced on all four paws, looking over my shoulder the way that I had come. I wanted her to follow me. Obediently, Summer followed, but not before latching the leash around my collar. I nearly collapsed with relief at the reassuring tether between us. We were connected again. I wasn't sure I'd ever be tempted to chew the clamp off of the lead again.

I led Summer into the woods along the trail, but my wolf was not waiting where I had left him behind. My tail drooped, dejected, and I whined at Summer. He had just been right there!

Summer leaned down to my level and I licked her fingertips. "What is it Willow?"

I whined, at Summer, at myself, at my wolf. I had wanted to say thank you! To say good bye! I'd been so lost, and he had saved me. The humans had made him seem so fierce but he had been so good to me. Surely we could show Summer, and she could tell others!

As Summer stood, not knowing what she was looking for, I called out to the forest, but it hid the wolf well. He may have saved me, but now he was gone.

"Let's go home, Will," Summer beckoned. Devastated, I allowed her to guide me back to the truck in a daze. Normally, I would be so excited to get to go for a ride, but now I was just desolate. I climbed into the cab, and Summer patted my sides and lifted my paws, checking for injuries. "Are you okay?" she asked, and I whimpered, licking her face weakly. She gave me some water, and I drank because my mouth was parched, but my heart wasn't in it. When I was done, she ruffled my ears and shut the door, circling the truck to get to the other side. I rested my head on the window sill, and my breath fogged up the glass.

Summer got in the driver's side, and just as she shut her door I spotted him, standing just at the tree line, eyes sharp on mine.

My ears perked up.

"The Rescue I got you from said a group of firefighters had found you not far from here after the big fire in Wyoming a few years ago, you know." Summer said as she turned the key in the ignition. The truck roared to life beneath us, and I caught my reflection in the passenger mirror. Summer had groomed me the week before, brushing out my undercoat so that I would not have to deal with blowing out my winter coat, so my short, stiff bristled coat was thinner and several shades paler than his, but our eyes—our amber eyes—they were exactly the same. I swiveled my head back toward him, afraid he had vanished like an apparition, but he remained, steadfast and still, in the forest. We looked exactly the same, he and I.

"We're going to need to find some other way to deal with your separation anxiety; I think that all of those Animal Programs you watch while I'm at work are giving you delusions of grandeur. What were you thinking, running off like that?"

I kept my eyes fixed on him as we went, my tail thumping against the seat, and I remembered not in images, but in scent: the smell of soft fur and family in my nose from long, long ago. We turned a hill, and I leaned against the window to try and catch even one last glimpse of him. He disappeared around the bend. I knew that our goodbye had been inevitable from the moment that our gazes had first met from across the spring, so the wave of anguish that flooded me was that much more unexpected. Bereft, I tilted my head back, closed my eyes, and howled.

Summer drove, not demanding my silence but rather placing a hand between the blades of my shoulders and rubbing me briskly. "It's okay baby; we'll be home soon."

She stilled her hand and just touched me, and I lowered my head, eyes still closed, as I thought about what I had lost and what I had gained. Like him, I would never be able to have a litter of my own. A cold trip to a sterile room that I could only barely remember had taken care of that; but that didn't mean that I was alone. Having a family, even one that you had made for yourself, meant that you never had to be alone.

From where we had come, the wolf answered my call with a howl of his own.

"What the-?" Summer checked her rearview mirror and further in the distance, two more voices joined in, and then three more.

To me, it sounded as though the wolves were saying, "Be well."

I laid my head down on Summer's lap, and her fingers found their home in the fur between my ears. Every breath I took filled my lungs with the scent of family and home and love, and I knew that I would be.

ROLAND JENKINS
BUCK PROOF

Bio

Roland Jenkins lives in Raymond, Washington but has seen much of the country, a true, seasoned adventurer. Other than writing short stories, he writes articles for newsletters surrounding his other two hobbies: martial arts and animal rescue. He is a volunteer for Harbor Area Volunteers for Animals and the National Wolf-watcher Coalition.

Here Jenkins tells of one of his most memorable companions and the journeys they had together. This story is real-life proof that love very often transcends the boundaries between man and animal.

We have to tear down a section of wood slat fence and replace it with new wire fencing. It is one of the things listed on our to-do list so the Home Insurance Policy can be renewed. Until we get that done we are installing a temporary fence within the property to keep our dogs in. As we were coming in today Polly asked me if the new fence was "Buck Proof." I got a good laugh out of that one.

She was referring to Buck One, my first canine friend. Polly had made a trip from Denver to Minneapolis where I was visiting my Uncle to deliver Buck when he was old enough to leave his Mom. We were relaxing after lunch one afternoon when I got the call from Polly telling me she was in town with Buck and wanted to know how to get to Uncle Rol's house. When we finally figured out where she was, amazingly only about two miles from the house, Rol and I drove over to escort her in.

We spent the evening there, Aunt Diane made up a bed for Polly in the girls bedroom and made one for me on the couch. What she did not know was that Polly and I were just close friends at that time and she had nothing to worry about. The next day Polly and I left to go up North and visit more of my family. She had brought Buck's Mom, JJ, with her so the four of us were off in her 1960 Ford Falcon pickup.

After about a week she and JJ headed back to Denver and Buck, and I stayed with an old school buddy Simon just north of Little Falls, Minnesota. I managed to get a job replacing the roof on the barn of his neighbor Ray and ended up spending the summer on Ray's dairy farm. Buck and I were inseparable. My cousin Butch sold me his old Ford Econoline Van, and I made a bed in there for Buck. Whenever I could not take him in somewhere he stayed in the van.

It was a long hot summer on the farm, working on the west side of the barn roof in the morning until the sun hit it then helping around the farm with haying, or other chores till the sun was far enough down to work on the east side. Ray the farmer had four children still living at home, and a couple times each week I would load them up, stop at their friends' farm and pick up two more kids and head out with them and Buck to Sandy Lake. You could walk out about 100 yards before the water got too deep, and the whole floor of the lake was white sand. I taught Buck how to swim by carrying him out as far as I could, set him in the water and dog paddle back to shore alongside him. He would be so tired from that he would just shake off, go find a cool spot to lie down, and just watch us. If he did get up I would go get him and repeat the swim lesson.

I was having trouble training him to stay and always come to me when I called. We would go out into the meadow behind the farm house, and I would have him sit and continually tell him to stay then command him to come. As the days went by I could get farther and farther away and even turn my back on him as I walked away repeating the command to stay. The one problem I had was if he found something more interesting his puppy curiosity would win out.

One day when he would not come I started walking toward him telling him to come; when I got close he took off so I took off after him. We crossed the meadow, crossed the dirt road and into the corn field. The corn had been cut down so there was no hiding, and he stopped about 100 feet away. I kept walking toward him, and he would take off when I got close. We crossed that corn field, went through a grove of trees, followed the creek to the alfalfa field and got halfway through it before he finally stopped and waited for me. When I got to him I just sat down beside him and started talking to him about partnerships. Soon I got up; told him to stay, walked away from him about

100 feet all the while softly saying "Stay". I turned around and he was sitting there looking at me. I said, "Come" and he did. We never had to have that talk again.

While I was working on Ray's roof in the late afternoon heat, a neighbor who had bought the old school house in town stopped by to talk to me. He was planning to put a new roof on it and figured if Ray had hired me I was good enough to do his roof also. This roof had some shade, and the pitch was not as steep as the barn roof, so I would set up a platform for Buck and started training him to climb the ladder with me. I put a bowl of water up there for him, and he would just sit there watching me work. Sometimes he would get up and walk around, but never went near the edge.

Bob, the owner of the converted school house was a foreman at the local paper mill. He ran the de-barking plant where the logs were brought in and stripped of their bark. When I finished his roof he got me a job working with him. Buck would go to work with me, and every two hours I got a ten minute break. I would let him out and go for a run with him then get back to work. We kept this up into the winter. I made a cave of blankets for him and when it got frigid I would have to go out and start the van, let it run for the ten minutes while he and I took our walk then plug it back into the tank heater for two hours.

I had met a family that lived in town and rented their basement from them to get away from that 10 mile drive in the snow and cold. One day I let Buck out back to go to the bathroom, and he did not come back. I took the day off work and searched for him. Finally I called the Dog Pound and described him. They had him, and it was going to cost a fortune to get him out, because while Polly had got his shots he was not up to date. I got directions to the Pound and headed out. We had just had about 12 inches of snow, and the wind had blown 4 to 6 foot high drifts. I made a wrong turn and was pulling into a driveway that had just been shoveled out. As I rounded the snow bank there in the middle of the drive stood Buck! I don't know who was more surprised; he looked at me and ran to my door. I opened it he jumped up on my lap and over to his seat, sat down and looked at me as if to say, "Man am I glad to see you!" Then he just looked out his window as if nothing happened.

The snow and cold had worn me down, and I did not want to take another chance of Buck getting busted so the very next payday Buck and I headed back to Colorado. Polly and Ray were living out on a farm south of Denver, and Buck and I joined them. Over the next couple of years Buck and I were inseparable. We hitch-hiked to Illinois when work got too slow and back to Colorado when I built up a stash of cash. I could write a book on hitch-hiking, but the big key to success in getting rides is to have a good-looking dog with no leash, at your side. He got me rides I never dreamed of. There was this Mom with two young kids, a nun, a young lady going to her girlfriend's house to listen to her record collection and more. The one thing they all had in common was they just loved my dog and any one that could have such a companion had to be ok. I never let my pride get the better of me. Buck was my ticket.

There were games he and I played. When he was young and had his sharp baby teeth I would put on as many gloves as I could on my right hand and let him grab hold then we would fight. As he got older I trained him to grab my two fingers behind his canines and hold on with just enough pressure to not slip off, but not so much as to break my fingers. I could actually pull him off his feet without him hurting me. We use to stage one hell of a fight. I would take off running and as he caught up to me I would stick out my hand with the two fingers extended. He would jump up and grab hold. We would growl at each other and have a tug of war. I could get nose to nose with him each of us growling with him showing one beautiful set of canines. He knew it was a game and never lost control.

One time I went to visit my Grandmother at the Crosby Senior Center. I knew which window was hers. There was about a foot of snow on the ground when Buck and I staged one of our "fights". When I was worn out I looked up at her window and there she was with a great big grin on her face along with a couple staff members. I went to the back door, they let me and Buck in to go visit with Grandma.

The other thing I worked with Buck on was jumping. I was always challenging him to jump over things. He got so good that I could sit on a bar stool, hold my leg out, and have him jump over it. He loved doing it. One time I was doing it, and my friend next to me stuck his leg out also. Buck jumped both without touching them. The next time not only the guy next to me but the guy next to him did it. Buck jumped two of us, but the third one he had to touch with his feet. He did not land, but just sprang off the leg.

Another of my favorite games to play with him was whenever he would get ahead of me in the woods I would find a place to hide and make him come find me. He always did. One time I made it real tough for him. I climbed a tree and he passed under the tree several times finally coming back to it and just standing there he slowly looked up at me with those jet black eyes glaring at me. He usually would wag his tail when he found me, but this time I got the message that he did not like the game anymore.

Right from the get-go I started training him to "stay". Over the years it got to the point I could lay my shirt down, tell him to stay and walk into a building. When I came back he would still be there. The only thing that would challenge that training was if another male dog came by. Then I would have to go out and break up a fight.

In 1974 my family was heading up to Crosby for a big family reunion. I was in Colorado and hustled to Lisle to ride up with them, but missed them by a few hours. Buck and I hit the road, and after a couple of short rides getting me just over the border into Wisconsin a woman in a station wagon pulled over. She had four kids in the car with the oldest about 8 years old. One jumped in the back so Buck could sit next to me. Again I had to ask why she felt ok picking me up. The kids loved the dog! I played games and drew pictures with the little rascals all the way to Little Falls, Minnesota. When they dropped me off outside a café on the main drag it was raining a steady downpour. I threw down a shirt by the door where Buck would have a little cover and went in to use the phone to call my Mom and get something for us to eat. Before I even sat down the waitress told me that Buck could come in and sit with me. When she brought out my cheeseburger she had a plate of scraps and a bowl of water for Buck. You bet I tipped her good.

One night I had gone down out of the mountains east of Denver to a friend's house. The next morning I was back up in the mountains and woke up with a hell of a hangover. I went out to the van, but Buck was not with me. I panicked thinking I left him out east of Denver. I drove down there and spent the whole day looking for him. I called up the Whippletree and was talking to Wagon about not being able to come into work until I found Buck. Wagon told me Buck was outside, that he had been there all day waiting for me. Man, I was relieved and felt incredibly stupid at the same time.

The last time I hitch-hiked out to Denver from Lisle I got a ride to Saint Louis with my Dad and Mom. They were headed south from that point so after lunch with them at the Truck Stop, Buck and I walked down the entrance ramp on I-70 and waited where the entrance merged with the traffic lanes. The key to success in hitch-hiking is to be clearly visible and be in a safe, easy to pull over area. It was pushing one hundred degrees, and the sun was directly overhead. I threw a sweatshirt down for Buck to sit on as the pavement was just about melting. I put his water dish down and put just a little water in it. If he did not drink it I did not want to waste it. I had him facing traffic so I straddled him so as to provide him some shade and stuck out my thumb. I wasn't there five minutes and this lady pulled over. It was the Nun! After we got on the road and settled in I just had to ask her why she stopped. Yes it was my handsome canine friend. He looked so miserable and that I did not have a leash on him meant that I must be a good person.

I told her I was going to Denver, but that I was going to stop to see a friend in Kansas City. She was going to Kansas City just a couple miles from where I was going. We had a pleasant conversation, and she actually went the couple miles out of her way for Buck and me and dropped us off at my friend's apartment complex. There were two pools at this complex and when Mary, Buck, and I went to take a dip the one pool was way too crowded, but there was no one at the smaller second one. Mary was sitting on the edge of the pool; Buck was sitting down at the other end of the pool by the gate, which I had left open. The fence was only three foot high so a closed gate meant nothing to Buck. When I was talking to Mary I could see a troubled look appear on her face. I quickly turned my head there was a woman walking her little poodle down the sidewalk alongside the pool; Buck had stood up and was taking a step forward. He was about to eat that Poodle. I yelled "STAY!" He froze in place; I continued to softly give the command to stay as I climbed out of the pool, walked over to the fence and closed the gate. Mary said: "Wow, now that's control!" We decided it was time to go back to the apartment.

Mary took me out to I-70 and down to the rest area about five miles down the highway. It was night time, and I felt that would be the best place for me to find a ride. After she dropped me off I was walking down the ramp, and a State Trooper pulled up behind me. He read me the riot act about hitch-hiking on the freeway and about not having Buck on a leash. I had a piece of rope with me so I fashioned it into a leash. Buck and I were sitting in the back of his squad being respectful and finally I asked him why he was being so rude to me. I understood he had a job to do and that I needed to get off the freeway, but asked him if he could just treat me like a human. He told me he did not like dogs! I did not get a ticket, but he told me if he saw me again tonight I was going to jail. After he pulled away, Buck and I started jogging. We jogged for 3 miles to the next exit which was the state highway that paralleled the freeway.

It was late, and I was worn out. We crawled up under the bridge that allowed the state highway to cross under the freeway. The old style bridges had platforms at the top that were wide enough to camp out on. I made myself as comfortable as I could and had Buck lay down alongside me. We had a deal: he was to protect me from animals, and I would protect him from humans. He kind of did both, but I tried. I was asleep when I awoke to his low warning growl. I looked up over his back, and there was a man at the base of the sloped concrete embankment. He had taken one step up it toward us and froze when Buck started to growl. I had my six-inch blade in my right hand, and I just lifted it up without saying a word. The man just turned and walked on down the road.

We made it back to Colorado, and one day while staying at some friend's house south of Evergreen Buck and I went for a walk. There was the Rock outcropping you could see from the road that I wanted to climb. As we got about halfway to it we had to cross over a wooden post and pole fence. We were no more than a hundred feet in when I heard then saw two big German Shepherds running straight at me. I saw about one hundred feet behind them this young woman with a big grin on her face. Buck was up and off to my right when I looked at him I saw he realized what was happening, and he bolted straight on an interception course. When the two Shepherds were within fifty feet of me Buck had gotten on their back sides. They made a sharp left half turn and took off for what I now saw was a log cabin a couple hundred yards away, with Buck barking and chasing them. I looked back at the woman, and her expression had changed from one of pleasure to one of terror. She started yelling at me that I was trespassing. I was yelling at Buck to come back. When he finally turned around and was running back to me I addressed the woman, apologizing for trespassing, but also telling Buck what a good job he had just done.

Eddie, a friend of ours in the Bergen Park area, had a beautiful Wolf named Shea. Buck and Shea were buddies, and when Shea was in heat no matter how hard Eddie tried to prevent continuous litters her and Buck made puppies. One time I had Buck locked in the patio area of the Bar. There was an 8 foot high solid wood lath fence. Eddie had Shea locked in his van. We were inside shooting pool when Eddie took a look out in the patio area and could not see Buck. He yelled "Oh Crap" and ran out to the front to check on Shea. The side door was open; we both ran around back, and there they were locked up.

The next time she was in heat he actually kenneled her at the Vet's place about two blocks from the Whippletree. We don't know how or when for sure but she had another litter of Buck puppies. They were always the most beautiful puppies, and there was no doubt this was also Bucks doing. He had to have broken in, mated with her, and then broke back out.

Pound for pound I never knew another dog as tough as Buck or with as much spirit. He just did not know how to back down from a fight, and more often than not the other dog did not even know it was going to be fighting until Buck was on top of it. One time there was this bully of a bulldog, but the first time Buck met him he got ahold of the bulldog's collar and somehow twisted it choking the dog. By the time I got Buck's jaw unlocked and off the dog he had passed out. From that day forward he was a changed dog. I never saw him pick on another dog again.

There was however this one time Polly and I were at a field party down by Conifer. Our friends opened up their house and the fields around their house to a massive get-together. I was playing volleyball when I could hear Buck yelping. It was strange so I looked to see what was happening. I saw Buck backing up still yelping and then from behind a couple of pine trees I saw these two huge Great Danes just walking toward him. I yelled up to Buck, "You tell 'em Buck!" and the crowd roared. Everyone knew Buck, but they also knew he was intelligent enough to know when to back away.

One summer my brother Bob had come to live with Polly and me at our Cabin up in Echo Hills. Bob and I were up by the Elk Ponds harvesting some firewood when I heard that yelp again. I told Bob that Buck must have found some Elk. He asked me how I knew, and I told him the sound of his bark. We walked over the ridge with Bob about 20 feet in front of me. He stopped behind a pine tree and as I crested the ridge I could see about 50 feet down the slope six female elk had a newborn calf surrounded, and they were all facing my three dogs. Suddenly one lowered her head and started walking toward Buck. Buck kept yelping but started backing up. He backed up within five feet of where Bob was standing and the elk was walking right toward Bob. Then I hear Bob lose it and start saying "Whoooooooaaaa". The elk hears and sees him then bolts back to the group and they all run off, but only as fast as the newborn can.

I had a friend visit me, and he wanted to get a chance to spot some elk. We started up the mountain when he told me he did not want the dogs along as they would scare the elk away. I reluctantly agreed and put the dogs in the house. After we were gone a couple hours Polly let them out. When we got back to the cabin the dogs were gone. I retraced my steps that day and the next and the next. I never saw my Buck again.

Buck. Roland Jenkins. Photograph.

Buck II. Roland Jenkins. Photograph.

RACHEL GARDNER
SEARCHING FOR HER SHADOWS, HOWL, & LONGING FOR CONNECTION

Bio

Rachel Gardner is a Houston-based artist and Art Affiliate at Houston Baptist University. She recently received her Master of Fine Arts from there as well. Though she has always loved nature, her love for wolves developed during her thesis studies. She began to fall in love with the beautiful creatures and empathize to the fact that they are often misunderstood. Gardner proceeded to not only paint the wolf, but she created an entire life-sized wolf pack installation out of paper mache. She has displayed her work at countless exhibitions. When she is not making art, she loves to travel, stay active, and spend time with family and friends.

Searching for Her Shadows. Rachel Gardner. Charcoal on paper.

Howl. Rachel Gardner. Paper mache sculpture.

Longing for Connection. Rachel Gardner. Mixed media on canvas.

TAYLOR CAVAZOS
THE THREE MILLION PIGS

Bio

Taylor Cavazos is a student at Vanderbilt University. She is specializing in English and Communication in a Diverse America. Her hobbies include reading, writing, hiking, and riding horses.

The following story manages to invert the classic "Three Little Pigs" story while providing a critique on environmental destruction, pollution, and how history is always rewritten by the victors.

Once upon a time there were three million pigs.

They built houses with straw, with sticks, and with bricks. Their houses covered the entire land, and every day, the pigs would build more and more. Every time they finished a house, the pigs sang and danced and celebrated in their new city.

On the edge of their metropolis lived a lonely wolf. Every day, he saw the pigs build their houses. Day by day, night by night, the pigs danced and sang closer and closer to his house. Every night, he hoped a great wind would come and blow everything down.

They used the trees, the rocks, and the soil to build their great houses. Before long, the beautiful land lay barren and naked. The pigs began looking for more straw, more sticks, and more bricks. Only so they could build more houses.

One day, the pigs walked by the wolf's house and said, "What a beautiful house this will make!" The wolf overheard the pigs, and feared that the pigs would come after his home.

One day, three big pigs came to his front door.

KNOCK, KNOCK, KNOCK

"Let us in!"

"NO!" said the wolf

The pigs tried to blow his house down, but they were not strong enough.

They tried to tear it down, but the wolf's house would not budge.

Finally, the pigs confronted the wolf's house with a giant machine. The wolf had never seen anything like it.

It had great, big claws, and as it traveled down the road, thick, black smoke escaped from the top of it. On the side, the machine read "Pig Builders, Inc." and the wolf saw the silhouette of a pig inside the belly of the great, metal beast.

The monstrosity made its way to the wolf's front door. But there was nothing he could do.

The wolf simply sat and watched as the metal giant, exhaling heavy smoke, huffed. And puffed. And blew his house down.

Nelli Smith
Evolution

Bio

One of our youngest contributors, Nelli Smith is a seventh-grader from Gaithersburg, Maryland. She writes as a hobby and has a great passion for all animals, especially wolves.

Past.
Wild wolves.
Powerful hunters. Majestic animals.
Some, less wary, came to us.
They ate our food scraps and stuck around.
We learned to hunt together.
Artificial selection. Domestication.
Dogs.

MARISSA MOLIVIATIS
WOLVES IN WINTER

Bio

Marissa Moliviatis has been living in a small town-like city called Athens in Southeastern Ohio. She is a student attending Hocking College, pursuing an Associate of Science Degree. She plans to transfer to Ohio University to obtain a major in Wildlife and Conservation Biology. She has written two children's books throughout her elementary school years, The Lone Wolf *being her most prized piece.*

It was a cold winter night when I heard the wolves sing.
Their voices carried softly by a gentle frozen breeze.
I hear the whispers seeping out from the shadows.
The trees sway with the slow dance of the snow.
The wilderness announces its presence.
I can hear the soft rustle of life beneath the snow.
I can smell the crisp scent of a world buried in white.
The silence, it engulfs me, until I'm consumed by it.
But I am not afraid...
When suddenly, out of the frigid darkness, golden eyes glow.
I freeze, out of wonder, not fear.
The soft crunch of frozen flakes under padded paws grows ever louder.
A silvery white mist climbing up to the blanket of black from cold, wet
    noses.
A shiver moves through me, but I am still.
The mysterious songs of the winter forest are given a form.
All at once, they appear before me.
All at once, I hear them sing.

Darren Greenidge
What's the Time, Mr. Wolf? & Children of the Forest

Bio

Darren Greenidge lives in a market town in Hertfordshire in the United Kingdom and is surrounded by Roman archaeology in his town and close by. The ruins of Berkhamsted Castle where William the Conqueror helped stake his claim on England are close by too as is Verulamium; modern day St. Albans. It's all inspiration to him.

Darren is interested in archaeology and history and wolves of course as well as many other subjects that are the usual suspects. He has previously interviewed singer/songwriter Amy MacDonald for Q Magazine *online in the UK.*

He set up the blog Caliburnus Rises *in March 2011. His dream is to write for* Doctor Who *and maybe play him too one day!*

What's the time Mr. Wolf?

*'Late morning,' says the Wolf
as he runs and hides*

What's the time Mr. Wolf?

*'Midday,' says he
as shots ring out and
his pack scatters*

What's the time Mr. Wolf?

*'Evening,' says he sadly,
as he looks at the carnage
about him, metal teeth drawing
blood*

What's the time Mr. Wolf?

'Too late,' says the Wolf
with tears in his eyes, now
the last of his kind as the
hunter takes aim…

What's the time Mr. Wolf?

Silence
No more howls
Time has run out…

Children of the Forest

A thin mist wisps through
the trees
The Dragon's breath
alive
As it snakes around
rock and wood
And over still
waters
The forest is quiet
today
Not a bird
chirps
Not a rustle in
the undergrowth
Not a whisper
in the trees
As the mountains
rise in the distance
Lording over all
below
Snow melting in
rivers
Giving life to
its children

And then a
noise
So quiet it's
barely heard
Quiet falls on
the forest bed
Move with careful
guise
Then from the
mists
Comes a sight to
behold!
Magnificent in
their glory
Appearing like
otherworldly beings
These creatures
of Mother Nature
These children of
the forest
These custodians
of all we take for granted
Come and go
as if wraiths of the forest
Into the mist
and into memory
Finally into myth
and legend
Until just a
story to be told
These misunderstood
children of the forest

FEDERICA GUIDOTTI
WE ARE ALL CONNECTED

Bio

Federica Guidotti lives in Ticino, Switzerland. She studies biology and draws in her free time. She hopes to help with wolf conservation throughout her country.

We Are All Connected. Federica Guidotti. Sketch markers on paper.

ELIZABETH WINDHAM
PROWL

Bio

Elizabeth Windham is a longtime animal enthusiast who works at a pet store as she is pursuing an education toward a veterinary technician's license. She plans to pursue a Master's degree in anthrozoology. She has published a poem about her feral cat rescue.

Prowl. Elizabeth Windham. Pencil on paper.

JONATHAN W. THURSTON
WOLF KING'S LULLABY

Bio

Jonathan W. Thurston received his B.A. in English at Vanderbilt University with a minor in Japanese. He specializes in studying Animal Literature, but he also has a fondness for literary fiction. He has written two novels Farmost Star I See Tonight *and* Where Carnivores Meet. *He has also published a poem in* Gifted *and a short story in the anthology* Lupus Animus. *He is the founder of Thurston Howl Publications and an editor in his spare time.*

Thurston lives near Nashville with his dog Temerita and a house full of books.

Here the new wolf king struggles to learn the secret of his father's mysterious past and the crystal lake that is tied to finding all the answers.

Points of light dotted the sky, illuminating the darkness of the night, while Arin the Wolf King left the comfort of his cave to embrace the chill of the summer breeze. His eyes shifting left and right, he scanned the area for other beasts that treaded the way. His heart relaxed as he realized he was alone. With paws quick as the wind itself, he ran from his castle, his den, his home. Trees passed either side the gray-haired king.

Despite his crown, he was young. When his father had died a few months ago, Arin had stepped in to rule the packs. He was the alpha of alphas, the ruler of the night, the moon whisperer. Yet, the moon had muttered neither recommendations nor advice to his lonely ears. It was as silent to him as it had been before he had been crowned king.

The branches tore at his flawless, rich fur; the rocks ripped at his strong, thick paws. The mass of forest around him obscured his vision, but his nose led him better than his eyes ever could. He could smell the spot. He knew it was there.

"Your Majesty!"

Instead of slowing down, Arin accelerated and leaped onto an overhanging limb, hiding amongst the trees. He froze as he gazed downward, searching for the caller. It was a gray wolf like him. After it stepped beneath him, he recognized him to be the alpha from the Kotane pack Kiehr.

"Your Majesty?" Kiehr said as he looked around the forest right beneath the hidden Wolf King. "I know you're out there. I saw you leave the den. What are you doing? Her Majesty the Wolf Queen said you were not to be allowed out this late at night."

Arin clenched his teeth. Kiehr did not know his place. His job was to lead the Kotane pack but also to follow any of Arin's orders. Why would Mera, his wife, have any say in what he did? Well, he knew very well how Mera could have scared any of the other alphas: Mera spoke constantly to his mother, the previous Wolf Queen. That gave her almost as much power as he had. For some reason, once the Wolf King had died, Arin's mother began having special talks with his mate. Now, Mera made as many orders as he did. It was not right.

"Your Majesty?"

With a low growl, Arin the Wolf King sprang from the branch and landed behind Kiehr. "What is it, Kiehr?"

The smaller wolf jumped as he turned to face his king. "Your Majesty, Her Majesty Lady Mera would want you to return to the den. This area is forbidden."

Arin raised a brow. "Forbidden?" He turned back to gaze at the direction he was headed. "Why is that? My father went there all the time."

"I'm sorry, Your Majesty, but Her Majesty Lady Mera and your own mother have advised that you not be allowed to go there." Kiehr shuffled his feet, and his eyes lowered to the ground, yet his voice remained confident and almost aggressive.

By contrast, Arin stood tall, proud, staring Kiehr down. "Would you try to stop me then?" He leaned closer to the alpha. "Stand down, Kiehr. I am the Wolf King, and if you try to regulate my daily actions, you might as well be challenging me directly. Go home and tell no one about this."

He turned to leave, but Kiehr only stepped forward. "Um, pardon me, Your Majesty, but…"

"What is it?" Arin roared, whipping back to face Kiehr with a growl.

"It's just…the Lady Mera threatened to kill me if you got past me…"

Arin took a step back. "You…you were a night watcher? To keep me in the den?"

Kiehr only nodded at this but kept his head low to the ground.

"What did Mera or my mother tell you about this place I'm going to?"

"Just that you're not allowed there."

Arin stopped to think. His father had come to this place every night. It was a clearing by a lake. He had always told Arin that it was easy to lose oneself in the moonlit water, in the air that sparkled with fireflies, in the scent of flowers amongst the pines. It was a magical place where the old Wolf King would do his nightly thinking and plan how to keep the packs together, ward off enemy packs, and survive. Arin had never been there, this place his father had called Lake Laria. When Arin had asked the wolf elders about Lake Laria, they knew nothing about it. No one did. His father had told him how to get there though, but he had never tried...until now.

"Well then, come with me."

Kiehr cocked his head sideways. "What?"

"When we get back, just say that you couldn't dissuade me but that you led me elsewhere."

Kiehr shuffled his feet again but nodded in acquiescence.

Arin smiled. "Come on."

As they stepped through the forest, Arin eyed Kiehr. The smaller wolf had a long scar across his face from a fight several years ago. By far, Kiehr was older and more experienced than Arin, but Arin was the largest and the strongest. Kiehr had earned his title through years of diligent training and even a little bit of luck. Still, Arin knew that Kiehr was more than just muscle. Those worn muscles came with an intelligent brain, one that had helped Arin's father on more than one occasion.

Kiehr was curious too. He knew that the old Wolf King had went into the dark woods every night, though no one knew what wisdom he had found there. Everyone whispered it though: the old Wolf King spoke to the moon. He could predict the weather and summon prey into their plains by talking to the great moon herself. Everyone had their own story of the power of the great old Wolf King, but now, he was gone. Now, this young wolf Arin was king. Kiehr knew better than to question the line of command. Arin was his king, and he held no bitterness toward him.

"Kiehr?"

"Yes, Your Majesty?"

"What did you know about my father?"

Kiehr slowed his pace as he considered. "He was a great and wise Wolf King. All loved him, and no enemy lasted long under his iron paw."

"No," Arin said, shaking his head. "I meant besides what you're supposed to say to me. Speak candidly, Kiehr."

Swallowing, Kiehr started, "Well, maybe he wasn't loved by everyone…"

Arin glanced sideways. "What?"

"Well, Her Majesty his wife, your mother, planned to kill him on numerous occasions, but he escaped her every move. His natural death was his way of letting his spirit laugh at her."

This was all news to Arin. "My mother…hated my father?"

"No one knows. As you can tell, she has gained no power from his death. Though she might speak words into Her Majesty Lady Mera's ears, she means nothing but the best for the packs, as do you, Your Majesty."

"Why would she do that?" Arin asked, more to himself than to Kiehr.

Kiehr was silent.

The branches brushed across their heads, leaving thin leaves and nettles in their pelts. The ground softened as they trekked, but the night continued to envelop them. It took mere minutes until Arin could smell the lake ahead.

What is it about this place? Why did my father go to it every night, and why are my mother and Mera trying to stop me from reaching it? What secrets does this Lake Laria hold?

Beside him, he sensed Kiehr's wariness and anxiety. If Mera had threatened his life, then Kiehr was probably hoping they would not be able to reach the hidden lake. Arin grinned to himself. Whatever his family was hiding, he was about to discover it. Light pierced the trees as the forest thinned. His eyes widened.

The trees cleared as a view of the shallow lake spread before them. The lake was crystal clear, and the pale image of the full moon shone on the water's surface. Beautiful red flowers lined the edge of the forest, and the mixed aroma of pines and roses filled their senses. Because their eyes had become accustomed to the darkness of the forest, the thousands of fireflies were dazzling as they floated through the air.

"What…what is this place?" Kiehr stammered.

Arin smiled. His father had been right. "This is Lake Laria, the place my father came to every night. I shall come here now too to glean what sacred knowledge he possessed." He sniffed the air again, searching. It took him just seconds to locate his father's scent. The place had not washed it away yet. He ambled forward to the edge of the lake, where the scent was strongest. He could smell that another wolf had been here as well.

Kiehr stood where he was, admiring the beauty of the summer scene. Enchanted, he was the only one who heard the bushes shake behind him. He jumped and crouched into an offensive position, ready to strike whatever manner of creature lay in wait. He saw a pair of eyes between the leaves and struck the beast. He had not expected it to be a loathsome porcupine. Face full of quills, Kiehr ran yelping through the woods, no longer concerned about the actions of Arin the Wolf King.

Arin did not have to look back to see what had happened to Kiehr. He sat and drank from the lake, admiring the place's serenity. Then, he looked up at the moon. "Oh moon, what is it about this place? Why did my father come here so often? What secrets can you impart?"

Though he asked such questions of the celestial body, he had not expected to receive an answer. "Oh wolf, who was your father who came here so often? Who are you to ask such things of the moon?"

Arin stepped backward, mouth agape. "I...I...my name is Arin. My father was the Wolf King, but...he has died, and I have taken the crown. He used to tell me he came here and found magic and wonderment here."

The voice responded, *"You* are the new Wolf King?"

"Yes, that is correct."

The moon laughed with a hint of coldness. "You want to learn to whisper to the moon and learn all my secrets?"

"Yes, I would. I would seek to become the great and wise king my father was."

There was silence. Arin risked several glances around. The voice surrounded him, coming from all sides. The trees swayed in the delicate breeze, spreading their scents across the lake. The fireflies twinkled like the stars above, and the moon stood silent above him.

Had the moon just been talking to him?

"Wolf King Arin, if you speak truth, then you must know that your father learned no great secrets here. All that he knew, he learned on his own. I gave him no advice on those affairs." The voice echoed across the lake, filling Arin's ears, and his heart resonated, beating in rapid time with the echo.

"But he was the moon whisperer though?"

The moon chuckled. "Yes, he whispered sweetly into my ear on many a night, yet I gave him no instructions. Why are you here, Wolf

King?"

Arin lowered his snout to examine his reflection in the still lake. "He told me how to get here. Back then, I was having trouble with my mate, and he told me that if things got…too bad, then I should come here, and I would find that the place would soothe my lonely heart."

A breeze picked up and swayed his fur in undulating ripples, but the moon hesitated. "And you have such a lonely heart? You are having troubles with your mate still?"

Clenching his eyes shut, Arin fought back tears. He had never told anyone besides his father about the growing distance between he and his mate. "Moon, this is not easy for me…"

The moon's voice grew sweeter. "Please, I understand. Tell me what ails you."

"I…Mera has always been good to me, yet I do not love her anymore. There is no passion. There is no romance. She is power-hungry like my mother. She berates me and does not acknowledge my own feelings. When my father died, she and my mother rushed to crown me, even though I was not fully ready at the time." He lowered his head again and muttered, "I still wonder if I'm ready."

The moon's reflection rippled as the water shook. "You are more than ready, Wolf King. You have your father's eyes, his step, and his humility. I did give your father much to ease his problems with his mate. Loneliness is a hard sorrow to bear."

"But what am I to do about it? I can't just leave her, but I am not sure that I can tolerate her forever."

"Do you think your father did?"

Arin raised his head and gazed at the moon's pale face with confusion written on his face. "What?"

The moon laughed again. "Your father first came here to escape his mate, and he continued to come after he saw how I helped him. I did not advise him to leave his mate or to fight her. I taught him how to tolerate it."

Shaking his head, Arin responded, "Tolerate it? How did he do that? Did he hate her as much as she hated him?"

Sighing, the moon replied, "She had tormented him so it would be easier for her to rule the packs while he was so stressed with their relationship. It was pure manipulation at its finest. When your father came to me, I taught him how to see through that. I gave him magic and light that I would refresh him with every night, so that he was able to concentrate for every day of his reign."

Arin took three steps into the water, his ears perked up, and his tail wagged. "Magic? Light? Can you give me that as well, oh Moon?"

The moon's voice took a warmer tone. "My name is not Moon, you know. But yes, I can give you that same respite and relief. It is not magic so much as magical though. Tell me, Wolf King, what is it your father told you about this place?"

The Wolf King looked behind him in the direction of home, at the pines. He closed his eyes and said, "He had said it was easy to lose yourself in the moonlit water, in the air that sparkled with fireflies, in the scent of flowers among the pines. He called it magical. He always told me that the lake was called Lake Laria, though no one else seemed to recognize the name."

"You may yet lose yourself, Wolf King."

At the opposite end of the small lake, he saw a fair wolf walk toward him from the trees. Her pelt was pearl white, and her sapphire eyes twinkled in the glow of the moon. Mouth agape, Arin walked toward the angelic creature. The breeze blew her fur around her, as if her pelt was made of the feathers of a dove. His eyes locked with hers as they circled the lake to meet halfway at the eastern edge.

"Oh moon," Arin stammered. "Who is this lovely wolf you are showing me?"

The pearl wolf grinned as she said, "There is no talking moon, Wolf King."

Arin's eyes opened wide. "But...I was just..." What was going on? What was happening to him? Where was the voice of the moon?

She stepped forward and put her muzzle next to his erect ear. His muscles tensed and froze at her touch. "I am the voice of the moon. I can ease your lonely heart as I once eased your father's. Do you still seek that respite and relief?"

"I...I..." Arin managed before nodding. He swallowed.

She brushed her nose against his snout. "I am Laria."

He left that sacred place with the smell of pines and roses and even the moon embracing him. His father had been right. He had lost himself in that magical place. That night, Arin the Wolf King learned much about love and magic, but, most of all, he learned why his mother had fought so hard to keep him from coming here.

JUSTIN KILBY
LIGHT IN THE DARK

This is my tribute to the unnecessary loss of life in the wolf population by poachers would be hunters and trappers.

The dark so heavy,
cold piercing through my hair,
my breath rushing over me,
the snow falls from the weighted branches of the trees,
the run has taken over me,
my brothers close never breaking from me,
I look up and see the hanging lights,
we stop and stare,
the lights catch us and hold us here,
this is where I belong,
family surrounding me,
BANG!!!!....
I am gone, where did I go?
where's my family?,
are these the lights we saw?
what's this warmth and glow around me,
am I light now?,
I miss my family,
Why did I have to go?

KATT REINGRUBER
FIVE BROTHERS

Five Brothers. Katt Reingruber. Photograph.

Five Brothers

As a recent widow who moved to Albuquerque, New Mexico, from Laguna Niguel, California in September of 2012, I found myself needing something to do with my time.

Since my daughter and grandson as well as grand-daughter and family have lived in Albuquerque for several years, I had visited several times. Each time I always wanted to go to the Rio Grande Zoo. Well now I find myself living in Albuquerque and the Zoo is a place I want to be at. But since I am living on a limited income, I needed to find a job at the Zoo. Not an easy thing to do. What I did find was the volunteer program offered. I could become a Zoo Docent, Greeter or work in the gardens.

First sign up was for the Horticulture volunteer program offered by the BioPark Botanic Gardens. Requested site to work in was the Zoo. This gave me unlimited access to the Zoo, any hours it was opened. So I pulled weeds, raked leaves and planted a shrub or two. But when the volunteer time was over, I could do whatever I wanted while in the Zoo.

I have also enjoyed photography as a hobby for several years. Now I have the best of two worlds that I enjoy. Being at the Zoo, and photographing animals at the Zoo.

The BioPark only offers Docent Training once a year, but as soon as August came in 2013, I couldn't sign up fast enough. It is a very intense learning program, having to understand the various animals, conservation concerns and well as endangered species.

It was the Mexican Gray wolf that has given me the greatest passion I have ever known for a cause. The morning I took the picture of the "Five Brothers", I had arrived as soon as the gates opened and spent a better part of four hours, watching the wolves move about their enclosure, taking pictures. With every Zoo guest that came by, they would say they had never seen the wolves move about. But since they are elusive naturally, you have to be aware of their habits, and I just happen to come on a rather cool morning, and all the wolves were up and about. One picture after another, snap, snap, snap.

It wasn't until I reviewed the photos later at home that I realized I had captured all five of the wolves in one shot. Trust me, if I got three, couldn't get the fourth in the frame. Then since the two on the left really blended in, I even caught myself off balance when I realized I had all five in one frame.

My excitement led me to send a copy of the photo to the BioPark's Facebook page. They responded stating they didn't even have a photo that caught all five of the brothers in one frame.

The Albuquerque BioPark Zoo is a holding facility for the endangered Mexican Gray Wolves. These boys were to have advanced on to a release program, but when the releases started to get delayed, their chance to become release wolves passed.

So now I take pictures of the beautiful boys. Hope to hear them howl one day, you know, about the time you least expect it. Maybe that one morning I come in a little earlier than need be or the last walk out after a long day, or now, on one of the "Twilight Tours" I have gotten to lead this year as a Docent of the Zoo. After hour tours through the Zoo, only offered a few times in the Summer, but at a time that the wolves could give up one of their howls.

GENEVIEVE MARIANI
LEARNING TO HOWL, FREE WOLF, & AMETHYST WOLF

Bio

Genevieve Mariani is a resident of Los Angeles, an avid animal welfare activist, illustrator, and sculptor. Much of her work revolves around issues regarding endangered species, and relationships between humans and non-humans. She has been featured in many gallery shows, completed countless commissioned works, as well as having her own solo show at the El Dorado Nature Center. Genevieve has two rescue dogs whom she enjoys hiking with in her free time.

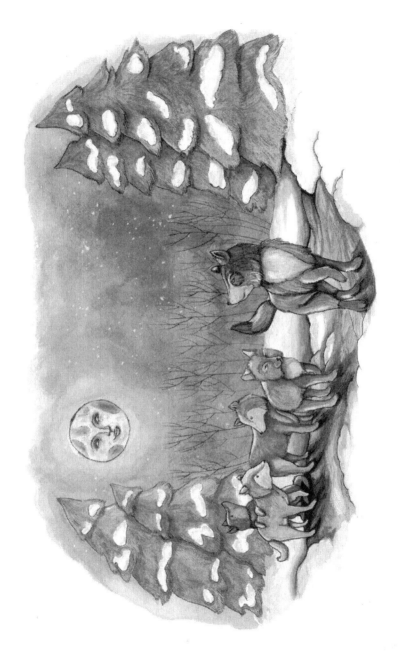

Learning to Howl. Genevieve Mariani. Watercolor on paper.

Free Wolf. Genevieve Mariani. Acrylic on wood panel.

Amethyst Wolf. Genevieve Mariani. Watercolor on paper.

Jeremy G. Hearn
Lone Wolf

Bio
Jeremy G. Hearn lives in Lexington, Tennessee. He has published one other poem entitled "Monster of Darkness." His hobbies include drawing, playing guitar, and writing. He is presently working on a novel manuscript.

Tonight I sit, howling at the moon
Because the sadness of losing so many weighs heavily upon my back.
All my family and friends
Even my whole pack,
They're all gone too soon.
Tonight I sit, howling at the moon
Wondering why you abandoned me
In my time of need and sorrow,
Knowing there's no promise of tomorrow.
My paws are bloody
From a past so clouded and matted from regrets,
Filled with difficulties not so easily overcome,
Somehow sweet yet also gruesome.
Tonight I sit, howling at the moon
Wondering why we have to be worlds apart
Yet still close and inseparable,
In a place that matters most, in the heart.
Tonight I sit, howling at the moon
Because in my canine heart there's a hole
That goes deeper, even into my soul,
Oh tell me why you had to go so soon?

KATE JOHNSTON
AN ESSAY ON WOLF RESCUE

Bio

Kate Johnston was born on Cape Cod, and raised in New Hampshire where nature and wildlife stirred her imagination. She knew she wanted to be a writer when she wrote a story about a good wolf. She thinks words are magical, enticing, and more-ish. Brew them together, and she creates stories. Family dramas with heart and a touch of magical realism.

Married with two children and living in Dover, NH, she works as a freelance writer for non-profit organizations and teaches creative writing to kids. She is an aspiring novelist and works on her novels at 4 in the morning, the best time of day for writing without interruptions.

Her short story, "Treasures," was published in The Greensilk Journal, *spring 2011. She blogs about her writing quest at 4amWriter. When she's not writing, she loves to take nature hikes, bake ooey-gooey desserts, and let her kids beat her at sports.*

The following essay details the struggles and complications inherent in rescuing wolves and gives a shout-out to the organizations that do work so hard daily to make such rescues possible.

**A wolf howling in the wild
belongs there
and he ain't leaving
without a fight**

I thought I wanted to be a vet when I grew up. I used to rescue all sorts—snakes, squirrels, frogs, turtles, birds, chipmunks, rabbits, groundhogs, bats, opossums. I even helped a fox once. Oh, and an eel.

But, I'm kind of squeamish. I can't handle blood, any kind of bodily fluids actually. Knowing part of a vet's job would require me to put animals to sleep, even though I knew it would help them feel better, was beyond my tolerance. I'm great at comforting the sick, calming the traumatized, but setting a broken bone or plunging a needle into flesh or easing the spirit into the next world? Not so much.

So, I dropped the idea of being a vet.

As I turned to my other passion, writing, I wrote about animals instead. Some of my favorite stories I wrote were about wolves. I made the wolf the good guy, unheard of when human beings were on the verge of killing off the entire population of wolves in the United States.

In 1926, the last wolf pack had been killed in Yellowstone (though there were ongoing reports of lone wolves). In 1974, the grey wolf had been listed as an endangered species, and in 1975 recovery was mandated under the Endangered Species Act.

Wolves were reintroduced to Yellowstone in 1995—20 years after they were first listed as endangered. They have had a hell of a roller coaster ride overcoming the odds.

As a kid, I didn't know what the wolves were going through. I just knew that they always got a bad rap in books.

I wanted to change that.

As I grew older, I followed their story of revival, their comeback, cringing with every obstacle they faced. I joined a national organization, Defenders of Wildlife, to help their recovery. That outreach stimulates and energizes me. It's like cheering on my favorite "underdog" team from the sidelines.

Wouldn't it be wonderful if every single person on this planet fought for something wild? Imagine how much we would save. I don't care if it's a wolf, a river, a flower, or a mollusk. If we all chose one wild thing that mattered to us and fought for it, this world would be a healthier, happier place.

There are some amazing people who have given their lives to wildlife. I would love to meet them all, tell them *thank you.*

One such amazing woman, Brenda, lives a couple of hours from me, in Limington, Maine. Brenda runs a wolf rescue and education center, called *Runs with Wolves Sanctuary.* The pure wolves that come to her are usually born in captivity, kept as "pets," mismanaged and abused, or abandoned. She also takes care of wolf-dogs (half-wolf, half-dog), who were generally kept as pets but ultimately abandoned or mistreated.

When owners give up on their "pet" wolves, those animals cannot be returned to the wild. They are too familiar with people and can't survive on their own. Instead, they must be surrendered to rescue facilities or euthanized.

Brenda's place is the end of the line for these wolves. She does not breed them as she is morally opposed to creating more captive wild animals. But, if she has a chance to rescue a wolf who might otherwise be euthanized or bred, she does everything she can to step in. She pens them for their protection, and gives them the closest experience as possible to living wild. Make no mistake—this isn't the ideal solution, but it's all they have.

Brenda gives wolves a second chance at life. Maybe these animals can't exactly live on the wild side like they are meant, but their survival is a clear indication of how much one human being can do to help.

As a busy mom, I don't get to do as much legwork for Defenders or local organizations like Brenda's as I would like. Contributing money, supplies, volunteer time is mostly what I do.

And I talk about them, write about them. As much as I can (without annoying people). Every time I talk or write about the wolves and educate someone about the realities, I feel like I'm helping a wolf, somewhere.

Giving them a fighting chance is one of the best feelings, ever.

MARC LATHAM
SEASON DANCER, FOREST ILLUMINATOR

Bio

Dr. Marc Latham graduated from the University of Leeds in 2005. He has since been working as a freelance writer and poet in the city. His greenygrey website base has a wolf logo, and animal welfare and environmentalism background theme. After his first three books were published, he self-published his latest two. His fiction and poetry often feature wolves and wildlife, with the Greenygrey fictional character a Scooby Doo-inspired traveling vegetarian werewolf.

Marc invented the Folding Mirror poetry form, and it was included in Prof. Lewis Turco's authoritative Book of Forms. *"Season Dancer, Forest Illuminator" is an example of a Folding Mirror poem, with the word count mirroring in either half of the poem, title and middle. The ekphrastic poem was inspired by a photo in a wolf calendar sent by his brother's family living in Ohio. On one visit to Ohio, Marc was thrilled to meet a three-quarters wolf hybrid.*

fire melting gold
fall full flow
leaves oval shaped
seem to poke
fun behind rump
tongue-twisting
on thin reaching branches
both rise from rock, wolf and tree harmony
under strong running legs
tree-like
paws resemble plinths
keep head grounded
feminine tongue smiles
sunrise eyes shine
below mountain peaks

KATI WILLIAMS
NORTHERN LIGHTS

This static world is blanketed with fragments of color, twisting across the ice like light shining through gemstones. Mirages of emotion interrupting the stars in all their withdrawn beauty, flashing across the sky in riots of pirouettes and arabesques. They are too beautiful to dance without a song.

All is still save for the crystalline light casting its reflection through the frosted overhangs and the breath that pours from your lips like earthly apparitions. You lament to break the silence, crying to a love you can never touch. Ears flat, head tilted you raise a call in companionship with the flickering pastels; wishing you could touch the stars as they can. Before, you could have sworn there was no end to this barren landscape, but as your sweet melody echoes in the hearts of your brothers and sisters, you don't feel so alone.

RYAN NOOE
SNOW

Bio

Ryan Nooe is a 21-year-old resident of Indiana. He is pursuing a Master's degree in Anthropology at the University of North Carolina-Charlotte. He has written countless short stories and enjoys poetry, drawing, singing, aeronautical/astronomic design, and the scientific study of supernatural objects.

Here is the tale of a man, a wolf, a lady, and, most of all, snow. When you walk out into the blizzard, you will find that not even the howl of a wolf can chill you anymore.

I can recall the snow. I can remember what I saw. I was stepping in the frozen white-water, burying my legs to my knees. The ground and sky were illuminated by the white, giving me no sense of time. Morning, noon, or near-night; I could not have known the difference. Not with the snow swirling round me, confining my vision to only a few feet in any direction, and the wind forcing my eyes shut. Most would not have gone into the white as I did, but I knew that if I kept my feet straight, I would find the trees where I meant to go. Once there, I could find my way on to the place I called home. The wind was constant, and as long as it struck my right side, I knew I was not veering far from a proper course.

I stepped long in the frozen white-water, gripping my arms to press my coat against my chest. I kept my gaze forward, toward the wall of downward-falling snow, hoping that I would see something new and know that I was not just moving in place. And I did see something new. At first, I saw only a shadow; a formless gray ghost not far beyond me. I did not assume it was alive, not until I saw her. When the wind and snow between us grew thin, I saw that the gray ghost was actually a white woman. I say white not because of her skin, which was actually rather olive in shade, but because of her hair. It was not silver, nor was it gray or blonde. It was as if the snow itself had frozen upon her head. But it did not move as ice. The wind was harsh, and her blank mane seemed to float by the command of the cold air. I could see only that and her shoulders, but it was not until I got closer that I realized she was bare. She wore not a single bit of cloth, and by the time I saw the near whole of her body through the snow, I had stepped too close. Her hair whipped round as she turned to set her gaze on me. I stopped, and she stared. She did not shiver in the cold or seem to care. Instead she locked her eyes on mine, eyes that were surely green, but held a gray hue; enough for one to mistake the color for blue. Although we seemed to watch each other for an endless time, it was but a second until the woman turned again and disappeared into the white and the gray.

Truly she must have been a ghost to have been gone from sight so fast. I continued forward, my pace hastened. Before I could decide why I wanted to follow her, I became lost in the endless wall of snow, hoping to see that shadow again. The roaring wind conquered the sound of my steps, although I cared not for what noise I made. I remained focused on the wintry abyss ahead. Each time forward was hard. I forced the snow up from the surface as I pushed through. My sight grew more strained. I was blinded by the white that encased me and my right arm became stiff from the cold. I began to realize that seeing the woman again was not important. Why she was there, absent clothing in the snow, was not my concern. Finding the forest was what mattered. I maintained the straightness of my feet, hoping to see the dark of trees ahead. But I did not see trees. I saw only white, until I saw gray. It was but a shadow in the storm. I halted, then moved forward slowly. The gray grew clear until it became white. I saw that it was her, only now I did not look at her back. She stood, turned towards me. Her eyes were locked with mine, but her gaze was soft. The snow seemed to hide her body, for I saw no bare skin. I thought she had, perhaps, taken up a coat, but a coat from where? It was not until the wind calmed that I saw it was not a coat.

Her face was not of an olive tint because it was covered in white hair. Her mouth was long, and her ears were high and pointed. Her hair swayed in the wind and I saw that the white hair I had mistaken for a coat held much closer to her skin. Her chest gave noticeable evidence for her gender, even though it was covered in fur. Her eyes captivated me. Although I quickly saw that my stare was upon the head of a wolf,

I could see that she was a woman, even just in her face. She seemed to pause for a moment. It was as if she, like me, wanted to become caught in this same game of eyes. I could not have moved even if I had wished to. I was not afraid of what I saw. I was willfully trapped in the snow, feeding my eyes with this bizarre sight. She was the first to move. Her eyes turned down, and her head turned away, as if she were ashamed. Then, just as quickly as she had reappeared, she was gone. I was determined now. I had lost hope that I would find her before, only to see her again. Only now, she had become different. Her colorless hair had become a natural shield from the cold. I had to see her. Even as my legs and my right arm began to fall numb, I stepped forward with strong pace.

I could feel the blood rushing to my face as the cold burned my bare skin. The sight ahead became familiar; angle-falling snow, and an endless whiteness. Flakes clung to my brows, and I brushed them off, only to wipe my face with the flakes that clung to my arm. The wind seemed to push me off course, as if it did not want me to find her once more. Nevertheless, I maintained whatever straight path I could, having only a uniform ground below me and a wall of snow before me. With warmth dissipating within me, I found it hard to muster the strength to continue. My leg muscles became stiff, for while they were also cold, one will find that it is much harder to move in high snow than on grass or dirt. Exhausted, I began to stare at the ground. My eyes were now shielded from the snow, but I was starting to fall into a trance. My mind went blank as if to give its strength to my legs. All I could do was step forward, my left foot then my right. It became harder and harder to accomplish, and my thighs felt sore. I held my thoughtless stare on the colorless mass I stepped on, occasionally managing to look up and search for my once-gray ghost. I saw nothing, nothing but the snow. It was difficult not to fall from consciousness. When one is surrounded by uniformity, there is nothing to gain attention. With nothing new to be aware of, just a blank ocean void of uniqueness, it is hard to be alert and hard to keep your eyes open. I remember my vision blurring. It was then that I realized I was no longer looking at the snow before my feet. Instead, I now stared straight down at my feet as they stepped. Before I could tell myself that I would not make it much further, my knees gave out. My view of the ground was magnified; my face brought closer as I fell. Once my legs had collapsed, little else could have maintained my upward position. As soon as I struck the snow below me, I found myself moving forward. My chest and my face went deep into the snow upon my fall. I managed to lift my mouth to the open air and breathe, but I did not sit up or stand. Somehow, the snow felt warmer as I lay there. I felt tired and had no real desire to get up. The pain in my legs was gone, and I could feel no other sensation than the chill of the wind and the odd warmth the frozen water seemed to give me. I wanted to sleep. I had never wanted anything more. My whole body seemed to beg me for rest, and I had no desire to deny it. My eyes slowly began to shut. The white became gray, and the gray became black. I could only hear the wind as it roared above me.

As I started to drift from consciousness and the sound of the wind faded, I heard something else. It was quiet, but it stopped me from falling into sleep. Suddenly, I heard it again; a step in the snow like the crunch of a nearly-dry leaf. I opened my eyes. The new stimulus gave me reason to focus; gave me something to focus on. Turning my head to one side, I had hoped to find the source, but I saw only snow. The step came again; it was light but it was also close. I forced my head up and looked toward the sound. At first, I saw nothing; only the white of the snow. Then I noticed that although the snow continued to fall, the white immediately in front of me did not move. Regaining some acuteness of vision, I saw that it was not snow. It was fur. A large, white front leg stood steady only inches from my face. Whatever paw lay at its end was buried, and so I was forced to see what the leg was attached to. I lifted my head higher until my gaze met someone else's. Eyes that were surely green, but held a gray tint stared back at mine across a great muzzle with the commanding, yet easily feminine, features of a white wolf. It was her. I had found my mysterious gray ghost. Only now, she stood not on two legs, but on four. She looked down at me with eyes that gave away her concern. From some unknown origin, I gathered the energy to push myself up. My hands and my knees were down in the snow. Now, I too stood on all fours. I did not feel as though I could rise any further, until the woman turned her head so as to direct my attention. I looked to my left and saw what I had been looking for all along: the forest. The she-wolf came to my side and nudged me, commanding me to stand. Again, even though I had been drained of strength, I found the energy to rise. Hunched over and still feeling weak, I turned toward the trees. The she-wolf stood by my side as I walked, watching me to ensure I did not fall again. Why she cared for me was beyond my knowledge. Even though a stranger may occasionally aid a stranger, this was quite different. I knew what she was, and I knew well what another may have done to her were they in my position. The weight of humanity's foolishness was heavy on my shoulders, and yet the woman walked beside me without hesitation. Perhaps it was because I followed her at first. Many would have turned away in fear, but I stepped forward out of curiosity. Regardless of my motives for that step, had I not taken it, I would not have found my destination. Now I walked with the guidance of a woman whose beauty was just as great in one form as it was in all others.

The white she-wolf stepped alongside me, looking up at me as I held my arms crossed to keep my chest warm. The wind and snow no longer blew in my face, but my body remained numb and stiff just as before. I was still exhausted, and I found myself surprised with each new step I took. I looked down at the woman-turned-wolf, and she looked back at me. One could have thought that, with how much we stared at each other, we were holding entire conversations within our own minds. However, I neither had the energy nor the desire to converse with anyone. I looked forward and saw that we had reached the edge of the forest. The trees were thick, providing a fair shield from some of the wind and snow. I would have a greater chance of surviving within the woods, but I quickly realized that I no longer had the strength to finish my journey. I stopped just inside the trees. The she-wolf stopped and looked at me, noticing that I was breathing heavy. The back of my throat was cold and sore. I matched gazes with the wolf once more, sighing as if to tell her that I could go no further. Again, my legs gave. I came to the ground beside a large tree and leaned up against it. It was still cold, but nowhere near as harsh as it was in the open white. I looked into the deep realm of brown towers, round at their bases and frayed like ropes at their tops. I thought that, perhaps, I might die. If I stayed there, beside that tree, it would most certainly be my fate. However, just as I began to accept that I would not make it, the lady-wolf came over to me. She owed me nothing. In truth, it was because of her that I had made it so far. I was a fool to think I could make it through the storm. And yet, without any reason for doing so, nothing to gain, the lady-wolf came close to me and lay down. She rested against my side and set her head below mine. The warmth of her fur penetrated my coat. Her head stole the cold from my neck, and I welcomed the theft. The olive-skinned woman that was now a white-furred she-wolf stayed with me. I could feel her chest fill with cold air, then release it, the rhythm growing calmer as she fell to rest. I knew as I leaned against the tree and lay with her that, even if I did die soon, I would die with nothing more than what I needed. For nothing waited for me at home; only more of the same life I lived and, apparently, took for granted. With the cold that teased me and the warmth beside me, I did not miss my home. I accepted whatever would come of my falling beside the tree, and I would pass into a cold sleep with my gray ghost beside me; my she-wolf with fur as blank as the snow.

SHAUNALEE "SILVERWOLF" MCKEAN
PURPLE SKY

Bio

Shaunalee "Silverwolf" McKean has long been a wildlife conservationist, working with several wildlife groups to help promote wolf education and conservation. In her spare time, she is an artist.

Her evocative short story here shows one wolf's spiritual journey amongst the stars. Only there can one find the song.

A soft and tattered whisper; Night's fingers within the wind.

There was a romance of gray upon the waters where all things begin.

But the beauty of this place had been tainted and a violet sea ran cold.

The Lights of the Ancients no longer offered wisdom for the Soul.

Something ancient here, yes; somewhere deep within. I must find it for I can feel its call and its pull within me; a voice I've known before, one I cannot ignore. Massive paws seek purchase upon turf and earth that swallows the sound of every stride; every muscle I can feel burning as each bunch and extension spreads and demands as much as I can fly. Speed...speed pushed to burning, old wounds start to complain, but I cannot stop, it won't let me. It cannot be denied, but must be obtained.

Ears push back and swivel to rest against shimmering neck, and every few paces a tickle from manes threads as wind ripples past me. My eyes...burning; a liquid both forming and being stung away as I give everything inside me to the push from rear legs to throttle me forward. Tails level out like banners flowing behind, and yet I can feel the pull of their weight against my hip, almost like the speed in which I Travel threatens to rip them from my hide.

There, yes! I can hear it, my chest pounding as feet seize and scratch ruts upon the ground as my momentum grinds to a sudden halt. Yes...I close my eyes, ears erecting and tilting just so. A twitch in my shoulder, the fur rippling under muscles' protest. Lifting my muzzle to the alluring weaves of the wind, and upon it dancing messages caught by my wet and flaring nose. I was close now. Too close. Closer than I should be, but I wasn't close enough yet...not yet...It was still calling me...the hum becoming a soft song and an urgent plea.

Spinning on my heel I throw myself back into stride, nose now pointed North, ears occasionally rising then falling back along lightning's line. Turf became colder, grass faded to rock, and greens gave way to white which covered all things. The crunch and shift of the snow under foot gave argument to my feet and tried to slip me up, but opal talons sunk in deeply, never giving way, gaining acceleration at my muscles reverent protests, against the fire in my lungs.

Slowing to a trot, then to a chest heaving stop. The waters to my left slumbered deeply with their covers of ice pulled snug and black against its breast. The mountains were Awake now; they knew I was here, and even to their peaks where fog gave way to storms, their majesty was uncontested. I listened for a while, closing silver eyes as their deep murmuring was given a tentative beat by the thunder; turning exhaled rhythms to a song.

But this was not the song that was Calling: this was not the song I followed. This was the song guiding me, telling me where to go. I opened silver orbs as a shadow mutely passed. An owl on whispered wings, cloaked in Winter's dress, quickly faded into the surroundings, a predator at its best. I watched it until it faded as winds tugged at my coat, and even they seemed to tell me that I still had a ways to go.

My body was regretting my instinctual decisions to continue; having run through the Ways of Summer into the Embraces of the Winter. Seasons spent running, turning as I passed, and yet I knew it was needed, but I didn't understand quite why. Nevertheless of reason I once again found speed, frozen trunks of Birch and Ash, leafless and naked accompanying me. To my left were still the slumbering waters, the drifts of snow upon its ice only making its black depths seem more ominous; a void in these deep sleeping lands. Forests to my right as the land before me started to slope, and so I loped against this fortress of steadily rising earth.

Silence never found me, but even if it could, it would be lost to the vast quiet around me. Still I was pulled. Panting breath formed clouds before me, flared nostrils to the cold and black line of lupine lips pulled tight and teeth closed. I slowed as leaves dusted the snow before me; leaves that should not be. Red and gold and a withering bronze with the soft smell of pine sap and evergreen arms. I walked to the rim of this rise I had climbed, and what stretched out before me is what I sought to find.

High above this frozen world I saw a gift of hue, the purple sky above me reflected like crystal dew. The waters arched around my cliff like a dark crescent moon below, and on their far shores arose the Ancient Mountains, draped in their finery of fog and snow. Between two eons-old peaks slipped a spill of color, undulating like a serpent just below the sky. As it weaved and rippled like a ribbon caught up on the wind, its colors touched upon everything like lost and curious kids. Magenta and cobalt, emerald and rose, and as it shot its track upon the heavens it headed directly for my nose.

As the wave splashed over me, my body felt Alive, electrified with a Knowledge of every wolf alive. The colors split around me, cupping me in its midst, and far in the distance thunder echoed in StormSkin. I inhaled deeply, closing my eyes as the Lights of the Ancestors wove through me, splitting upon me to travel Beyond, and when I opened my eyes, I finally could see the Singer of All Songs.

The fog released its embrace upon the Mountains and behind them; across the breath and span of their magnificent towers, were Her branches; reaching hundreds of fingers, thousands of arms, cupping the very sky. Her enormity couldn't be captured, even by my eyes, but even from where I was She brought tears to my eyes. All those woven mazes that formed her golden and knotted bark shimmered with leaves upon Her; twinkling like the stars. The color of good maple, rich and well and True, I stood upon the cliff, then decided I should Sing, too.

Throwing back my head and reaching past my lungs, from my very heart so broken, dripping with such love. Welling up like a tempest and pushed out from my throat, upon my lips sung Harmony to all the Broken Ghosts. A voice of a wolf in timber, echoed a thousand times, dripping hums of Ether in every dip and rise. A howl that rolled like thunder, and ebbed away with a quake; I found myself so tired that I just collapsed where I stayed. Paws hanging over the edge and up so very high, the last image in silver orbs was Boundless before lids closed against a gentle sigh.

KELLY DESSEL
HOWLING WITH THE MEXICAN GREY WOLF

Bio

Artist Kelly Dessel was born in San Luis Obispo, California and now resides in the San Diego area. She has been drawing and painting since she was three years old. Kelly Dessel enjoys working in various mediums such as Acrylics, Inks, Pastels, Oils, and Watercolors. Dessel also loves to create free form ceramics and sculpture. She likes to give a voice to cultures and species of long ago and the present through her paintings and drawings. Dessel has a show at the 4S Ranch Library in San Diego. Her exhibit is called Wildlife of the World: Past and Present.

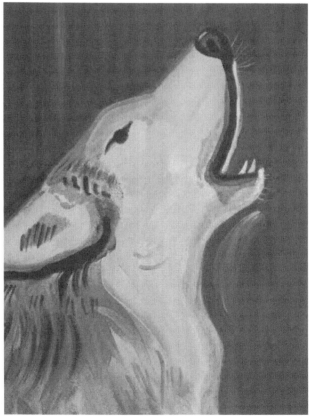

Howling with the Mexican Grey Wolf. Kelly Dessel. Acrylics.

MATT STONE
SPIRIT OF THE WOLF

Bio

Matt Stone (aka Matt Folkmuse Stone) is a folk and americana songwriter from Temecula, California. His first full length album, Northern Lights, *was released in 2013. Moved by the news of her death, Stone created a video tribute to Lamar Vally's alpha female '06, combining his song "Spirit of the Wolf" with images of the Lamar Canyon pack contributed to the project by photographer Jimmy Jones. The song, which was written in Big Sur in 2011, has since taken Matt on a continuing odyssey to share the song and support efforts to protect and restore America's wolves. Along the way he has met an incredible group of dedicated individuals and learned their stories, shared in their triumphs and sorrows. His favorite way to perform the song is in an intimate setting, to a quiet audience, late at night with the lights down. Matt continues to write songs and perform locally and on the occasional tour. He plans to return to the studio to record his second album in the near future.*

I stand here on this ridge
My fur covered in fresh snow
And I look down at the lights
That fill the valley far below

We roamed these hills forever
We knew these mountains well
And our wisdom has been worn
Into a thousand forest trails

Our brothers the Comanche,
The Cherokee and Sioux
Worshipped the Great Spirit
And taught from our totems too

The ranchers and the trappers
They shot us out of fear
Blocked us off with barbed wire
Caught our feet in deadly gear

Late at night
When you're safe at home
You will hear my voice calling
Across the valley far below
I am calling to my pack
I am calling to my clan
"This is our land! This is our land! This is our land!"

I have met the ghost of Black Elk
Running through these granite hills
My heart is full of sorrow
For the blood that has been spilled

Trapped into the camps
Some made into slaves
But he never gave up dreaming
Of the land they took away

Late at night
When you're safe at home
You will hear the voice of Black Elk
When the cold north wind blows
He is calling to his people
He is calling to his tribe
"This is our land! This is our land! This is our land!"

Oh the mothers who were slaughtered
And their children who were killed
The suffering I've seen is something
I could never tell

They told stories of their visions
And they danced around the fire
They kept it all alive somehow
Through times so dark and dire

Late at night
When you're safe at home
You will hear my voice calling
Across the valley far below
I am calling to my people
I am calling to my pack
"This is our land! This is our land! This is our land!"

And now we have returned
Along the mighty Yellowstone
But our brothers never made it
To their ancient land and home

They were scattered on the Four Winds
Pushed out for mortal gold
But their tie to these mountains
Is too sacred to let go

Late at night
When you're safe at home
You will hear my voice calling
Across the valley far below
I am calling to my people
I am calling to my pack
"This is our land! This is our land! This is our land!"

I am the Spirit of the Wolf
And I am witness
To it all…

MITCH RAND
THE TATTERED FLAG OF THE WOLVES

Bio

Mitch Rand lives in Dayton, Ohio, though he often spends time in other states, including Alaska and Florida. He is a contributor to the blog The Life of a Wolf. *Besides writing short stories and working with mixed media, Rand writes how-to guides and is a foam dart war enthusiast.*

The Tattered Flag of the Wolves. Mitch Rand. Electronic/photograph. (poem on next page).

The flag of the wonderful wolves is worn.
Its canton is ripped, its stripes are torn.
Strands hang free and corners sag.
This is the state of the canid flag.
Red has faded and grey is dark.
White and black are covered in marks.
Though it has stood through a perilous fight,
The standard is in a terrible plight.
The wolves who guard it are red and grey.
Though the last of their kinds may fade away.
But hope still sparks within their eyes
As long as the canid flag still flies.
The flag of the wolves can still be saved,
Though its fabric is tattered and state is grave.
If those who care can take a stand,
The flag may return throughout the land.
Until then we can only mourn,
The flag of the wonderful wolves is worn.

CELIA CASTRO
WOLF GIRL

Bio
Celia Castro is 27 years old and lives in Miami, Florida. She has been an artist since she was a child and loves drawing mythological beings.
(Artist dedication: Thanks to all the people who supported and helped me throughout the years for my Art and Comic drawings and thanks to my sweetheart Christian and Jin and my little girl Malinda. This drawing was drawn for Gary Fonseca, her ceramics friend/teacher.)

Wolf Girl. Celia Castro. Pen and paper.

Cornelia Hutt
Endangered Means There is Still Time—A Status Update on the Red Wolf

Bio
Cornelia N. Hutt chairs the board of directors of the Red Wolf Coalition and is the author of the K-12 red wolf curriculum Far Traveler. *She was Education Chair on the board of the International Wolf Center for 11 years, and she currently serves as a member of the* International Wolf *magazine editorial team. She is a patron of the UK Wolf Conservation Trust, and she writes regular articles for their publication* Wolf Print *and for* International Wolf. *She received the International Wolf Center's 2012 "Who Speaks for Wolf" award. She is a retired public school language arts and writing teacher, and she lives in northern Virginia where her family includes dogs, cats, horses, and assorted resident wildlife.*

Hutt's essay speaks out for red wolves, explaining their present situation and what there is to do about it.

Since the world's only wild population of red wolves lives in the U.S. (in northeastern North Carolina), we need to begin with a frequently-asked question: What exactly *is* a red wolf? Some wolf opponents have made a concerted effort to make a case for what the red wolf *isn't*. "There is no such species as *Canis rufus*, the red wolf, " they insist. Their list of reasons for denying these rare predators recognition and legal protection usually includes an attempt to invoke serious science. "Studies," they insist, "show the red wolf is not a wolf at all. It's a hybrid mutt, a coyote mixed with gray wolf and domestic dog." Pressed to produce the "studies," the detractors might cite a blog written by an obscure, self-described "expert" with a negative bias and no credible data to back up the taxonomic conclusions.

But the bottom line is that after decades of healthy debate and disagreement, most scientists and geneticists now agree that the red wolf is a distinct and legitimate canid species. Like the eastern wolf (sometimes called the eastern timber wolf), the red wolf is thought to have evolved, along with its smaller relative the coyote, in North America. The gray wolf, on the other hand, is believed to have evolved in

Eurasia and is not related to the coyote or to the red wolf.

Although its origins remain an enigma, most taxonomists agree that this shy wolf was the top canid predator of the Southeast and Mid-Atlantic regions of the U.S. for thousands of years until ferocious human persecution and habitat loss drove the final survivors to eke out a marginal existence in the marshlands of the Texas/Louisiana Gulf Coast. There, the last red wolves were captured for a pioneer captive breeding program just in the nick of time as hybridization with resident coyotes in the region threatened to swamp the remnant red wolf population.

Protected under federal law (the Endangered Species Act), red wolves were returned to the wild in 1987 on northeastern North Carolina's Albemarle Peninsula, a rural region that was coyote-free at the time. There the wolves established a small but robust population, hunting and raising their wild-born pups in the coastal forests and croplands.

But the hard-won success of the recovery years is now threatened by hybridization with encroaching coyotes that have migrated eastward and filled the niches left by the extirpated wolves. Like the larger gray wolves, red wolves have little tolerance for other canids in their pack territories, but a red wolf will sometimes mate with an eastern coyote if it can't find another red wolf for a partner, and the two will produce hybrid offspring. This threat looms especially large with the loss of 9 wild red wolves (all of breeding age) to illegal gunshot in the past year. Seven wolves were killed in late October and early November of 2013, and a radio-collared red wolf was found shot on January 7, 2014. At this time (July 2014), the wild red wolf population is estimated to number fewer than 100.

Why the sudden alarming rise in gunshot mortality in the five-county red wolf recovery region? There is disagreement among the stakeholders, including both wolf advocates and wolf haters. Justified or not, hunters get a big share of the blame, but the counterpoint to that accusation is that ethical hunters, who abide by established regulations and who value wildlife and habitat conservation, are among the first to condemn the deliberate killing of an endangered species.

A significant number of people have a more ominous theory regarding the spike in illegal gunshot mortality. They maintain the fatal shootings of red wolves are no accident and not cases of careless misidentification with their smaller cousin, the coyote. The wolves, they say, are being targeted.

This conclusion forces yet again an examination of humankind's bias against predators, specifically canid predators. A particularly ugly hatred for wolves and coyotes runs deep in the United States. It doesn't take an exhaustive search to discover Facebook pages devoted to the conviction that humans are justified in exterminating these so-called varmints, "pests" and nuisance species, often by the most savage methods imaginable.

Other proponents of systematically eliminating wolves and coyotes from the landscape cling to the belief that indiscriminate killing of canid predators (particularly coyotes) will "control" and reduce their numbers to an acceptable level, whatever that is. There are data that demonstrate otherwise, but open season on predators with no limits and no reporting required is staunchly supported in many places including North Carolina. The recent decision by a federal court to issue a preliminary injunction to halt coyote hunting in the five-county red wolf recovery region has ignited anger and resentment among some landowners who put coyotes in the same category as cockroaches.

Despite the U.S. Fish and Wildlife Service Red Wolf Recovery Program's 27 years of management innovation, some vocal critics have seized upon the recent illegal gunshot deaths and the reduction of the number of red wolf breeding pairs as evidence of the program's failure and what they deem is now a waste of taxpayer money. That argument ignores the fact that 28 years ago, the number of wild red wolves was zero. Today, there are still perhaps 90 known wolves thriving in the coastal habitat of the Albemarle Peninsula, going about the business of finding food (nutria, deer, raccoons, marsh rabbits) and raising their families on the three national wildlife refuges and on private lands in a region laced with waterways and stitched together by a labyrinth of back roads. These resilient and tenacious animals have hung on in spite of the campaigns to exterminate them, functional extinction in the wild and relatively limited public interest or engagement in their long-term survival.

But they need help. Endangered means it's not too late to save this imperiled species—unless people are apathetic about the illegal killing of these animals and unless our own species denies the great predators like wolves living space among us in an increasingly crowded world. Is it worth the time, expense, energy and will it takes to maintain a species our ancestors hunted and trapped and poisoned until they were all but gone? We can't restore the ecosystems that once nurtured them in the wild, but perhaps we can give them a chance in a small portion of their historical range. To do that, organizations like the Red Wolf Coalition with its partners, including the National Wolfwatcher Coalition and the UK Wolf Conservation Trust, must continue to raise their collective voices and increase the efforts to stop the illegal killing of red wolves.

The Red Wolf Coalition, the Red Wolf Recovery Team and the Coalition's partner wolf organizations are working to bring national and international attention to the plight of the red wolf. Social media like Facebook, Pinterest and Google Plus Communities are making a huge impact on red wolf awareness. Betty and Hank, the lively red wolf ambassador couple at the Red Wolf Education Center in Columbia, North Carolina, are frequently showcased on the Red Wolf Coalition and the Wolfwatcher Facebook pages. Betty and Hank are participants in the Red Wolf Species Survival Captive Breeding Program, which Wolfwatcher has highlighted on their Facebook page by showcasing each of the captive breeding facilities in the U.S. Additionally, the red wolf now has a Pinterest board and a Google Plus Community, thanks to the initiative of our Wolfwatcher partners who have also launched a spectacular Junior Wolfwatcher web site that gets kids involved with red wolf restoration.

New pups each spring, both captive and wild-born, renew our belief that we can save the red wolf from slipping into extinction. If we allow that to happen, if we give up on an animal that our ancestors ruthlessly persecuted, what does that say about our view of wild nature? And what does it say about us? The Cherokee, who once lived throughout most of red wolf country, ascribed these cautionary words to the great predator of the Southeast: "I am a hunter's hunter, my track a sign of hope, its absence a warning." We need to pay heed, now more than ever before.

ELAINE BENWELL
THE ENCOUNTER

Bio

Elaine Benwell is the author of Beyond the Blue Door, *a story of love, loss, and redemption. She lives in Northern California where she obtained degrees in History and Religious Studies. Elaine loves wolves, the Beatles, and cloudy skies.*

Benwell tells the story of her first encounter with a wolf and how it has stayed with her forever.

I remember I hated camping. But my parents were alfresco types, and every weekend it happened. On Friday night we would pack up the camper, stuffing and cramming supplies for a two-day trek to the great outdoors. Drive, drive, drive, seemingly endless highways and then the campground. The smell of bacon and coffee in the morning mingled with the sharp fragrance of forest pine or the moist tickle of salt air, depending on where the weekend excursion took us. We'd just get settled, and then it was time to pack it all up and go home. So much hassle, so much inconvenience. Hurry up to get there, hurry more to get home, home to glorious flush toilets and soft beds.

But one extended vacation stands out—a two week trip to Yellowstone National Park. Geysers and hail and bears, oh my! My ten-year-old self had never seen anything like it. It was cold, and there were still patches of snow on the ground even though it was early summer. We drove slowly through the park, marveling at the wonders of nature along the way. At one point the road curved around to the left in a long, graceful arc. To the right was an open expanse of grassland, and to our left was a lightly wooded area. As we rounded the curve we came upon a small hill where a copse of trees stood like sentinels, protecting the life around them. The green on the trees contrasted with the patchy snow that lay across the dark humus on the ground. It was a lovely scene, but considering the wildness that surrounded us, there was nothing extraordinary about it. Nothing, that is, until the leaves rustled, and through the stand of trees there emerged a large gray wolf. We stopped the car and sat to gaze at his magnificence. He paused to look back at us, stately and serene. There was no fear there, nor hostility. There was not even curiosity. He stood motionless, regarding us with eyes that penetrated deep into us, through us, and beyond us into eternity. I was entranced, and for an oh-so-brief moment I experienced something so timeless, so precious, that it remains with me to this day. All too soon the wolf, having his fill of us, turned back into the stand of trees and disappeared from our sight. My father started the car, and we were again on our way. It was such a small thing. But that night I dreamed of wolves, and for the rest of my days I would hold that encounter in my heart as one of the most wondrous experiences I've ever had.

MADELINE HARRIS
SILVER & SONG OF THE WOLF SPIRIT

Bio
Madeline Harris is a new author and wolf activist.

Silver
Like wolves in winter
As they run through the pines
Their paws rush over hidden trails
The moonlight is their guide

Gold
Like the forgotten stories their howls hold
When there is nothing but the wind to carry their voices
In the chill of night nothing speaks
Only whispers sift through the leaves

Black
Like the silence of night
A complete echo of all we lack

It's in those lonely howls we hear ourselves reflected
It's in those hidden trails we feel ourselves revealed
It's in the silver of the moon we see the choices we've made
And the consequences left behind

Song of the Wolf Spirit

Only a mere shadow among the night
Alone, but for the silent silhouettes
The moon hanging high before song takes flight
Rising, his chest fills with a hollow breath
His call may fall unheard, but still rings clear
Wandering with only shadows as kin
The moonlight is his only guidance here
Lost and lonely, looking for his brethren
Thought abandoned and forgotten by them
Forever left to search and sing his song
He allowed darkness to envelope him
As the wind carried his lingering call
Listen closely to the trees to hear it
Misunderstood Song of the Wolf Spirit

LEONA M. PEASE
GRAY WOLF

Bio

Leona M. Pease is a medical assistant in Southwest Michigan. Her hobbies include painting, writing, reading, photography, and walking. She has a Bachelor's in Business Management.

Gray Wolf. Leona M. Pease. Watercolor.

CHLOE VINER
FRUIT OF THEIR FRIGHTENED SELVES

Bio
Chloe Viner lives in Randolph, Vermont with her husband Shane, and their rescue animals Milo (cat) and Haley (dog). Chloe's chapbook Naked Under an Umbrella, *was published in 2011 by Finishing Line Press. Chloe has been published in a wide range of markets including recent publications in Grey Sparrow Print and Poetry Quarterly. Chloe received a Masters in Environmental Law and Policy and a Juris Doctor degree from Vermont Law School in 2012, her work focuses on protecting endangered species and conserving the environment. In her free time, Chloe bakes and enjoys the great Vermont outdoors.*

People fear the wolf
she is too beautiful for this world
her mysticism frightens them
born of a no-winters kind of world
having no familiarity with hibernation
they lift large rock slabs over their bodies to shelter
themselves from inevitable death
not knowing she comes to nourish them
her fangs covered in berries
the fruit of their frightened selves
taste so bitter.

If you waded in the waters
far enough to reach her den
you would find a dignity
not known among men.

The wolf displays humanity while
men cower beneath rocks
weapons raised
brutal animals.

DEIRDRE COCHRAN
CANIS LUPUS

Bio

Deirdre Cochran was born in the northeast and moved to Colorado as a single parent with her young son. She has been a wolf advocate and volunteer for around fifteen years now. What follows is just one of her poems that honor the wolf.

Cold as ice and wind piercing without you;
Snow deep and cumbersome.
Lakes frozen through;
He hides and no one can see him—silent.
Clear eyes of color—amber to green;
His fur blending with the forest.
He feels no inconveniences;
All that matters is his family.
Learned never to trust humans;
Assassinated for centuries;
All fear him—elusive and mysterious.
I know his soul is wild and free;
The way it should be.
From the rocky hill;
Always protecting what's his.
He is one of God's creatures;
Here with a purpose.
A predator of love howling to the Moon;
Waiting for you.

SOPHIE POLLARD
WOLF FAMILY

"Hello, my name is Sophie. I am eleven years old and have loved wolves since I was about four or five. Instead of presents for my birthday, I have asked for gift money to donate to wolves. Some of my hobbies are horse riding, which to me is more like my sport, I like to draw, play games, write, read, and do lots of other things. I love wolves for many reasons. One because they are like volcanoes, they are peaceful like a mountain when they are not erupting, and when they are it is like a surge of power and dominance. I love the fact that they are loyal to each other and like a family altogether and that when the two alphas mate they are loyal to each other forever. I drew my picture because they are a family that protects each other."

Wolf Family. Sophie Pollard. Pencil on paper.

Sophie Pollard is the youngest contributor in this anthology and intentionally the finale of this volume. Many traits can make a warrior: Fell's strength, Rufus C. Paddington's bravery, Willow's dedication. But the characteristic we should always value most is simply family. No work represents the innocence and purity of that notion as well as Ms. Pollard's own piece of art. Rudyard Kipling once said, "The Strength of the Pack is the Wolf, and the strength of the Wolf is the Pack." As we move forward into our own struggles, facing wolf hunters, one-sided myths and fairy tales, and personal problems even, it would do us all well to remember that we do form a pack. We form a family. It is the heart of the warrior that defines us.

Onward.

13475516R00215

Printed in Great Britain
by Amazon.co.uk, Ltd.,
Marston Gate.